An Introduction to Linear Programming

An Introduction to Linear Programming

Second Edition

G. R. WALSH

Department of Mathematics
University of York

A Wiley–Interscience Publication

JOHN WILEY & SONS
Chichester · New York · Brisbane · Toronto · Singapore

Library of Congress Cataloging in Publication Data:

Walsh, G. R. (Gordon Raymond), 1925–
An introduction to linear programming.

'A Wiley–Interscience publication.'
Bibliography: p.
Includes index.
1. Linear programming. I. Title.
T57.74.W35 1985 519.7′2 85-642

ISBN 0 471 90719 7

British Library Cataloguing in Publication Data:

Walsh, G. R.
An introduction to linear programming.—2nd ed.
1. Linear programming
I. Title
519.7′2 T57.74

ISBN 0 471 90719 7

Typeset by Macmillan India Ltd., Bangalore.
Printed by Page Bros. (Norwich) Ltd.

Contents

* Sections marked with an asterisk may be omitted on a first reading.

Preface to the First Edition

The aim of this book is to present a simple, concise, mathematical account of linear programming.

Linear programming, in common with many other mathematical techniques, was developed for the purpose of solving practical problems. During World War II many problems arose in connection with the optimal deployment of aircraft, submarines, men, materials and transport. Immediately after the war similar problems arose in industry and government, ranging from the economic manufacture of pig foods to the best choice of shipping routes. The most general problem of this kind may be described as the 'optimal allocation of scarce resources'. Classical methods of calculus and algebra fail to solve these problems because the problems are formulated in terms of inequalities rather than equations. In a large sub-class of such problems every variable appears linearly, both in the inequality constraints (which indicate the scarceness of the resources) and in the objective function (which describes the quantity to be maximized or minimized). The subject of linear programming deals with the formulation and solution of problems in this sub-class.

Electronic computers were being developed and brought into use from 1945 onwards. These made possible the rapid solution of full-scale industrial linear programming problems, and soon paid for themselves many times over by finding solutions which achieved dramatic cost reductions in the companies' operations. Linear programming flourished and became popular. It was soon apparent, however, that many interesting and worthwhile problems could not be accurately formulated within the confines of linear programming; hence nonlinear programming was developed as an extension of linear programming. Nonlinear programming may also be regarded as an extension of the classical theory of constrained maxima and minima to the case when inequality constraints are included; either the objective function or the constraints (or both) are nonlinear. The term 'mathematical programming' is now used to include both linear and nonlinear programming. More generally, an 'optimization technique' is *any* method for finding a maximum or minimum value of a function, with or without constraints. Optimization techniques are currently being applied to a wide range of problems in physics, engineering, economics and operational research.

This book provides a first course in linear programming for any student of mathematics or allied science (or art) who wishes to acquire a working knowledge of the subject. The material presented here is an extended version of a course of lectures given to second-year Mathematics/Economics and

Mathematics/Education students in the University of York. It is natural that linear programming should be described mathematically by linear algebra, and it is assumed that the reader is acquainted with the methods of linear algebra: an ability to manipulate vectors and matrices, and an understanding of the notion of the linear dependence of vectors are all that is required.

Chapter 1 begins with the formulation of the general linear programming problem; the rest of the chapter deals with the two-dimensional problem and introduces the simplex method. The main algebraic proofs concerning the simplex method appear in Chapter 2. In the penultimate section of Chapter 2 it is shown how the two-dimensional geometrical description of the simplex method can be extended to any number of dimensions. The final section of this chapter gives the theory of the perturbation method for avoiding degeneracy. The major part of the theoretical development is concluded by a discussion of duality in Chapter 3. Two well-known alternative simplex algorithms—the dual simplex method and the revised simplex method—are described, and the chapter ends with some useful results in sensitivity analysis. Chapter 4 is concerned with the application of linear programming to the problems of transportation and assignment, and with the relationships between linear programming and the theory of games. In particular, detailed descriptions are given of the *uv*-method for the solution of the transportation problem, and of a variant of the Hungarian method for the solution of the assignment problem. In concentrating on the mathematical aspects of linear programming, other aspects (e.g. industrial and economic applications, high-speed computation) have necessarily been neglected in a book of this size. These specialized aspects of the subject are dealt with in many of the texts listed on pages 219–221. Sections that are marked with asterisks deal with the more difficult or the less fundamental topics, and may be omitted on a first reading.

Most of the exercises at the end of each chapter are numerical, and these are intended to be worked out exactly, using pencil and paper only. Experience shows that time is saved by making frequent arithmetical checks; the row-sum check (Exercise 3, Chapter 2 and Exercise 22, Chapter 3) is highly recommended.

The notation has been made as consistent and standardized as possible. Matrices are denoted by bold type capital roman letters; column vectors by unprimed bold type lower case letters; column and row vectors in component form by square and round brackets, respectively; transposes (including row vectors) by primes; and linear dependence coefficients by lower case Greek letters.

I would like to thank my colleague, Dr N. Anderson, for his careful reading of the first draft of this book, and for his many valuable comments. I would also like to acknowledge with gratitude the contributions of Mr L. C. Carpenter of Bradford University and Mr M. L. Chambers of Lancaster University, both of whom suggested many improvements in the content and presentation of the text.

Preface to the Second Edition

This edition differs from its predecessor in one major respect: an entirely new chapter, on the theory of the ellipsoid method, has been added. An account of how this method can be used to determine whether or not a set of linear constraints is consistent was first published by Khachiyan in 1979; the application to the solution of linear programming problems has since been considered by many authors. At present, Khachiyan's results are of great theoretical interest but have little practical value, and so the emphasis here is on the mathematical theory.

The opportunity has also been taken to expand the section on Sensitivity Analysis, to add further exercises for the reader, to bring the References and Suggestions for Further Reading up to date, and to correct a number of errors and misprints.

I am particularly indebted to my colleague, Mr M. J. Smith, for many helpful discussions on the ellipsoid method and for his careful reading of an early draft of Chapter 5. I would also like to thank the staff of John Wiley and Sons Ltd for their very able assistance at all stages of the production of this new edition.

G. R. W.

York, October 1984.

1

Introduction

1.1 Statement of the Problem

The most general linear programming problem is that of maximizing or minimizing a linear function

$$z = c_1 x_1 + \ldots + c_n x_n \tag{1.1}$$

of n real variables, $x_1, \ldots, x_n$, where the c_j are given constants, and the variables must also satisfy m linear constraints. The function z is called the *objective function*. By a 'constraint' we mean either an inequality or an equation. Symbolically, the constraints may be written

$$\left.\begin{array}{l} a_{11}x_1 + \ldots + a_{1n}x_n \leqslant, =, \geqslant b_1, \\ a_{21}x_1 + \ldots + a_{2n}x_n \leqslant, =, \geqslant b_2, \\ \ldots \\ a_{m1}x_1 + \ldots + a_{mn}x_n \leqslant, =, \geqslant b_m, \end{array}\right\} \tag{1.2}$$

where the a_{ij} and b_i are given constants. Each constraint may be of the $\leqslant$, $=$ or $\geqslant$ type, though strict inequality constraints are excluded in order to avoid absurd problems such as that of minimizing x_1, given that $x_1 > 2$.

It is both convenient and conventional to assume that the variables $x_1, \ldots, x_n$ take only non-negative values. These conditions are known as the *non-negativity restrictions*:

$$x_1 \geqslant 0, \ldots, x_n \geqslant 0. \tag{1.3}$$

Statements (1.1), (1.2), and (1.3) represent the complete formulation of the general linear programming problem.

Vectors and matrices will be used throughout this book because of the clarity and conciseness with which they express the basic ideas of linear algebra. There are many introductory texts on linear algebra: for example, references [5], [8], and [31].

In vector-matrix notation the general linear programming problem is that of maximizing or minimizing

$$z = \mathbf{c}_0{}'\mathbf{x}_0, \tag{1.4}$$

subject to the constraints

$$\mathbf{A}_0\mathbf{x}_0 \leqslant, =, \geqslant \mathbf{b} \tag{1.5}$$

and the non-negativity restrictions

$$\mathbf{x}_0 \geqslant \mathbf{0}, \tag{1.6}$$

where $\mathbf{c}_0' = (c_1, \ldots, c_n)$ is an n-component row vector, $\mathbf{x}_0 = [x_1, \ldots, x_n]$ is an n-component column vector, $\mathbf{A}_0 = \{a_{ij}\}$ is an $m \times n$ matrix, and $\mathbf{b} = [b_1, \ldots, b_m]$ is an m-component column vector. Vector inequalities, such as those of (1.5) and (1.6), must be interpreted component by component. The suffix $_0$ is used merely for notational convenience; its significance will become apparent in Section 2.1.

In principle, every linear programming problem can be solved, provided that a solution exists. The simplex method, devised by George B. Dantzig [10] in 1947, is an algorithm which produces the required solution in a finite number of steps. Various forms of the simplex method have been devised which differ in computational detail, but no other general method has been found which is more efficient than the simplex method.

Before discussing the simplex method, it is instructive to consider the geometrical interpretation of the linear programming problem involving only two variables.

1.2 Linear Programming in Two Dimensions

Example 1.1

Consider the problem of maximizing

$$z = 4x_1 + 3x_2,$$

subject to the constraints and non-negativity restrictions

$$\left.\begin{aligned} 3x_1 + 4x_2 &\leqslant 12, \\ 7x_1 + 2x_2 &\leqslant 14, \\ x_1, x_2 &\geqslant 0. \end{aligned}\right\} \tag{1.7}$$

Solution

The constraints are represented graphically by drawing the lines

$$\begin{aligned} 3x_1 + 4x_2 &= 12, \\ 7x_1 + 2x_2 &= 14, \end{aligned}$$

and using arrows which point into the region where the constraints are satisfied (Figure 1.1). An easy way of determining the directions of the arrows is to consider whether or not the origin (0, 0) satisfies each constraint.

In Figure 1.1, the shaded region OABC, called the *feasible region*, includes all points (x_1, x_2) which satisfy the constraints *and* non-negativity restrictions of the

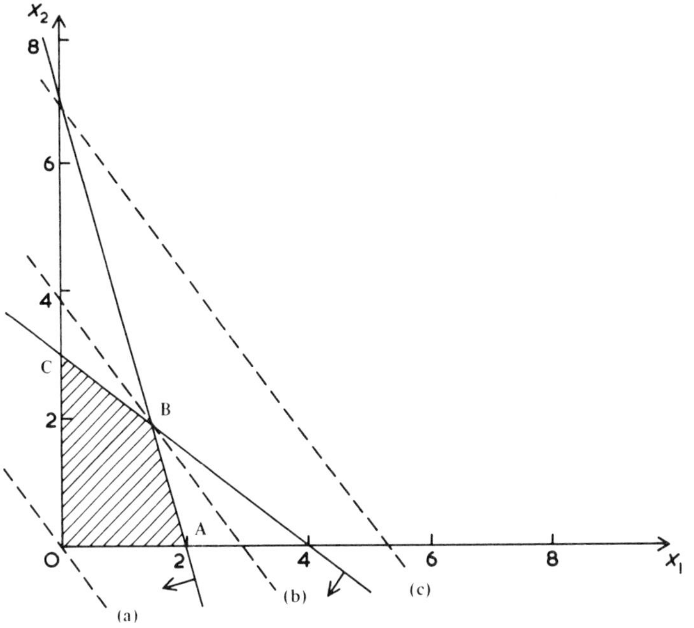

Figure 1.1 Solution of Example 1.1

problem. Any point (x_1, x_2) in the feasible region represents a *feasible solution* of the problem. A point which satisfies the constraints, but which violates one or more of the non-negativity restrictions, represents a *non-feasible solution*. The definitions of this paragraph apply, with suitable modifications, to the general linear programming problem with n variables.

The linear programming problem (1.7) thus reduces to a search in the feasible region for a point which maximizes the objective function. The parallel broken lines in Figure 1.1 are

$$\begin{aligned}
&\text{(a)}\ 4x_1 + 3x_2 = 0,\\
&\text{(b)}\ 4x_1 + 3x_2 = 127/11,\\
&\text{(c)}\ 4x_1 + 3x_2 = 21.
\end{aligned}$$

Along each of these lines the objective function takes a constant value; this value increases as the distance of the line from O increases.

At this stage the essential conflict arises: the line representing the value of the objective function must be moved as far as possible in the direction of increasing z while, at the same time, the solution must remain feasible. It is clear from Figure 1.1 that the broken line through the corner B of the feasible region provides the required maximum value of z, that is, the point B (16/11, 21/11) represents the *optimal solution.* Note that the optimal solution is necessarily feasible since it must satisfy the non-negativity restrictions. The maximum value of z is 127/11.

The linear programming problem of Example 1.1 was given in a standard mathematical form; in a practical problem there is the important preliminary step of expressing the problem in this standard form.

Example 1.2

The total area of a garden is 300 yd². Unfortunately, the part-time gardener can spend only 7 hours per week in his garden, so he has decided to divide the space between grass and flowers, and may even leave some land unused. He estimates that each week an hour's work is required for every 60 yd² of grass or for every 30 yd² of flower beds. His children insist that at least half the garden should be grass, and his wife would like at least one-third to be flowers. The objective function can be described loosely as 'pleasure', and must be maximized.

Solution

Let x_1, x_2 denote the number of square yards of grass and flower beds, respectively. The constraints are

$$\left.\begin{aligned} x_1 + x_2 &\leqslant 300, \\ \frac{x_1}{60} + \frac{x_2}{30} &\leqslant 7, \\ x_1 &\geqslant 150, \\ x_2 &\geqslant 100. \end{aligned}\right\} \tag{1.8a}$$

The non-negativity restrictions are satisfied automatically, because of the last two constraints. 'Pleasure' must now be expressed as a linear combination of 'grass' and 'flowers'; this illustrates the point that it may sometimes be absurd to force a problem into the linear programming form. However, in the present case let us assume that the gardener derives pleasure from equal areas of grass and flower beds in the ratio 3 : 2. Then the problem is to maximize

$$z = 3x_1 + 2x_2, \tag{1.8b}$$

subject to the constraints (1.8a).

Figure 1.2 is self-explanatory and shows that the optimal solution, represented by the point A, is

$$\begin{aligned} x_1 &= 200 \text{ yd}^2 \text{ of grass}, \\ x_2 &= 100 \text{ yd}^2 \text{ of flower beds}. \end{aligned}$$

It is instructive to refer back to the original problem for which (1.8a) and (1.8b) are the mathematical model. We see that

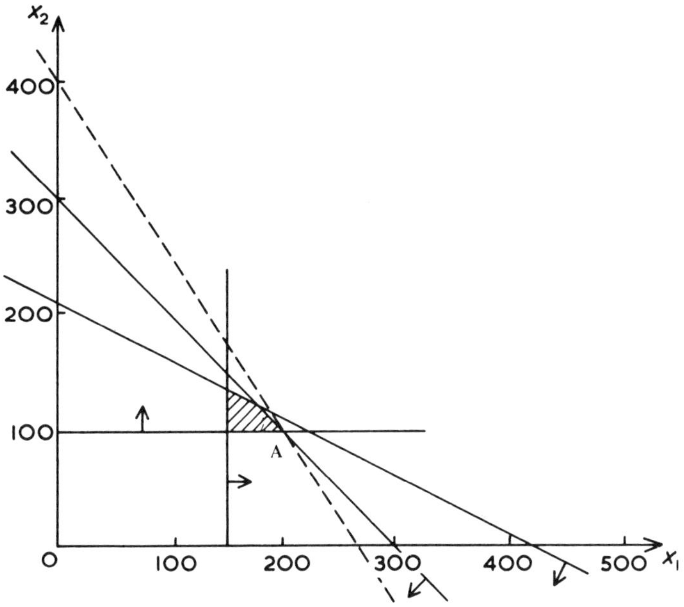

Figure 1.2 Solution of Example 1.2

(a) there is no spare land,

(b) the optimal solution involves working only $6\frac{2}{3}$ hours per week in the garden,

(c) the children are delighted,

(d) the wife is happy,

(e) the 'pleasure' is 800 units.

There is no essential difference between a minimizing problem and a maximizing problem, since the optimal solution (x_1^*, x_2^*) which minimizes z also maximizes $-z$, and

$$\min z = -\max(-z). \tag{1.9}$$

(Asterisks will be used to denote optimal values.) Consequently, every minimizing problem can be solved by changing the sign of every term in the objective function, solving the maximizing problem, and finally changing the sign of the optimal value of the objective function. In general, it is largely a matter of taste whether one solves a minimizing problem directly or changes it into a maximizing problem; in two-dimensional graphical solutions the direct method is preferable, as shown by the next example.

Example 1.3

$$\text{Minimize } z = 5x_1 + 2x_2,$$

subject to the constraints and non-negativity restrictions

$$\begin{aligned} 3x_1 - 2x_2 &\geqslant 6, \\ x_1 + 2x_2 &\geqslant 8, \\ x_1 + x_2 &\leqslant 7, \\ x_1, x_2 &\geqslant 0. \end{aligned}$$

Solution

The optimal solution is represented by the point A (7/2, 9/4) of Figure 1.3. This point is obtained by moving the line $5x_1 + 2x_2 = z$ as far as possible in the direction of decreasing z, while keeping at least one point of the line in the feasible region. The minimum value of z is therefore 22.

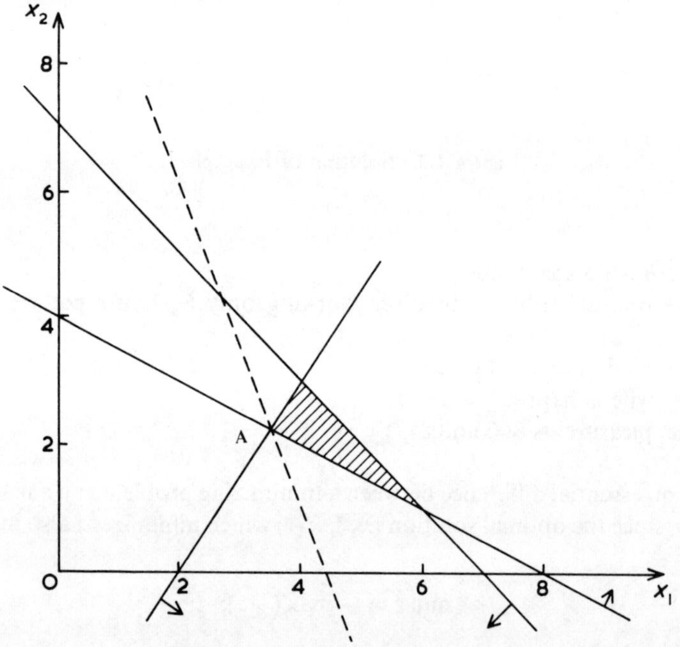

Figure 1.3 Solution of Example 1.3

If the constraints and non-negativity restrictions are unaltered in Example 1.3, then Figure 1.3 also solves the problem:

$$\text{Maximize } \bar{z} = -5x_1 - 2x_2,$$

where $\bar{z} = -z$. The maximum value of $\bar{z}$ is -22, and it follows that the minimum value of z is 22, as found above. Thus nothing is gained by solving Example 1.3 as a maximizing problem.

In every example so far the optimal solution has occurred at a corner of the region of feasible solutions. A general feature of all linear programming problems is that if an optimal solution exists, and is unique, then it occurs at a corner of the feasible region. (It will be seen in Section 2.9 that the notion of 'corner' is easily extended to the n-dimensional case.) In certain circumstances, however, there may be other optimal solutions, as shown by the following typical example.

Example 1.4

$$\text{Maximize } z = 6x_1 + 2x_2,$$

subject to the constraints and non-negativity restrictions

$$\left.\begin{aligned} 4x_1 + 5x_2 &\leqslant 20, \\ 3x_1 + x_2 &\leqslant 6, \\ x_1, x_2 &\geqslant 0. \end{aligned}\right\} \quad (1.10)$$

Solution

Referring to Figure 1.4, we see that the line representing the maximum value of the objective function coincides with the constraint boundary $3x_1 + x_2 = 6$. Any point on the line segment AB therefore represents an optimal solution: we say that the points of AB represent *alternative optima*. In particular, the points A and B, which are corner points of the feasible region, represent optimal solutions. The maximum value of z is 12.

Example 1.4 is typical of the cases in which alternative optima appear, and it may be stated quite generally that a linear programming problem has either no optimal solution, a unique optimal solution, or an infinite number of optimal solutions—there can never be a finite number ($\neq 1$) of optimal solutions. This result is proved in Section 2.8.1.

A well-formulated linear programming problem will always have a finite optimal solution, i.e. one in which the variables at the optimum point take finite values. Occasionally it happens that owing to errors in formulation or in arithmetic a problem has no finite optimal solution; Example 1.5 illustrates this case.

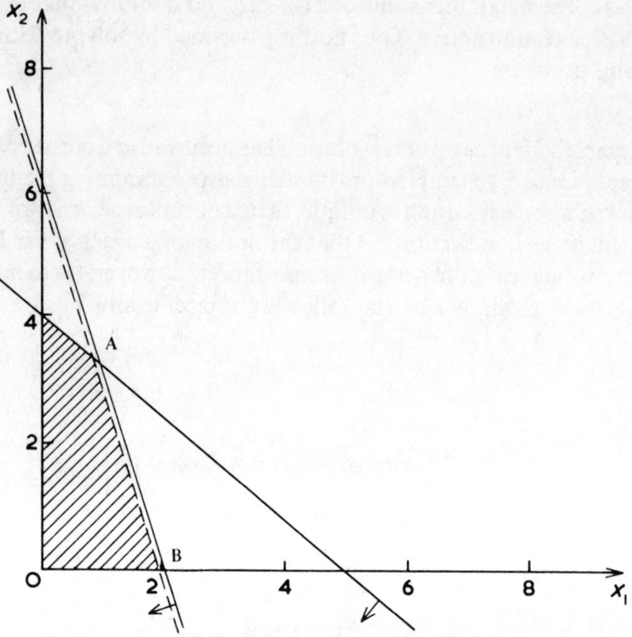

Figure 1.4 Solution of Example 1.4 (alternative optima)

Example 1.5

$$\left.\begin{aligned} &\text{Maximize } z = x_1 + x_2, \\ &\text{subject to the constraints and non-negativity restrictions} \\ &\qquad x_1 - x_2 \geqslant 1, \\ &\qquad x_1 - 3x_2 \geqslant -3, \\ &\qquad x_1, x_2 \geqslant 0. \end{aligned}\right\} \quad (1.11)$$

Solution

Figure 1.5 shows that there is no finite point in the feasible region at which z attains a maximum. The problem has an *unbounded solution*, with an unbounded value of z.

In Example 1.5 the objective function z is unbounded, but it may happen that an unbounded solution occurs with a *finite* value of the objective function. This case may be demonstrated by considering the problem of minimizing

$$z' = x_1 - 3x_2,$$

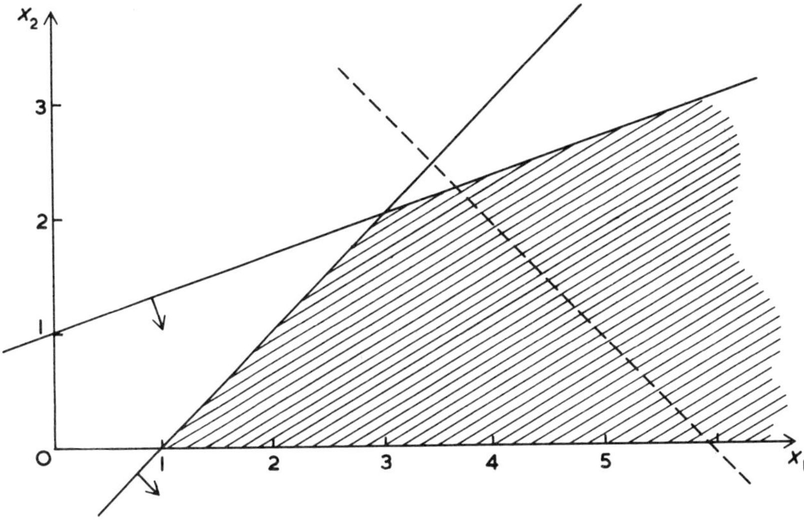

Figure 1.5 Solution of Example 1.5 (unbounded solution)

again subject to the constraints and non-negativity restrictions of (1.11). The line representing the minimum value of the objective function z' now coincides with the constraint boundary

$$x_1 - 3x_2 = -3.$$

Hence, although there is an unbounded solution (among the alternative optima on this constraint boundary), the minimum value of z' is -3, which is finite.

Unbounded solutions, with finite or unbounded values of the objective function, may also occur in the general linear programming problem with n variables. Finally, we note that by convention an unbounded solution is not regarded as optimal.

1.3 The Simplex Method in Two Dimensions

The simplex method is an iterative procedure for solving the general linear programming problem, and it is described in detail in Chapter 2. However, as a prelude to the development of the general theory, it will be valuable to show how the method (or algorithm) works in two dimensions. We do this by solving Example 1.1 by the simplex method.

The problem is to maximize

$$z = 4x_1 + 3x_2, \tag{1.12}$$

subject to the constraints and non-negativity restrictions

$$3x_1 + 4x_2 \leqslant 12, \quad (1.13)$$

$$7x_1 + 2x_2 \leqslant 14, \quad (1.14)$$

$$x_1, x_2 \geqslant 0. \quad (1.15)$$

The inequalities (1.13) and (1.14) are equivalent to the equations

$$3x_1 + 4x_2 + x_3 = 12, \quad (1.16)$$

$$7x_1 + 2x_2 + x_4 = 14, \quad (1.17)$$

provided that

$$x_3 \geqslant 0, x_4 \geqslant 0. \quad (1.18)$$

A solution of equations (1.16) and (1.17) is

$$x_1 = 0, x_2 = 0, x_3 = 12, x_4 = 14. \quad (1.19)$$

From (1.12) this solution gives $z = 0$. Equations (1.19) illustrate an essential feature of the simplex method: the number of variables taking non-zero values never exceeds the number m of constraints (in this case $m = 2$). Normally, in each iteration of the simplex method, a variable with a zero value is given a non-zero value, and another variable with a non-zero value is forced to take the value zero.

The present state of the variables is shown by equations (1.19). From (1.12) we see that z can be increased by increasing either x_1 or x_2. Let us choose to increase x_1, since it has the larger coefficient in the expression for z. At the same time we must make either x_3 or x_4 zero. The value of x_2 is kept fixed at zero throughout these operations. There are now two outstanding questions:

(a) By how much can we increase x_1 from zero?

(b) Which of x_3, x_4 should be made zero?

In order to answer these questions, consider equations (1.16) and (1.17). We have $x_2 = 0$ throughout. From equation (1.16), when $x_3 = 0$ we find $x_1 = 4$. From equation (1.17), when $x_4 = 0$ we find $x_1 = 2$. Equation (1.17) is therefore the critical equation, for if x_1 is made greater than 2, then x_4 will become negative, which contradicts (1.18). Hence x_1 can be increased by 2 at most, and is, in fact, increased by exactly 2. At this stage x_1 becomes non-zero and x_4 becomes zero.

The new values of the variables are shown clearly by solving equations (1.16) and (1.17) for x_1, x_3 (which have non-zero values) in terms of x_2, x_4 (which have zero values):

$$x_1 = 2 - \tfrac{2}{7}x_2 - \tfrac{1}{7}x_4, \quad (1.20)$$

$$x_3 = 6 - \tfrac{22}{7}x_2 + \tfrac{3}{7}x_4. \quad (1.21)$$

Thus, at the present stage,

$$x_1 = 2, x_2 = 0, x_3 = 6, x_4 = 0. \quad (1.22)$$

The new value of z is 8. Again this is shown clearly by expressing z in terms of x_2, x_4. From equations (1.12) and (1.20) we find that

$$z = 8 + \tfrac{13}{7}x_2 - \tfrac{4}{7}x_4. \tag{1.23}$$

One iteration of the simplex method has now been completed; the rest is pure repetition. The next question is:

(c) Can z be increased further?

We have to increase either x_2 or x_4 from zero. Equation (1.23) shows that z will be increased if we increase x_2. Now, question (a) applies to x_2 and question (b) applies to x_1, x_3. Proceeding in exactly the same way as for the previous step, we write equations (1.20) and (1.21) in the form of equations (1.16) and (1.17):

$$x_1 + \tfrac{2}{7}x_2 + \tfrac{1}{7}x_4 = 2, \tag{1.24}$$

$$x_3 + \tfrac{22}{7}x_2 - \tfrac{3}{7}x_4 = 6, \tag{1.25}$$

and note that x_4 is zero throughout this iteration. From equation (1.24), when $x_1 = 0$ we find $x_2 = 7$. From equation (1.25), when $x_3 = 0$ we find $x_2 = 21/11$. Equation (1.25) is therefore the critical equation; hence x_2 is increased from zero to 21/11, and x_3 becomes zero. Corresponding to equations (1.20)–(1.22), we now have, from equations (1.24) and (1.25),

$$x_1 = \tfrac{16}{11} + \tfrac{1}{11}x_3 - \tfrac{2}{11}x_4, \tag{1.26}$$

$$x_2 = \tfrac{21}{11} - \tfrac{7}{22}x_3 + \tfrac{3}{22}x_4, \tag{1.27}$$

$$x_1 = 16/11,\ x_2 = 21/11,\ x_3 = 0,\ x_4 = 0, \tag{1.28}$$

and from equations (1.23) and (1.27), we find

$$z = \tfrac{127}{11} - \tfrac{13}{22}x_3 - \tfrac{7}{22}x_4. \tag{1.29}$$

Another iteration of the simplex method has now been completed. The new value of z is 127/11. We ask question (c) again and note that in order to proceed with the simplex method we must increase either x_3 or x_4 from zero. But equation (1.29) shows that z can only be decreased by this procedure. Therefore we have already reached the optimal solution, with

$$x_1{}^* = 16/11,\ x_2{}^* = 21/11;\ z^* = 127/11, \tag{1.30}$$

and the process terminates.

Referring to Figure 1.1, a simple geometrical interpretation of the two steps of the simplex method which were used in this example is that the solution point moves along the two edges OA, AB of the feasible region, reaching the corner A after one step and the (optimal) corner B after two steps. It will be seen later (Section 2.9) that there is an analogous geometrical interpretation of the simplex method when more than two variables are involved.

Exercises

Solve the following linear programming problems graphically, and also solve numbers 1 and 7b by the simplex method. Assume that the objective functions have to be optimized subject to the given constraints, and that all the variables satisfy non-negativity restrictions.

1. $$\text{Maximize } z = 4x_1 + 3x_2.$$
$$2x_1 + 3x_2 \leqslant 6,$$
$$4x_1 + x_2 \leqslant 4.$$

2. $$\text{Maximize } z = 2x_1 + 5x_2.$$
$$2x_1 - 3x_2 \geqslant -6,$$
$$7x_1 - 2x_2 \leqslant 14,$$
$$x_1 + x_2 \leqslant 5.$$

3. $$\text{Maximize } z = -2x_1 + x_2.$$
$$0 \leqslant x_1 - 3x_2 \leqslant 3,$$
$$x_1 \geqslant 2.$$

4. $$\text{Minimize } z = x_1 + x_2.$$
$$x_1 + 2x_2 \leqslant 4,$$
$$x_1 - 2x_2 \leqslant -6,$$
$$8x_1 - x_2 \geqslant 8.$$

5. $$\text{Minimize } z = 12x_1 + 2x_2.$$
$$x_1 - x_2 \leqslant 0,$$
$$x_1 + x_2 \geqslant 7,$$
$$6x_1 + x_2 \geqslant 12.$$

6. $$\text{Maximize } z = 2x_1 - 5x_2.$$
$$7x_1 + 4x_2 \leqslant 28,$$
$$x_1 - x_2 \geqslant 3,$$
$$3x_1 + 8x_2 \geqslant 16.$$

7a. $$\text{Maximize } z = 2x_1 + 9x_2.$$
$$4x_1 + 5x_2 \leqslant 20,$$
$$3x_1 + 7x_2 \leqslant 21.$$

7b. $$\text{Minimize } z = 20x_1 + 21x_2.$$
$$4x_1 + 3x_2 \geqslant 2,$$
$$5x_1 + 7x_2 \geqslant 9.$$

Notice that the coefficients and constants in Exercise 7b are those of Exercise 7a in a specially rearranged order; 7a and 7b are called *dual problems*. Notice also a remarkable fact about the optimal values of the objective functions for the two problems.

8a.

$$\text{Maximize } z = 2x_1 + 5x_2.$$
$$4x_1 - 3x_2 \geqslant -12,$$
$$x_1 - 4x_2 \leqslant 5.$$

8b.

$$\text{Minimize } z = 12x_1 + 5x_2.$$
$$-4x_1 + x_2 \geqslant 2,$$
$$3x_1 - 4x_2 \geqslant 5.$$

N.B. Exercises 8a and 8b are also dual problems.

9. A farmer has 100 acres of land which he has decided to make part arable and part grass. Part of the land may also lie fallow. He can make an annual profit of £15/acre from arable land and £10/acre from grass. Each year arable land requires 25 hours work per acre, and grass requires 10 hours work per acre. The farmer does not want to work more than 2 000 hours in any year. How should he divide his land between arable and grass so as to maximize his annual profit?

10. A furniture company produces tables of two different sizes. The cost of manufacturing a table depends on two factors—construction costs (materials) and finishing costs (smoothing and polishing); these costs include labour. There are upper limits to the costs per day that can be incurred, owing to the shortage of suitable skilled labour. All the costs (in £) are shown here in tabular form.

	Large table	Small table	Maximum cost per day
Construction of one table	20	12	160
Finishing of one table	10	4	60

The profit on a large table is £7, and on a small table £4. How many tables of each size should be produced each day in order to maximize the total profit?

11. A motor car company manufactures cars for the home market and for export. Company policy is to export at least 60 per cent of its cars. Not more than 150 cars can be produced each week. The delivery costs payable by the manufacturer are £5 and £20, respectively, for cars for the home market and for export, but the delivery firm specify that the total delivery costs must not be less than £1 600 per week. Each car for the home market requires 120 man-hours to be spent on bodywork, 35 man-hours on the engine, and 10 man-hours on checking and testing. The corresponding figures for cars for export are 150, 40, and 15 man-hours, respectively. The total number of man-hours available per

week is 25 000 for bodywork, 5 500 for engine work, and 2 000 for checking and testing. The net profit on a car for export is k times that on a car for the home market, where k may lie between 2 and 0.

How many cars of each kind should be produced each week if the company wishes to

(a) minimize the excess of cars for export over those for the home market?
(b) maximize its net profit?

12. Discuss the following linear programming problem.

$$\text{Maximize } z = c_1x_1 + c_2x_2,$$

subject to the constraints and non-negativity restrictions

$$\begin{aligned} a_{11}x_1 + a_{12}x_2 &\leqslant 0, \\ a_{21}x_1 + a_{22}x_2 &\leqslant 0, \\ x_1, x_2 &\geqslant 0. \end{aligned}$$

2

The Simplex Method

2.1 Introduction

The graphical method of Chapter 1 can be extended in two different directions. First, the method may be used when the constraints or the objective function (or both) are nonlinear: no essential difficulty is introduced, apart from the necessity of drawing accurate curves when a numerical solution is attempted. Secondly, it is possible to display graphically the linear programming problem in three dimensions: the feasible region becomes a solid, bounded by plane faces, and the objective function is represented by a plane which moves parallel to itself until the optimal solution is reached. However, such three-dimensional drawings are not recommended for general use since they tend to be confusing, even when carefully drawn and shaded. In any case, a purely algebraic method is needed to solve problems having four or more variables; the simplex method was devised for this purpose.

We shall now develop the theory of the simplex method, or algorithm, in detail. For future reference, the particular version of the method described in this chapter is called the 'standard simplex method'. The steps of the method are collected together for reference at the end of Section 2.5.

The general linear programming problem, which was introduced in Section 1.1, may be formulated as follows:

Maximize the linear objective function

$$z = c_1 x_1 + \ldots + c_n x_n, \tag{2.1}$$

subject to the linear constraints

$$\left.\begin{aligned} a_{11}x_1 + \ldots + a_{1n}x_n &\leqslant, =, \geqslant b_1, \\ a_{21}x_1 + \ldots + a_{2n}x_n &\leqslant, =, \geqslant b_2, \\ \ldots & \\ a_{m1}x_1 + \ldots + a_{mn}x_n &\leqslant, =, \geqslant b_m, \end{aligned}\right\} \tag{2.2}$$

and the non-negativity restrictions

$$x_j \geqslant 0, \quad j = 1, \ldots, n. \tag{2.3}$$

The definitions of feasible region, feasible solution, etc. given in Section 1.2 for the two-dimensional problem also apply to the n-dimensional problem, provided that in these definitions we replace 'the point (x_1, x_2)' by 'the point $(x_1, \ldots, x_n)$'.

The vector $\mathbf{b} = [b_1, \ldots, b_m]$ is called the *requirements vector* and, without loss of generality, may be assumed non-negative, since any of the constraints (2.2) may be multiplied throughout by -1, if necessary. The vector $\mathbf{c}_0 = [c_1, \ldots, c_n]$ is called the *price vector*, and its rth component c_r is called the *price* of the variable x_r.

The first step in the simplex method is to change every inequality constraint in (2.2) into an equality constraint, as follows. Suppose that the first a constraints are of $\leqslant$ type, the next b constraints of $\geqslant$ type, and the remaining $(m-a-b)$ constraints of $=$ type; the constraints (2.2) can always be arranged in this order. A *slack variable* is added to the left-hand side of each $\leqslant$ inequality. Typically, if the pth constraint is of $\leqslant$ type, it becomes

$$a_{p1}x_1 + \ldots + a_{pn}x_n + x_{n+p} = b_p, \tag{2.4}$$

where x_{n+p} ($\geqslant 0$) is the slack variable for the pth constraint. Similarly, a *surplus variable* is subtracted from the left-hand side of each $\geqslant$ inequality, so that if the qth constraint is of $\geqslant$ type, it becomes

$$a_{q1}x_1 + \ldots + a_{qn}x_n - x_{n+q} = b_q, \tag{2.5}$$

where x_{n+q} ($\geqslant 0$) is the surplus variable for the qth constraint.

Let the slack and surplus variables together form a vector

$$\mathbf{x}_s = [x_{n+1}, \ldots, x_{n+a+b}], \tag{2.6}$$

where $x_{n+1}, \ldots, x_{n+a}$ are slack variables and $x_{n+a+1}, \ldots, x_{n+a+b}$ are surplus variables. The constraints (2.2) may then be written in the form

$$\mathbf{A}_0\mathbf{x}_0 + \begin{pmatrix} \mathbf{I}_a & \mathbf{O} \\ \mathbf{O} & -\mathbf{I}_b \\ \mathbf{O} & \mathbf{O} \end{pmatrix} \mathbf{x}_s = \mathbf{b}, \tag{2.7}$$

where $\mathbf{x}_0 = [x_1, \ldots, x_n]$ is the vector of *main variables*, and $\mathbf{I}_a$, $\mathbf{I}_b$ are unit matrices of orders a and b respectively. The non-negativity restrictions are now

$$\mathbf{x}_0 \geqslant \mathbf{0}, \quad \mathbf{x}_s \geqslant \mathbf{0}. \tag{2.8}$$

Next we assign a price of zero to each slack and surplus variable. Then (2.1) may be replaced by

$$z = \mathbf{c}_0'\mathbf{x}_0 + \mathbf{c}_s'\mathbf{x}_s, \tag{2.9}$$

where $\mathbf{c}_s$ is the zero vector with $(a+b)$ components.

The problem of maximizing the objective function (2.9), subject to the *equality* constraints (2.7) and the non-negativity restrictions (2.8), is entirely equivalent to the original problem with mixed constraints, defined by (2.1), (2.2), and (2.3). The original problem may therefore be expressed in the form

$$\left.\begin{array}{ll} & \text{Maximize } z = \mathbf{c}'\mathbf{x}, \\ \text{subject to} & \\ & \mathbf{A}\mathbf{x} = \mathbf{b} \quad \text{and} \quad \mathbf{x} \geqslant \mathbf{0}, \end{array}\right\} \tag{2.10}$$

where

$$\mathbf{A} = \left(\mathbf{A}_0 \begin{array}{|cc} \mathbf{I}_a & \mathbf{O} \\ \mathbf{O} & -\mathbf{I}_b \\ \mathbf{O} & \mathbf{O} \end{array} \right), \quad \mathbf{x} = \begin{pmatrix} \mathbf{x}_0 \\ \hline \mathbf{x}_s \end{pmatrix}, \quad \mathbf{c} = \begin{pmatrix} \mathbf{c}_0 \\ \hline \mathbf{0} \end{pmatrix}.$$

It is now apparent that the reason for attaching a suffix $_0$ to the quantities in (1.4)–(1.6) is to distinguish those quantities from their counterparts in (2.10). From now on we shall regard (2.10) as the standard form of the general linear programming problem.

The main purpose of the manipulation of this section has been to replace all the inequality constraints by equality constraints: the latter, of course, are much easier to handle algebraically. It is now clear that the ingenuity in the simplex method lies in the fact that it does three things at the same time:

(a) solves the simultaneous equations $\mathbf{Ax} = \mathbf{b}$,

(b) ensures that the non-negativity restrictions $\mathbf{x} \geqslant \mathbf{0}$ are satisfied,

(c) improves the value of the objective function z in each iteration (though sometimes z remains unchanged during an iteration).

A further important and, for practical purposes, essential property of the simplex method is that it makes no *a priori* assumptions concerning the equations $\mathbf{Ax} = \mathbf{b}$. Even if these equations are inconsistent, or if some of them are redundant, the simplex method still works, in the sense that it indicates unambiguously these peculiarities of the equations and finds an optimal solution if one exists.

2.2 Basic Solutions

The constraint equations $\mathbf{Ax} = \mathbf{b}$ of the general linear programming problem (2.10) may be written in the form

$$x_1\mathbf{a}_1 + \ldots + x_N\mathbf{a}_N = \mathbf{b}, \tag{2.11}$$

where $\mathbf{a}_1, \ldots, \mathbf{a}_N$, called *activity vectors*, are the column vectors comprising the $m \times N$ matrix $\mathbf{A}$, and

$$N = n + a + b.$$

We assume throughout this section that equations (2.11) are consistent. (Inconsistent constraints are discussed in Section 2.8.)

If m, the number of constraints, is equal to N, the number of variables, and if $\text{rank}(\mathbf{A}) = m$, then equations (2.11) have the *unique* solution

$$\mathbf{x} = \mathbf{A}^{-1}\mathbf{b},$$

and there is no optimization problem; the feasible region (if it exists) consists of a single point. If $m > N$ and $\text{rank}(\mathbf{A}) = N$, then $(m - N)$ of the constraint equations are redundant and can, in principle, be omitted. (Redundant constraints are discussed in Section 2.8.) Equations (2.11) again have a unique solution. Thus the cases in which $m \geqslant N$ and rank(**A**) is as large as possible are of little interest and are henceforth ignored.

Now assume $m < N$ and rank (**A**) $= m$. [The cases for which rank (**A**) $<$ min (m, N) need not be considered at this stage, since it is always possible, again in principle, to remove redundant constraint equations until the assumed conditions are satisfied.] Consider equations (2.11): it is useful to think of each variable x_j as being permanently associated with the corresponding column vector $\mathbf{a}_j$. If m linearly independent column vectors of **A** are chosen, and if the $(N-m)$ variables corresponding to the remaining columns of **A** are set equal to zero, then the resulting set of m simultaneous equations has a unique solution called a *basic solution.* (A different choice of the m linearly independent column vectors of **A** would produce a different basic solution.) The m variables of the basic solution—which are associated with the m linearly independent column vectors of **A**—are called *basic variables.* The corresponding column vectors of **A** are called *basis vectors* and together comprise the (non-singular) *basis matrix.* The remaining $(N-m)$ variables (which were set equal to zero) are called *non-basic variables.* It may happen that one or more of the basic variables takes the value zero; in this case the basic solution is said to be *degenerate.* Basic variables which take the value zero will be called *degenerate variables.* There cannot be more than ${}_NC_m$ basic solutions.

In the two-dimensional linear programming problem, basic solutions of the constraint equations correspond to corners of the polygon defined by the constraints. In particular, basic feasible solutions correspond to corners of the feasible region. Analogous statements may be made concerning the general n-dimensional problem—see Section 2.9.

Example 2.1

Find all the basic solutions of the simultaneous equations

$$4x_1 + 5x_2 + 8x_3 + 7x_4 = 10,$$
$$3x_1 + 2x_2 + 6x_3 + 9x_4 = 11.$$

Solution

Setting $x_1 = x_2 = 0$, and solving for x_3, x_4, we find

$$(x_1, x_2, x_3, x_4) = (0, 0, 13/30, 14/15).$$

Similarly, setting other pairs of variables equal to zero, in turn, we obtain four more basic solutions:

$$(x_1, x_2, x_3, x_4) = (0, 13/31, 0, 35/31), (0, -2, 5/2, 0), (13/15, 0, 0, 14/15), (5, -2, 0, 0).$$

N.B. There is no basic solution corresponding to $x_2 = x_4 = 0$, since the column vectors $\binom{4}{3}$, $\binom{8}{6}$ are linearly dependent, or, equivalently, the value of the determinant $\begin{vmatrix} 4 & 8 \\ 3 & 6 \end{vmatrix}$ is zero.
The following theorem is of fundamental importance in the theory of the simplex method.

■ **Theorem 2.1**

Let $\mathbf{Ax} = \mathbf{b}$ be a set of m simultaneous equations in N variables, with $m < N$ and rank$(\mathbf{A}) = m$. Then, if the equations have a feasible solution ($\mathbf{x} \geqslant \mathbf{0}$), they have a basic feasible solution.

Proof

Suppose that the given feasible solution satisfies

$$\sum_{j=1}^{p} x_j \mathbf{a}_j = \mathbf{b}, \qquad x_j > 0, \qquad j = 1, \ldots, p, \tag{2.12}$$

and

$$x_j = 0, \qquad j = p+1. \ldots, N. \tag{2.13}$$

There are two cases to consider.

(i) The vectors $\mathbf{a}_j$, $j = 1, \ldots, p$, are linearly independent. Rank$(\mathbf{A}) = m$ implies $p \leqslant m$. Thus the given feasible solution is already a basic feasible solution, non-degenerate if $p = m$ and degenerate if $p < m$.

(ii) The vectors $\mathbf{a}_j$, $j = 1, \ldots, p$, are linearly dependent. In this case we show that it is possible to reduce successively the number of variables taking strictly positive values until the column vectors $\mathbf{a}_j$ associated with these variables are linearly independent. The result then follows from case (i).

The linear dependence of the vectors $\mathbf{a}_j$ implies that there exist constants α_j, $j = 1, \ldots, p$, not all zero, such that

$$\sum_{j=1}^{p} \alpha_j \mathbf{a}_j = \mathbf{0}. \tag{2.14}$$

Suppose that $\alpha_r \neq 0$, and solve equation (2.14) for $\mathbf{a}_r$:

$$\mathbf{a}_r = -\sum_{\substack{j=1 \\ j \neq r}}^{p} \frac{\alpha_j \mathbf{a}_j}{\alpha_r}. \tag{2.15}$$

Substituting this expression for $\mathbf{a}_r$ into equation (2.12), we obtain

$$\sum_{\substack{j=1 \\ j \neq r}}^{p} \left(x_j - \frac{\alpha_j}{\alpha_r} x_r \right) \mathbf{a}_j = \mathbf{b}. \tag{2.16}$$

Equation (2.16) represents a solution of $\mathbf{Ax} = \mathbf{b}$ in which not more than $(p-1)$ of the variables take non-zero values, cf. (2.12). We ensure that these variables are all non-negative by choosing r such that

$$x_j - \frac{\alpha_j}{\alpha_r} x_r \geqslant 0, \quad j = 1, \ldots, p. \tag{2.17}$$

If $\alpha_j = 0$, then (2.17) is satisfied automatically, since $x_j > 0$, $j = 1, \ldots, p$. If $\alpha_j \neq 0$, we require

$$\frac{x_j}{\alpha_j} - \frac{x_r}{\alpha_r} \geqslant 0 \quad \text{if } \alpha_j > 0, \tag{2.18a}$$

and

$$\frac{x_j}{\alpha_j} - \frac{x_r}{\alpha_r} \leqslant 0 \quad \text{if } \alpha_j < 0. \tag{2.18b}$$

Both (2.18a) and (2.18b) are satisfied if we choose r such that

$$\frac{x_r}{\alpha_r} = \min_{j=1,\ldots,p} \left\{ \frac{x_j}{\alpha_j} : \alpha_j > 0 \right\}. \tag{2.19}$$

This condition requires that at least one α_j be positive: equation (2.14) can be multiplied throughout by -1, if necessary. If condition (2.19) is satisfied by more than one value of r, we choose any one of them.

Starting from a feasible solution (2.12), (2.13), with p of the variables taking strictly positive values, we have obtained a feasible solution (2.16) with not more than $(p-1)$ of the variables taking strictly positive values. The process can be repeated, if necessary, until the column vectors of $\mathbf{A}$ corresponding to the variables that take strictly positive values are linearly independent. That this situation is bound to arise ultimately is a consequence of the fact that (in the worst possible case) a single non-zero vector forms a linearly independent set. The proof is therefore complete.

Corollary

If condition (2.19) is satisfied by k values of r, say $r_1, \ldots, r_k$, then equation (2.16) becomes

$$\sum_{\substack{j=1 \\ j \neq r_1, \ldots, r_k}}^{p} \left(x_j - \frac{\alpha_j}{\alpha_r} x_r \right) \mathbf{a}_j = \mathbf{b}, \tag{2.20}$$

where the suffix r takes one of the values $r_1, \ldots, r_k$. The number of variables which take non-zero values in the feasible solution is reduced by k at this step.

The importance of Theorem 2.1, and its limitations, may be explained as follows. The theorem suggests that it is possible to solve a linear programming problem by examining *basic* feasible solutions only—and this is precisely what the simplex method does. In one iteration the simplex method proceeds from one basic feasible solution to another. The new basic feasible solution usually has an improved value of the objective function z, though occasionally the value of z remains unchanged during an iteration. Eventually the iterations lead to an optimal basic feasible solution (if one exists).

However, it is important to notice that Theorem 2.1 does not quite imply this last result. For if a linear programming problem has an optimal feasible solution, the theorem does not guarantee that it has an *optimal* basic feasible solution. In other words, we cannot claim from Theorem 2.1 that the simplex method will find an optimal feasible solution (if one exists) of the *general* linear programming problem. The necessary extension of Theorem 2.1 to cover optimal solutions is provided by Theorem 2.8, Section 2.9. Theorem 2.8 therefore leads to the important result that, in searching for an optimal feasible solution, we need consider only *basic* feasible solutions. Thus Theorem 2.8 will provide the final justification for the claim that the simplex method may be used to solve the general linear programming problem.

In this discussion, we have ignored the possibility that the simplex method will return to a previous basic feasible solution and thence go round and round in an endless cycle. We shall see later (Section 2.10) that *cycling*, as this process is called, can easily be eliminated by a slight modification of the simplex method.

2.3 Improving the Objective Function

In this section we examine in detail a single iteration of the simplex method. Starting with a given basic feasible solution of the general linear programming problem, we attempt to find a new basic feasible solution with an improved value of the objective function.

Consider the general linear programming problem in the standard form (2.10). Suppose that we are given a basic feasible solution of the problem, and let $\mathbf{B}$ be the $m \times m$ matrix whose columns are the basis vectors for this solution, so that $\mathbf{B}$, the basis matrix, is a nonsingular sub-matrix of $\mathbf{A}$. Let $\mathbf{x}_B$ be the vector of basic variables, and $\mathbf{c}_B$ the corresponding price vector. The equation $\mathbf{Ax} = \mathbf{b}$ becomes

$$\mathbf{B}\mathbf{x}_B = \mathbf{b}, \tag{2.21}$$

and the objective function is

$$z = \mathbf{c}'_B\mathbf{x}_B. \tag{2.22}$$

Since $\mathbf{B}$ is an $m \times m$ matrix, and $\text{rank}(\mathbf{A}) = m = \text{rank}(\mathbf{B})$, it is possible to express each column $\mathbf{a}_j$ of $\mathbf{A}$ as a linear combination of the columns $\mathbf{b}_i$ of $\mathbf{B}$ (the $\mathbf{b}_i$ are m of the $\mathbf{a}_j$, in some order):

$$\mathbf{a}_j = \beta_{1j}\mathbf{b}_1 + \dots + \beta_{mj}\mathbf{b}_m \tag{2.23}$$

$$= \sum_{i=1}^{m} \mathbf{b}_i \beta_{ij}$$

$$= \mathbf{B}\boldsymbol{\beta}_j, \tag{2.24}$$

where $\boldsymbol{\beta}_j$ is the column vector $[\beta_{1j}, \dots, \beta_{mj}]$. It is assumed that all the coefficients β_{ij}, $i = 1, \dots, m$, $j = 1, \dots, N$, are known for the given basic feasible solution. The new basic feasible solution is obtained from the given basic feasible solution in the simplest possible way: only one column of $\mathbf{B}$ is changed. Using a bar to denote new quantities, the first requirement is that $\overline{\mathbf{B}}$ must be non-singular. It is convenient to regard the matrix $\mathbf{A}$ as a reservoir of N column vectors, m of which form the basis matrix $\mathbf{B}$. Suppose that $\overline{\mathbf{B}}$ is formed from $\mathbf{B}$ by removing $\mathbf{b}_r$ from $\mathbf{B}$ and replacing it by $\mathbf{a}_k$ ($\neq \mathbf{0}$) from $\mathbf{A}$. We have seen that $\mathbf{a}_k$ can be expressed as a linear combination of $\mathbf{b}_1, \dots, \mathbf{b}_m$:

$$\mathbf{a}_k = \beta_{1k}\mathbf{b}_1 + \dots + \beta_{rk}\mathbf{b}_r + \dots + \beta_{mk}\mathbf{b}_m. \tag{2.25}$$

At this point we need the following well-known lemma [5].

Lemma

If the vectors $\mathbf{b}_1, \dots, \mathbf{b}_r, \dots, \mathbf{b}_m$ are linearly independent, and if $\mathbf{a} = \sum_{i=1}^{m} \beta_i \mathbf{b}_i$, then the vectors $\mathbf{b}_1, \dots, \mathbf{b}_{r-1}, \mathbf{a}, \mathbf{b}_{r+1}, \dots, \mathbf{b}_m$ are linearly independent if and only if $\beta_r \neq 0$.

Identifying $\mathbf{a}$ in the lemma with $\mathbf{a}_k$ in equation (2.25), we see that the columns of $\overline{\mathbf{B}}$ are linearly independent, i.e. $\overline{\mathbf{B}}$ is nonsingular, if and only if $\beta_{rk} \neq 0$. Thus our choice of k and r is restricted by the condition

$$\beta_{rk} \neq 0. \tag{2.26}$$

A further limitation, this time on the choice of r, is imposed by the condition that the new basic solution must be feasible. The analysis here closely resembles that of Theorem 2.1, Section 2.2. The given basic feasible solution satisfies

$$\sum_{i=1}^{m} x_{Bi}\mathbf{b}_i = \mathbf{b}, \tag{2.27}$$

which is merely another way of writing equation (2.21). Solving equation (2.25) for $\mathbf{b}_r$, and substituting the result in equation (2.27), we exhibit the new basic solution in the form

$$\sum_{\substack{i=1 \\ i \neq r}}^{m} \left(x_{Bi} - \frac{\beta_{ik}}{\beta_{rk}} x_{Br} \right) \mathbf{b}_i + \frac{x_{Br}}{\beta_{rk}} \mathbf{a}_k = \mathbf{b}. \tag{2.28}$$

This solution must be feasible, i.e.

$$\bar{x}_{Bi} = x_{Bi} - \frac{\beta_{ik}}{\beta_{rk}} x_{Br} \geqslant 0, \quad i = 1, \ldots, m, \quad i \neq r, \tag{2.29a}$$

and

$$\bar{x}_{Br} = \frac{x_{Br}}{\beta_{rk}} \geqslant 0. \tag{2.29b}$$

It may be helpful at this stage to consider in more detail the *replacement* of one basic variable by another, and the *changes in the values* of the basic variables, as we proceed from one basic feasible solution to the next. In this transformation all the basic variables *except one* remain basic, but in general the values of any number of basic variables may change. A typical case is shown in Table 2.1.

Table 2.1 Basic Variables in Consecutive Basic Feasible Solutions

Basic Variables		Values of Basic Variables	
Old	New	Old	New
$x_{B1} = x_2$	$\bar{x}_{B1} = x_2$	$x_2 = 15$	$x_2 = 8/3$
$x_{B2} = x_5$	$\bar{x}_{B2} = x_1$	$x_5 = 21$	$x_1 = 5/3$
$x_{B3} = x_7$	$\bar{x}_{B3} = x_7$	$x_7 = 11$	$x_7 = 22/3$

Returning to (2.29a) and (2.29b), we have

$$x_{Br} \geqslant 0,$$

because x_{Br} is a variable in a basic feasible solution. The cases $x_{Br} = 0$ and $x_{Br} > 0$ are considered separately.

If $x_{Br} = 0$, then (2.29a) and (2.29b) show that

$$\bar{x}_{Bi} = x_{Bi}, \quad i = 1, \ldots, m, \quad i \neq r, \quad \text{and } \bar{x}_{Br} = x_{Br} = 0, \tag{2.30}$$

so that in the new basic feasible solution the values of all the variables are unchanged from their old values. The only difference between the new and old solutions is that a different basic variable takes the value zero. Both solutions are degenerate.

If $x_{Br} > 0$, then (2.29b) shows that $\beta_{rk} > 0$, and (2.29a) then requires either

$$\left.\begin{aligned} &\beta_{ik} \leqslant 0, \\ \text{or} \quad &\beta_{ik} > 0 \quad \text{and} \quad \frac{x_{Bi}}{\beta_{ik}} \geqslant \frac{x_{Br}}{\beta_{rk}}. \end{aligned}\right\} \quad i = 1, \ldots, m, \quad i \neq r. \qquad \begin{aligned}(2.31a)\\(2.31b)\end{aligned}$$

Hence the new basic solution will be feasible if r is chosen such that

$$\frac{x_{Br}}{\beta_{rk}} = \min_{i=1,\ldots,m} \left\{\frac{x_{Bi}}{\beta_{ik}} : \beta_{ik} > 0\right\}. \tag{2.32}$$

This choice of r ensures that all the $(m-1)$ conditions (2.29a) are satisfied, as well as condition (2.29b). For brevity, each side of equation (2.32) is denoted by θ. Thus

$$\frac{x_{Br}}{\beta_{rk}} = \min_{i=1,\ldots,m} \left\{\frac{x_{Bi}}{\beta_{ik}} : \beta_{ik} > 0\right\} = \theta \geqslant 0. \tag{2.33}$$

The following special cases may arise.

(i) $x_{Br} = 0$. This is the case that led to equations (2.30); it is included here for the sake of completeness. Both the old and new basic feasible solutions are degenerate, and from (2.29a) and (2.29b) it is seen that the sign of β_{rk} $(\neq 0)$ is irrelevant.

(ii) The minimum in equation (2.33) does not determine r uniquely (though it must always yield a unique value for θ).

The choice of column vector $\mathbf{b}_r$ to be removed from $\mathbf{B}$ is made arbitrarily from among those $\mathbf{b}_r$ for which r satisfies (2.33). From equations (2.29a) and (2.33) we find that $\bar{x}_{Bi} = 0$ for all new basic variables for which i satisfies $(x_{Bi}/\beta_{ik}) = \theta$. Hence the new basic feasible solution is degenerate.

(iii) The given basic feasible solution is degenerate, and the β_{ik} corresponding to each degenerate variable x_{Bi} satisfies $\beta_{ik} < 0$.

Provided that r is uniquely determined by equation (2.33), the new basic feasible solution is non-degenerate; for in the determination of θ from equation (2.33), negative β_{ik} are ignored. Hence $\theta > 0$, and the result follows from (2.29a) and (2.29b), which can be written, respectively, in the form

$$\bar{x}_{Bi} = x_{Bi} - \theta\beta_{ik} \geqslant 0, \quad i = 1, \ldots, m, \quad i \neq r,$$

and

$$\bar{x}_{Br} = \theta \geqslant 0.$$

For this special case the above inequalities become 'strictly greater than' inequalities, and the non-degeneracy is proved.

(iv) There is no strictly positive β_{ik} as required by equation (2.33).

It will be shown in the next section that this case corresponds to an unbounded solution with an unbounded value of the objective function.

Finally, we determine the conditions that ensure $\bar{z} > z$ for the maximizing problem. These turn out to be conditions on k and θ. We have

$$z = \sum_{i=1}^{m} c_{Bi} x_{Bi}, \quad \bar{z} = \sum_{i=1}^{m} \bar{c}_{Bi} \bar{x}_{Bi}. \tag{2.34}$$

But $\bar{c}_{Bi} = c_{Bi}$, $i \neq r$, and $\bar{c}_{Br} = c_k$, while $\bar{x}_{Bi}$ and x_{Bi} are related by (2.29a) and (2.29b). Hence

$$\begin{aligned}
\bar{z} &= \sum_{\substack{i=1 \\ i \neq r}}^{m} c_{Bi}\left(x_{Bi} - \frac{\beta_{ik}}{\beta_{rk}} x_{Br}\right) + c_k \frac{x_{Br}}{\beta_{rk}} \\
&= \sum_{i=1}^{m} c_{Bi}\left(x_{Bi} - \frac{\beta_{ik}}{\beta_{rk}} x_{Br}\right) + c_k \frac{x_{Br}}{\beta_{rk}} \\
&= \sum_{i=1}^{m} c_{Bi} x_{Bi} - \frac{x_{Br}}{\beta_{rk}} \sum_{i=1}^{m} c_{Bi} \beta_{ik} + c_k \frac{x_{Br}}{\beta_{rk}} \\
&= z - \frac{x_{Br}}{\beta_{rk}} (z_k - c_k) \\
&= z - \theta (z_k - c_k),
\end{aligned} \tag{2.35}$$

where z_k is defined by

$$z_k = \sum_{i=1}^{m} c_{Bi} \beta_{ik} = \mathbf{c}'_B \boldsymbol{\beta}_k. \tag{2.36}$$

Also, z_k is known for the given basic feasible solution for any given k, since $\mathbf{c}_B$ and $\boldsymbol{\beta}_k$ are known. Since

$$\frac{x_{Br}}{\beta_{rk}} = \theta \geqslant 0,$$

equation (2.35) shows that $\bar{z} > z$ if and only if

$$z_k - c_k < 0 \text{ and } \theta > 0. \tag{2.37}$$

The condition imposed on k restricts the choice of column vector $\mathbf{a}_k$ from $\mathbf{A}$ to enter the basis matrix. In practice, when $z_k - c_k < 0$ for more than one value of k, it is usual to choose the value of k that makes $z_k - c_k$ a minimum. If $z_k - c_k$ is a minimum for more than one value of k, then any one of these values is chosen. It cannot be guaranteed that these rules for the determination of k make for efficient computation in every case, though they have the advantage of simplicity.

Note that conditions (2.37) may occur even when the given basic feasible solution is degenerate, for special case (iii) above shows that degeneracy does not necessarily imply $\theta = 0$ (although $\theta = 0$ does imply degeneracy). Also, it will be seen in the next section that if the given solution is non-optimal then there exists a value of k for which $z_k - c_k < 0$. If $\theta = 0$, then equation (2.35) shows that $\bar{z} = z$. The objective function is therefore not improved at this stage, but may be improved at a later stage if a subsequent basic feasible solution becomes non-degenerate through the operation of special case (iii) above.

Further investigation of the properties of equation (2.35) leads to a consideration of the various ways in which the simplex calculations may terminate. This is the subject of Section 2.4. Meanwhile, it is useful to summarize the main results of the present section. The following results refer to the *maximizing* problem in the standard form (2.10).

In a single iteration of the simplex method:

1. The vector $\mathbf{a}_k$ (the corresponding variable being x_k) is a candidate for entry to the basis matrix if k satisfies

$$z_k - c_k = \min_{j=1,\ldots,N} \{z_j - c_j \colon z_j - c_j < 0\}.$$

An additional condition on k, concerning the β_{ij} coefficients, is added later— see equation (2.54).

2. The vector $\mathbf{b}_r$ (the corresponding variable being x_{Br}) leaves the basis matrix, where r is determined from equation (2.33).

3. The objective function is improved if and only if $z_k - c_k < 0$ and $\theta > 0$, where θ is defined by equation (2.33).

2.4 Terminating the Simplex Calculations

A given linear programming problem has only a finite number of basic feasible solutions. Therefore by moving from one basic feasible solution to another the simplex method will either reach an optimal solution, if one exists, in a finite number of iterations (here we are anticipating Theorem 2.8); or reach an unbounded solution in a finite number of iterations; or cycle. Cycling can occur only in the presence of degeneracy, since a non-degenerate, non-optimal, basic feasible solution is always followed by a basic feasible solution with an improved value of the objective function—see (2.37), *et seq.*

The necessary and sufficient conditions for the objective function corresponding to a non-degenerate basic feasible solution to be improved are given by (2.37), with θ defined by equation (2.33). These conditions are violated in the following two cases.

(i) There exists at least one value of k for which $z_k - c_k < 0$, but θ does not exist because $\beta_{ik} \leqslant 0$ for each of these values of k and for all i, $i = 1, \ldots, m$.

(ii) There is no value of k for which $z_k - c_k < 0$. In other words, $z_j - c_j \geqslant 0$ for every column vector $\mathbf{a}_j$ of $\mathbf{A}$ which does not belong to $\mathbf{B}$.

These two cases correspond to the only two ways in which the simplex calculations can terminate with a non-degenerate basic feasible solution (including the special case which indicates the existence of an unbounded solution associated with a finite value of the objective function; this special case, which has already appeared in Section 1.2, is discussed in Section 2.8.1 under the heading of 'Alternative Optima'). We shall see that the simplex calculations also terminate in these two cases when the current basic feasible solution is degenerate. It will now be shown that in case (i) there is an unbounded solution with an unbounded value of the objective function, and that in case (ii) the current basic feasible solution is optimal. It should be pointed out that an unbounded solution can often be recognized, and the calculations terminated, before the situation described in case (i) arises. We shall prove this stronger result in Theorem 2.2.

■ Theorem 2.2

For the maximizing problem in the standard form (2.10), suppose that in the current basic feasible solution there exists at least one value of k for which $z_k - c_k < 0$ and $\beta_{ik} \leqslant 0$ for all i, $i = 1, \ldots, m$. Then the problem has an unbounded solution with an unbounded value of the objective function.
N.B. In comparison with case (i) above, we have replaced the conditions $\beta_{ik} \leqslant 0$ for *each* of the values of k for which $z_k - c_k < 0$, and for all i, by the conditions $\beta_{ik} \leqslant 0$ for *at least one* of these values of k, and for all i.

Proof

One of the rules of the simplex method, as shown by equation (2.33), is that if $\mathbf{a}_k$ enters the basis matrix then $\beta_{ik} > 0$ for at least one value of i. Let us now break this rule by allowing $\mathbf{a}_k$ to enter the basis matrix when $\beta_{ik} \leqslant 0$ for all $i, i = 1, \ldots, m$. (This procedure is valid *algebraically*.) Condition (2.26) becomes $\beta_{rk} < 0$, and equation (2.29b) then shows that $\bar{x}_{Br} = x_{Br} = 0$ if the basic solution is to remain feasible.

Instead of attempting to obtain another basic feasible solution, we break another rule of the simplex method and obtain a non-basic feasible solution as follows. The current basic feasible solution satisfies

$$\sum_{i=1}^{m} x_{Bi}\,\mathbf{b}_i = \mathbf{b},$$

i.e.
$$\sum_{i=1}^{m} x_{Bi}\,\mathbf{b}_i - \phi\mathbf{a}_k + \phi\mathbf{a}_k = \mathbf{b}, \tag{2.38}$$

where ϕ is arbitrary. But from equation (2.23) we have

$$\mathbf{a}_k = \sum_{i=1}^{m} \beta_{ik}\,\mathbf{b}_i,$$

so that equation (2.38) becomes

$$\sum_{i=1}^{m} (x_{Bi} - \phi\beta_{ik})\,\mathbf{b}_i + \phi\mathbf{a}_k = \mathbf{b}. \tag{2.39}$$

When $\phi > 0$, equation (2.39) represents a non-basic feasible solution with $(m+1)$ variables, all of which may take non-zero values, since $\beta_{ik} \leqslant 0$. The value of the objective function for this solution is

$$\bar{z} = \sum_{i=1}^{m} c_{Bi}(x_{Bi} - \phi\beta_{ik}) + c_k\phi$$
$$= z - \phi(z_k - c_k).$$

Since $z_k - c_k < 0$, the value of $\bar{z}$ can be made arbitrarily large by choosing ϕ sufficiently large, i.e. the problem has an unbounded solution with an unbounded value of the objective function.

Theorem 2.3 deals with case (ii) above, which may be regarded as the normal case.

■ Theorem 2.3

For the maximizing problem in the standard form (2.10), suppose that, in the current basic feasible solution, $z_j - c_j \geqslant 0$ for every column vector $\mathbf{a}_j$ of $\mathbf{A}$ which does not belong to $\mathbf{B}$. Then the current basic feasible solution is optimal.

Proof

We begin by proving that, for any basic feasible solution, $z_j - c_j = 0$ for every column vector $\mathbf{a}_j$ of $\mathbf{A}$ which *belongs* to $\mathbf{B}$. For suppose that $\mathbf{a}_j = \mathbf{b}_i$. Then $c_j = c_{Bi}$, and $x_j = x_{Bi}$. Equation (2.24) gives

$$\boldsymbol{\beta}_j = \mathbf{B}^{-1}\mathbf{a}_j = \mathbf{B}^{-1}\mathbf{b}_i = \mathbf{e}_i,$$

where $\mathbf{e}_i$ is the unit column vector $[0, 0, \ldots, 1, \ldots, 0]$ with the 1 in the ith position. Therefore

$$\begin{aligned} z_j - c_j &= \mathbf{c}_B'\boldsymbol{\beta}_j - c_j, \quad \text{by the definition of } z_j, \\ &= \mathbf{c}_B'\mathbf{e}_i - c_j \\ &= c_{Bi} - c_j \\ &= 0. \end{aligned} \tag{2.40}$$

Combining this result with the hypothesis of the theorem, we can state that, for the current basic feasible solution,

$$z_j - c_j \geqslant 0 \quad \text{for all } j, \quad j = 1, \ldots, N, \tag{2.41}$$

i.e. for *every* column vector $\mathbf{a}_j$ of $\mathbf{A}$.

Now, for any basic feasible solution, by eliminating the vectors $\mathbf{a}_j$ from equation (2.11) by means of equation (2.23), we obtain

$$\mathbf{b}_1\sum_{j=1}^{N} x_j\beta_{1j} + \ldots + \mathbf{b}_m\sum_{j=1}^{N} x_j\beta_{mj} = \mathbf{b}. \tag{2.42}$$

But from equation (2.21),

$$\mathbf{b}_1 x_{B1} + \ldots + \mathbf{b}_m x_{Bm} = \mathbf{b}. \tag{2.43}$$

Comparing equations (2.42) and (2.43), we see that

$$x_{Bi} = \sum_{j=1}^{N} x_j \beta_{ij}, \quad i = 1, \ldots, m, \tag{2.44}$$

since $\mathbf{b}$ is represented uniquely in terms of the linearly independent vectors $\mathbf{b}_1, \ldots, \mathbf{b}_m$.

The current value of the objective function is

$$\begin{aligned} z_c &= c_{B1} x_{B1} + \ldots + c_{Bm} x_{Bm} \\ &= c_{B1} \sum_{j=1}^{N} x_j \beta_{1j} + \ldots + c_{Bm} \sum_{j=1}^{N} x_j \beta_{mj}, \text{ using equation (2.44),} \\ &= x_1 \sum_{i=1}^{m} c_{Bi} \beta_{i1} + \ldots + x_N \sum_{i=1}^{m} c_{Bi} \beta_{iN}, \end{aligned}$$

i.e.
$$z_c = z_1 x_1 + \ldots + z_N x_N. \tag{2.45}$$

If z is the value of the objective function for *any* feasible solution $\mathbf{x} = [x_1, \ldots, x_N]$, then

$$z = c_1 x_1 + \ldots + c_N x_N. \tag{2.46}$$

But condition (2.41) holds for the current basic feasible solution. Hence equations (2.45) and (2.46) show that $z_c \geqslant z$, i.e. that z_c is optimal.

The proofs of Theorems 2.2 and 2.3 do not require the current basic feasible solutions to be non-degenerate. Thus, as stated earlier, the results of these theorems also apply when degeneracy is present.

To sum up, the simplex method is terminated when the conditions of either Theorem 2.2 or Theorem 2.3 apply. In the case of Theorem 2.3, equivalent conditions are that, in the current basic feasible solution,

$$z_j - c_j \geqslant 0 \quad \text{for all } j, \quad j = 1, \ldots, N.$$

These are known as the *optimality conditions* (for a maximizing problem). Taking Theorems 2.1, 2.2, and 2.3 together, remembering the special case of an unbounded solution with a finite value of the objective function, and anticipating Theorem 2.8, we have shown that, apart from the possibility of cycling, every linear programming problem falls into one of the following three categories.

1. There is no feasible solution.
2. There is an unbounded solution.
3. There is an optimal solution.

N.B. When a linear programming problem has an unbounded solution with a *finite* value of the objective function, it also has an infinite number of finite *optimal* solutions with the same finite value of the objective function—see Section 2.8.1.

There remains the possibility of cycling—examples have been constructed which show that cycling can occur. However, even before any such example had been constructed, a method for avoiding cycling had been devised by Dantzig [9]: the remedy was available before the disease appeared! The method is to perturb slightly the constant terms in the given problem in such a way that the basic feasible solutions of the perturbed problem become non-degenerate, while at the same time the corresponding basic solutions of the given problem remain feasible. It is a curious fact that, although degeneracy is quite common in practice, cycling has occurred only in artificially constructed problems. Since the perturbation method is of considerable theoretical significance, it is described in detail in Section 2.10, where an example which leads to cycling may also be found. Meanwhile, we shall ignore the possibility of cycling, knowing that it can be eliminated if necessary.

2.5 Simplex Rules

Equations (2.29a) and (2.29b) give the new values of the basic variables after a single iteration of the simplex method, and equation (2.35) gives the new value of the objective function. However, the iteration is not complete until we have also calculated new values of β_{ij} and $z_j - c_j$, the latter being more convenient for simplex calculations than z_j alone.

To calculate $\bar{\beta}_{ij}$, we assume, as usual, that $\mathbf{a}_k$ replaces $\mathbf{b}_r$ in the basis matrix, i.e. that $\bar{\mathbf{b}}_r = \mathbf{a}_k$, and we use equation (2.23) twice, to give

$$\mathbf{a}_j = \sum_{\substack{i=1 \\ i \neq r}}^{m} \beta_{ij} \mathbf{b}_i + \beta_{rj} \mathbf{b}_r \tag{2.47}$$

and

$$\mathbf{a}_k = \sum_{\substack{i=1 \\ i \neq r}}^{m} \beta_{ik} \mathbf{b}_i + \beta_{rk} \mathbf{b}_r. \tag{2.48}$$

Using equation (2.48) to eliminate $\mathbf{b}_r$ from equation (2.47), we obtain

$$\mathbf{a}_j = \sum_{\substack{i=1 \\ i \neq r}}^{m} \left(\beta_{ij} - \frac{\beta_{ik}\beta_{rj}}{\beta_{rk}} \right) \mathbf{b}_i + \frac{\beta_{rj}}{\beta_{rk}} \mathbf{a}_k. \tag{2.49}$$

The representation of $\mathbf{a}_j$ in terms of the new basis vectors is found by copying equation (2.47):

$$\mathbf{a}_j = \sum_{\substack{i=1 \\ i \neq r}}^{m} \bar{\beta}_{ij} \bar{\mathbf{b}}_i + \bar{\beta}_{rj} \bar{\mathbf{b}}_r. \tag{2.50}$$

Comparing equations (2.49) and (2.50), and remembering that $\bar{\mathbf{b}}_r = \mathbf{a}_k$, we find the required expressions for $\bar{\beta}_{ij}$:

$$\bar{\beta}_{ij} = \beta_{ij} - \frac{\beta_{ik}\beta_{rj}}{\beta_{rk}}, \quad i \neq r, \tag{2.51a}$$

$$\bar{\beta}_{rj} = \frac{\beta_{rj}}{\beta_{rk}}. \tag{2.51b}$$

To calculate $\bar{z}_j - c_j$, we copy the definition of equation (2.36):

$$\bar{z}_j - c_j = \sum_{i=1}^{m} \bar{c}_{Bi}\bar{\beta}_{ij} - c_j. \tag{2.52}$$

But $\bar{c}_{Bi} = c_{Bi}$, $i \neq r$, and $\bar{c}_{Br} = c_k$. Using equations (2.51a) and (2.51b), we have

$$\begin{aligned} \bar{z}_j - c_j &= \sum_{\substack{i=1 \\ i \neq r}}^{m} c_{Bi}\left(\beta_{ij} - \frac{\beta_{ik}\beta_{rj}}{\beta_{rk}}\right) + \frac{c_k\beta_{rj}}{\beta_{rk}} - c_j \\ &= (z_j - c_j) - \frac{\beta_{rj}}{\beta_{rk}}(z_k - c_k). \end{aligned} \tag{2.53}$$

Computational schemes for the simplex method take advantage of the striking similarities among the transformation equations (2.29a), (2.29b), (2.35), (2.51a), (2.51b), and (2.53); also, the simplex transformations become much clearer when the calculations are set out in tableau form, as shown in the next section. To conclude the present section, a summary of the rules for the application of the simplex method, incorporating all the results obtained so far, is given for reference. Since the basic variables and their values are of particular interest, a simplex transformation is regarded as an interchange of a basic and a non-basic variable, and we shall say that a variable 'becomes basic' or 'becomes non-basic'.

Maximizing problem

Assume that for the linear programming problem in the standard form (2.10) we have a basic feasible solution $\mathbf{x}_B$, and assume also that we know z, β_{ij} and $z_j - c_j$ (all i and j) for this solution. The steps in a simplex iteration are then:

1(a). Test for optimal solution. If $z_j - c_j \geqslant 0$ for all j, $j = 1, \ldots, N$, then the solution is optimal.

1(b). Test for unbounded solution. If there exists at least one j ($j = k$, say) for which $z_j - c_j < 0$, and $\beta_{ik} \leqslant 0$ for all i, $i = 1, \ldots, m$, then there is an unbounded solution with an unbounded value of the objective function.

1(c). When neither 1(a) nor 1(b) is applicable, there exists at least one j for which $z_j - c_j < 0$, and $\beta_{ij} > 0$ for at least one i for each of these j. The variable x_k becomes basic, where k is chosen by the rule:

$$z_k - c_k = \min_{j=1,\ldots,N} \{z_j - c_j : z_j - c_j < 0, \beta_{ij} > 0 \text{ for at least one } i, i = 1, \ldots, m\}. \tag{2.54}$$

If this rule does not determine k uniquely, then one of the values of k is chosen arbitrarily.

2. When 1(c) holds, the variable x_{Br} becomes non-basic, where r is chosen by the rule (2.32):

$$\frac{x_{Br}}{\beta_{rk}} = \min_{i=1,\ldots,m} \left\{ \frac{x_{Bi}}{\beta_{ik}} : \beta_{ik} > 0 \right\}.$$

If this rule does not determine r uniquely, then one of the values of r is chosen arbitrarily.

3. Compute $\bar{x}_{Bi}, \bar{z}, \bar{\beta}_{ij}$ and $\bar{z}_j - c_j$, for all i and j, from equations (2.29a), (2.29b), (2.35), (2.51a), (2.51b), and (2.53).

Minimizing problem

It was indicated in equation (1.9), Section 1.2, how a minimizing problem may be solved indirectly by changing it into a maximizing problem. However, it is sometimes desirable to solve a minimizing problem directly. Suppose that the problem is expressed in the standard form

$$\text{Minimize } z = \mathbf{c}'\mathbf{x},$$

subject to

$$\mathbf{Ax} = \mathbf{b} \quad \text{and} \quad \mathbf{x} \geqslant \mathbf{0}.$$

The simplex iteration for the minimizing problem differs from that for the maximizing problem only in step 1. For the minimizing problem, we have:

1(a). Test for optimal solution. If $z_j - c_j \leqslant 0$ for all $j, j = 1, \ldots, N$, then the solution is optimal.

1(b). Test for unbounded solution. If there exists at least one j ($j = k$, say) for which $z_j - c_j > 0$, and $\beta_{ik} \leqslant 0$ for all $i, i = 1, \ldots, m$, then there is an unbounded solution with an unbounded value of the objective function.

1(c). When neither 1(a) nor 1(b) is applicable, there exists at least one j for which $z_j - c_j > 0$, and $\beta_{ij} > 0$ for at least one i for each of these j. The variable x_k becomes basic, where k is chosen by the rule:

$$z_k - c_k = \max_{j=1,\ldots,N} \{z_j - c_j : z_j - c_j > 0, \beta_{ij} > 0 \quad \text{for at least one } i, i = 1, \ldots, m\}. \tag{2.55}$$

If this rule does not determine k uniquely, then one of the values of k is chosen arbitrarily.

Steps 2 and 3 for the minimizing problem are identical with those for the maximizing problem.

2.6 Simplex Tableaux

Simplex calculations are most conveniently performed with the help of a series of tables known as simplex tableaux. Consider again Example 1.1 of Section 1.2, which was solved graphically in Section 1.2, and by the simplex method in Section 1.3.

***Example* 2.2**

$$\text{Maximize } z = 4x_1 + 3x_2,$$

subject to

$$3x_1 + 4x_2 \leqslant 12,$$
$$7x_1 + 2x_2 \leqslant 14,$$
$$x_1, x_2 \geqslant 0.$$

Solution

Adding slack variables x_3, x_4, the constraints become

$$\left.\begin{aligned} 3x_1 + 4x_2 + x_3 &= 12, \\ 7x_1 + 2x_2 + x_4 &= 14. \end{aligned}\right\} \tag{2.56}$$

It is immediately obvious that a basic feasible solution is

$$x_1 = 0, x_2 = 0, x_3 = 12, x_4 = 14.$$

All the above information is set out in Tableau 1. We shall refer to this type of tableau as the *standard simplex tableau.*

Tableau 1 (Example 2.2)

	$\mathbf{c}'$		4	3	0	0
$\mathbf{c}_B$	Basic Variables		x_1	x_2	x_3	x_4
0 0	x_3 x_4	12 14	3 7*	4 2	1 0	0 1
	$z_j - c_j$	0	−4	−3	0	0

The *numbers* appearing in this tableau, in the present notation, are shown in Tableau 1a.

Tableau 1a (Example 2.2)

			c_1	c_2	c_3	c_4
$c_{B1} = c_3$ $c_{B2} = c_4$		$x_{B1} = x_3$ $x_{B2} = x_4$	β_{11} β_{21}	β_{12} β_{22}	β_{13} β_{23}	β_{14} β_{24}
		z	$z_1 - c_1$	$z_2 - c_2$	$z_3 - c_3$	$z_4 - c_4$

For Tableau 1, using equation (2.24),

$$\boldsymbol{\beta}_1 = \begin{pmatrix} \beta_{11} \\ \beta_{21} \end{pmatrix} = \mathbf{a}_1, \quad \boldsymbol{\beta}_2 = \begin{pmatrix} \beta_{12} \\ \beta_{22} \end{pmatrix} = \mathbf{a}_2, \text{ etc.,}$$

since the basis matrix at this stage is the unit matrix

$$\begin{pmatrix} 1 & 0 \\ 0 & 1 \end{pmatrix}.$$

The $z_j - c_j$ entries in the last row are obtained from the definition of z_j, equation (2.36):

$$z_j - c_j = \mathbf{c}_B'\boldsymbol{\beta}_j - c_j, \quad j = 1, \ldots, N. \tag{2.57}$$

Since $\mathbf{c}_B = \mathbf{0}$ for Tableau 1, equations (2.57) give

$$z_j - c_j = -c_j, \quad j = 1, 2, 3, 4.$$

A simplex tableau is constructed for each iteration of the simplex method: all the information that is required for the next iteration is included in the current tableau.

In order to obtain Tableau 2, the simplex rules for the maximizing problem (Section 2.5) are applied to Tableau 1. Paragraph 1(c) applies, and min $\{-4, -3\} = -4$, so that x_1 becomes basic. Likewise, from paragraph 2 of the simplex rules, we find that the variable to become non-basic is determined from

$$\min\left\{\frac{x_{B1}}{\beta_{11}}, \frac{x_{B2}}{\beta_{21}}\right\} = \min\left\{\frac{12}{3}, \frac{14}{7}\right\} = \frac{14}{7} = 2.$$

Hence $x_{B2} = x_4$ becomes non-basic. The element in the tableau at the intersection of the x_1 column and the x_4 row, indicating the pair of variables to be exchanged, is called the *pivot*. The pivot ($\beta_{rk} = \beta_{21} = 7$) is denoted by an asterisk—there should be no confusion between this asterisk and one which denotes an optimal quantity.

In connection with paragraph 3 of the simplex rules (Section 2.5) which refers, in effect, to the construction of the new tableau, a remarkable simplification is obtained by extending the β_{ij} notation to cover the whole of the tableau (apart from the prices). If we write

$$x_{B1} = \beta_{10},\ x_{B2} = \beta_{20},\ z = \beta_{30},$$
$$z_1 - c_1 = \beta_{31},\ z_2 - c_2 = \beta_{32},\ z_3 - c_3 = \beta_{33},\ z_4 - c_4 = \beta_{34},$$

then it follows from the equations quoted in paragraph 3 of the simplex rules that the whole transformation can be written in the form

$$\bar{\beta}_{ij} = \beta_{ij} - \frac{\beta_{ik}\beta_{rj}}{\beta_{rk}}, \quad i = 1, 2, \ldots, m+1, i \neq r, \quad j = 0, 1, \ldots, N, \tag{2.58a}$$

$$\bar{\beta}_{rj} = \frac{\beta_{rj}}{\beta_{rk}}, \quad j = 0, 1, \ldots, N. \tag{2.58b}$$

It is convenient to compute row r first, using equations (2.58b): divide each element in the old row r by the pivot β_{rk}. The numbers on the right-hand side of each of equations (2.58a) appear in the tableau at the corners of a rectangle:

$$\begin{matrix} \beta_{ij} & \cdots & \beta_{ik} \\ \vdots & & \vdots \\ \beta_{rj} & \cdots & \beta_{rk}^* \end{matrix} \quad \text{or} \quad \begin{matrix} \beta_{rj} & \cdots & \beta_{rk}^* \\ \vdots & & \vdots \\ \beta_{ij} & \cdots & \beta_{ik} \end{matrix} \qquad (j < k; \text{ similarly for } j > k)$$

depending on whether the element to be transformed (β_{ij}) is situated above or below the pivot. Note that equations (2.58a) can be written more symmetrically as

$$\bar{\beta}_{ij} = \frac{\beta_{ij}\beta_{rk} - \beta_{ik}\beta_{rj}}{\beta_{rk}}, \quad i = 1, 2, \ldots, m+1, \quad i \neq r, \quad j = 0, 1, \ldots, N;$$

this form is more suitable for hand computation. The computation of the elements in a new tableau may be speeded up even further by working row by row along the non-pivotal rows. Along the ith row,

$$\frac{\beta_{ik}}{\beta_{rk}} = \text{constant} = k_i, \text{ say,}$$

and the transformation equations (2.58a) simplify to

$$\bar{\beta}_{ij} = \beta_{ij} - k_i\beta_{rj}, \quad i = 1, 2, \ldots, m+1, \quad i \neq r, \quad j = 0, 1, \ldots, N. \tag{2.58c}$$

Thus the transformation equations (2.58a) and (2.58b) turn out to be unexpectedly easy to use. We can now construct Tableau 2.

Tableau 2 (Example 2.2)

	$\mathbf{c}'$		4	3	0	0
$\mathbf{c}_B$	Basic Variables		x_1	x_2	x_3	x_4
0	x_3	6	0	22/7*	1	−3/7
4	x_1	2	1	2/7	0	1/7
	$z_j - c_j$	8	0	−13/7	0	4/7

The columns headed x_1 and x_3 can be filled in immediately with 1's and 0's, since x_1 and x_3 are basic variables. For if $x_j = x_{Bi}$ is a basic variable, then $\boldsymbol{\beta}_j$ is the unit vector $\mathbf{e}_i$, and $z_j - c_j = 0$, as was shown at the beginning of the proof of Theorem 2.3. Alternatively, the columns in any tableau which correspond to basic variables may be omitted altogether. It is instructive to compare Tableau 2 with equations (1.20)–(1.23) of Section 1.3, which correspond to the same stage of the calculation.

The $z_j - c_j$ values of Tableau 2 were calculated by means of equations (2.58c); they could also have been obtained from equations (2.57). The latter equations should always be used as a check on the arithmetic, though they do not necessarily provide a complete check owing to the fact that zero multipliers may hide some errors. This check extends to the objective function $z = \mathbf{c}_B'\mathbf{x}_B$. The price vectors are included in the tableau solely for the purpose of checking: they play no direct part in the simplex transformations. A *complete* check on the tableau arithmetic may be obtained with only a small additional amount of computation, as described in Exercise 3 at the end of this chapter.

From Tableau 2, we see that x_2 will become basic at the next iteration. The variable to become non-basic is determined from

$$\min\left\{\frac{6}{22/7}, \frac{2}{2/7}\right\} = \frac{6}{22/7} = \frac{21}{11}.$$

This shows that $x_{B1} = x_3$ becomes non-basic. Hence the pivot is 22/7, and we are ready to construct the next tableau.

Tableau 3 (Example 2.2)

	$\mathbf{c}'$		4	3	0	0
$\mathbf{c}_B$	Basic Variables		x_1	x_2	x_3	x_4
3	x_2	21/11	0	1	7/22	−3/22
4	x_1	16/11	1	0	−1/11	2/11
	$z_j - c_j$	127/11	0	0	13/22	7/22

Tableau 3 is optimal, since $z_j - c_j \geqslant 0$ for all j. It should be compared with equations (1.26)–(1.29) of Section 1.3. The optimal solution is

$$x_1^* = 16/11,\ x_2^* = 21/11;\quad z^* = 127/11,$$

and for this solution the slack variables x_3 and x_4, being non-basic, take zero values.

2.7 Artificial Variables

After slack and surplus variables have been added to the constraints, it often happens that there is no immediately obvious basic feasible solution. The method used to overcome this difficulty is ingenious: the simplex method itself is employed to produce a basic feasible solution of the given problem, starting with a basic feasible solution of a different problem. An example will make the process clear.

Example 2.3

$$\left.\begin{aligned} &\text{Minimize } z = 2x_1 - 3x_2 + x_3,\\ &\text{subject to}\\ &3x_1 - 2x_2 + x_3 \leqslant 5,\\ &x_1 + 3x_2 - 4x_3 \leqslant 9,\\ &x_2 + 5x_3 \geqslant 1,\\ &x_1 + x_2 + x_3 = 6,\\ &x_1, x_2, x_3 \geqslant 0. \end{aligned}\right\} \tag{2.59}$$

Solution

First, we choose to solve the problem directly as a minimizing problem rather than change it into a maximizing problem. After slack and surplus variables have been introduced, the constraints become

$$\left.\begin{aligned} 3x_1 - 2x_2 + x_3 + x_4 &= 5,\\ x_1 + 3x_2 - 4x_3 + x_5 &= 9,\\ x_2 + 5x_3 - x_6 &= 1,\\ x_1 + x_2 + x_3 &= 6. \end{aligned}\right\} \tag{2.60}$$

There is no obvious basic feasible solution with which to start the simplex calculations. However, by adding *artificial variables* x_7 and x_8 to the third and fourth of equations (2.60), respectively, we can construct an *augmented problem* with an obvious basic feasible solution. The constraints (2.60) now become

$$\left.\begin{aligned} 3x_1 - 2x_2 + x_3 + x_4 &= 5,\\ x_1 + 3x_2 - 4x_3 + x_5 &= 9,\\ x_2 + 5x_3 - x_6 + x_7 &= 1,\\ x_1 + x_2 + x_3 + x_8 &= 6. \end{aligned}\right\} \tag{2.61}$$

An obvious basic feasible solution of equations (2.61) is

$$x_4 = 5,\ x_5 = 9,\ x_7 = 1,\ x_8 = 6.$$

N.B. Artificial variables satisfy non-negativity restrictions.

The simplex method can now be used to force the artificial variables to zero by assigning to each of them a large positive price M. Since we are solving a minimizing problem, the artificial variables are forced to become non-basic. (For a maximizing problem, we assign a large negative price, $-M$, to each artificial variable.) This device was first suggested by Charnes [7], and is known as 'Charnes' M-method'. The simplex calculations proceed in the usual way, apart from a minor modification to the $z_j - c_j$ rows in the tableaux.

Tableau 1 (Example 2.3)

	$\mathbf{c}'$		2	−3	1	0	0	0	M	M
$\mathbf{c}_B$	Basic Variables		x_1	x_2	x_3	x_4	x_5	x_6	x_7	x_8
0	x_4	5	3	−2	1	1	0	0	0	0
0	x_5	9	1	3	−4	0	1	0	0	0
M	x_7	1	0	1	5*	0	0	−1	1	0
M	x_8	6	1	1	1	0	0	0	0	1
	$z_j - c_j$	0	−2	3	−1	0	0	0	0	0
		$7M$	M	$2M$	$6M$	0	0	$-M$	0	0

With regard to the $z_j - c_j$ values of Tableau 1, it is convenient to write the terms involving M on a separate line. Because of the linear nature of the simplex transformation equations (2.58c) the two $z_j - c_j$ rows can be transformed independently; indeed, it is only necessary to write down the *coefficients* of the M terms—and this will always be done from now on—provided we remember that these terms always appear in the last row of the tableau.

Since M is regarded as being indefinitely large, the terms of $z_j - c_j$, $j = 1, \ldots, 8$, that are independent of M in Tableau 1 (i.e. those in the penultimate row) may be neglected when applying equation (2.55). Thus x_3 becomes basic and x_7 becomes non-basic; but x_7 is an artificial variable, and was introduced solely to obtain a basic feasible solution to an augmented problem. It has now become non-basic, its job is therefore done, and it may be ignored in subsequent tableaux. Similarly, any artificial variable that becomes non-basic is subsequently ignored.

Tableaux 2–7 require no further explanation.

Tableau 7 is optimal for Example 2.3 (a minimizing problem). The optimal solution is

$$x_1^* = 0, \quad x_2^* = 33/7. \quad x_3^* = 9/7; \quad z^* = -90/7.$$

Tableau 2 (Example 2.3)

	c′		2	−3	1	0	0	0	M
$\mathbf{c}_B$	Basic Variables		x_1	x_2	x_3	x_4	x_5	x_6	x_8
0	x_4	24/5	3*	−11/5	0	1	0	1/5	0
0	x_5	49/5	1	19/5	0	0	1	−4/5	0
1	x_3	1/5	0	1/5	1	0	0	−1/5	0
M	x_8	29/5	1	4/5	0	0	0	1/5	1
	$z_j - c_j$	1/5	−2	16/5	0	0	0	−1/5	0
		29/5	1	4/5	0	0	0	1/5	0

Tableau 3 (Example 2.3)

	c′		2	−3	1	0	0	0	M
$\mathbf{c}_B$	Basic Variables		x_1	x_2	x_3	x_4	x_5	x_6	x_8
2	x_1	8/5	1	−11/15	0	1/3	0	1/15	0
0	x_5	41/5	0	68/15	0	−1/3	1	−13/15	0
1	x_3	1/5	0	1/5*	1	0	0	−1/5	0
M	x_8	21/5	0	23/15	0	−1/3	0	2/15	1
	$z_j - c_j$	17/5	0	26/15	0	2/3	0	−1/15	0
		21/5	0	23/15	0	−1/3	0	2/15	0

Tableau 4 (Example 2.3)

	c′		2	−3	1	0	0	0	M
$\mathbf{c}_B$	Basic Variables		x_1	x_2	x_3	x_4	x_5	x_6	x_8
2	x_1	7/3	1	0	11/3	1/3	0	−2/3	0
0	x_5	11/3	0	0	−68/3	−1/3	1	11/3*	0
−3	x_2	1	0	1	5	0	0	−1	0
M	x_8	8/3	0	0	−23/3	−1/3	0	5/3	1
	$z_j - c_j$	5/3	0	0	−26/3	2/3	0	5/3	0
		8/3	0	0	−23/3	−1/3	0	5/3	0

In Charnes' M-method, as carried out on Example 2.3, we did not have to specify a value for M. When a digital computer is used to solve this type of problem, either M is assigned a large value, say 10^6 for the above example, or the *two-phase method* is used.

The two-phase method is very similar to the M-method. In phase 1, artificial variables are each given the price 1 for a minimizing problem or −1 for a

Tableau 5 (Example 2.3)

	c′		2	−3	1	0	0	0	M
c_B	Basic Variables		x_1	x_2	x_3	x_4	x_5	x_6	x_8
2	x_1	3	1	0	−5/11	3/11	2/11	0	0
0	x_6	1	0	0	−68/11	−1/11	3/11	1	0
−3	x_2	2	0	1	−13/11	−1/11	3/11	0	0
M	x_8	1	0	0	29/11*	−2/11	−5/11	0	1
	$z_j - c_j$	0	0	0	18/11	9/11	−5/11	0	0
		1	0	0	29/11	−2/11	−5/11	0	0

Tableau 6 (Example 2.3)

	c′		2	−3	1	0	0	0
c_B	Basic Variables		x_1	x_2	x_3	x_4	x_5	x_6
2	x_1	92/29	1	0	0	7/29*	3/29	0
0	x_6	97/29	0	0	0	−15/29	−23/29	1
−3	x_2	71/29	0	1	0	−5/29	2/29	0
1	x_3	11/29	0	0	1	−2/29	−5/29	0
	$z_j - c_j$	−18/29	0	0	0	27/29	−5/29	0

Tableau 7 (Example 2.3)

	c′		2	−3	1	0	0	0
c_B	Basic Variables		x_1	x_2	x_3	x_4	x_5	x_6
0	x_4	92/7	29/7	0	0	1	3/7	0
0	x_6	71/7	15/7	0	0	0	−4/7	1
−3	x_2	33/7	5/7	1	0	0	1/7	0
1	x_3	9/7	2/7	0	1	0	−1/7	0
	$z_j - c_j$	−90/7	−27/7	0	0	0	−4/7	0

maximizing problem, and all other variables (regardless of their true prices) are given a price of zero. Thus the objective function in phase 1 is the sum of all the artificial variables for a minimizing problem, and minus this sum for a maximizing problem. The simplex calculations are carried out in the usual way with the aim of making every artificial variable non-basic. Phase 1 ends when the objective function is either optimized (shown by the optimality conditions being satisfied) or made to vanish, whichever comes first—these two alternatives may coincide. At this point, one of the following three situations must have arisen:

1. All the artificial variables have become non-basic.
2. One or more non-degenerate artificial variables cannot be made non-basic.
3. One or more degenerate artificial variables cannot be made non-basic.

In case 1 we have found a basic feasible solution of the given problem, and phase 2 begins: the non-artificial variables are assigned their true prices, and the simplex calculations proceed normally.

In case 2 the given problem has no feasible solution; further details of this case are given in Section 2.8.2.

In case 3 we have found a degenerate basic feasible solution of the given problem. One or more of the constraints may be redundant, as explained in Section 2.8.3. We can proceed with phase 2 provided we ensure that the degenerate artificial variables remain degenerate throughout the rest of the calculation. (There is no similar problem in Charnes' M-method, because of the prices, $\pm M$, of the artificial variables.) Several computational schemes which satisfy this condition have been suggested. The simplest device is to make non-basic any degenerate artificial variable which would otherwise become non-degenerate, even though this procedure breaks the simplex rules. It is always possible to do this while maintaining a basic feasible solution, for the variable which replaces the degenerate artificial variable will itself be degenerate, as is made clear by considering the following tableau fragment:

$$
\begin{array}{l}
x_{Br} = 0 \ldots \beta_{rk} < 0 \\
\ldots \\
x_{Bt} = 0 \\
\ldots \\
x_{Bs} > 0 \ldots \beta_{sk}{}^{*} > 0
\end{array}
$$

Suppose that x_{Br} is a degenerate artificial basic variable and that x_{Bs} is a non-degenerate non-artificial basic variable, while the usual simplex rules indicate that x_k is to become basic and x_{Bs} non-basic, so that β_{sk} is the pivot. Then the new value of the artificial variable x_{Br} is $\bar{x}_{Br} > 0$. To avoid this result take β_{rk} to be the pivot; then x_k still becomes basic, but now $\bar{x}_{Br} = x_k = 0$, all degenerate basic variables (such as x_{Bt}) remain degenerate, and the new basic solution is feasible.

2.8 Special Cases

It is important to be able to recognize and interpret certain special properties of simplex tableaux when these properties appear. The simplex rules of Section 2.5 give the tests for an optimal solution and for an unbounded solution. In this section, we shall consider a further three special cases that may arise during the simplex calculations.

2.8.1 Alternative Optima

The question of the existence of alternative optima (see Example 1.4, Section 1.2) arises as soon as an optimal tableau is reached. An alternative optimal basic feasible solution exists if we can find a legitimate simplex transformation of the optimal tableau which leaves the value of the objective function unaltered. From equation (2.35) we see that this is possible in two cases, when (i) $\theta = 0$, (ii) $z_k - c_k = 0$.

Case (i), though technically an alternative optimum, gives no new information, for $\theta = 0$ implies $x_{Br} = 0$, from equation (2.33). Thence, using equations (2.30), the new and old solutions (both of which are optimal and degenerate) are seen to be identical, apart from the trivial fact that a degenerate basic variable and a non-basic variable have been interchanged.

In case (ii) an alternative optimal basic feasible solution exists when, for a given optimal basic feasible solution, there exists at least one value of k, corresponding to a non-basic variable, for which $z_k - c_k = 0$ and $\theta > 0$. Then x_k can replace x_{Br} as a basic variable, where r has been determined, as usual, by equation (2.32). The basic variables, in general, take new values.

The existence of an alternative optimal basic feasible solution implies the existence of alternative optimal *non-basic* feasible solutions. For if $\mathbf{x}_{B1}^*$ and $\mathbf{x}_{B2}^*$ are two optimal basic feasible solutions giving the same value z^* for the objective function, then

$$\mathbf{x}^* = \lambda \mathbf{x}_{B1}^* + (1-\lambda)\mathbf{x}_{B2}^*, \quad 0 < \lambda < 1,$$

also gives $z = z^*$, because z is a linear, homogeneous function of the variables $x_1, \ldots, x_N$. Hence $\mathbf{x}^*$ is also an optimal feasible solution, but in general will be non-basic. As λ varies between 0 and 1, an infinite number of such solutions is generated, as stated in Section 1.2. More generally, given the optimal basic feasible solutions $\mathbf{x}_{Bt}^*$, $t = 1, \ldots, T$, the solution

$$\mathbf{x}^* = \sum_{t=1}^{T} \lambda_t \mathbf{x}_{Bt}^*, \quad \sum_{t=1}^{T} \lambda_t = 1, \quad \lambda_t > 0,$$

is optimal and feasible, but in general non-basic. The solution $\mathbf{x}^*$ is described as a *convex combination* of the solutions $\mathbf{x}_{Bt}^*$.

Finally, there are alternative optima when, for a given optimal basic feasible solution, there exists at least one value of k, corresponding to a non-basic variable, for which $z_k - c_k = 0$, and θ does not exist because $\beta_{ik} \leqslant 0$, $i = 1, \ldots, m$. This is the case for which there exists an unbounded solution associated with a finite value of the objective function—see the sequel to Example 1.5, Section 1.2. A one-parameter family of optimal *non-basic* feasible solutions with finite z^* can be obtained by means of a simplex transformation of the type represented by equation (2.39), with the parameter ϕ satisfying $0 < \phi < \infty$. The solution becomes unbounded as $\phi \to \infty$, though the value of z remains at its finite optimal value.

Example 2.4

$$\text{Maximize } z = x_1 - 2x_2 + x_3,$$

subject to

$$\begin{aligned} x_1 - 2x_2 + x_3 &\leqslant 10, \\ 2x_1 - 3x_2 - x_3 &\leqslant 6, \\ x_1, x_2, x_3 &\geqslant 0. \end{aligned}$$

Solution

Add slack variables x_4 and x_5.

Tableau 3 is optimal, because $z_j - c_j \geqslant 0$ for all j. The optimal solution is

$$x_1^* = 16/3,\ x_2^* = 0,\ x_3^* = 14/3;\ z^* = 10.$$

Alternative optima are indicated by the fact that $z_j - c_j = 0$ for the non-basic variables x_2 and x_5. In the case of x_2, since $\beta_{12} < 0$ and $\beta_{22} < 0$, we can use

Tableau 1 (Example 2.4)

	$\mathbf{c}'$		1	-2	1	0	0
$\mathbf{c}_B$	Basic Variables		x_1	x_2	x_3	x_4	x_5
0	x_4	10	1	-2	1	1	0
0	x_5	6	2*	-3	-1	0	1
	$z_j - c_j$	0	-1	2	-1	0	0

Tableau 2 (Example 2.4)

	$\mathbf{c}'$		1	-2	1	0	0
$\mathbf{c}_B$	Basic Variables		x_1	x_2	x_3	x_4	x_5
0	x_4	7	0	$-1/2$	3/2*	1	$-1/2$
1	x_1	3	1	$-3/2$	$-1/2$	0	1/2
	$z_j - c_j$	3	0	1/2	$-3/2$	0	1/2

Tableau 3 (Example 2.4)

	c′		1	−2	1	0	0
$\mathbf{c}_B$	Basic Variables		x_1	x_2	x_3	x_4	x_5
1	x_3	14/3	0	−1/3	1	2/3	−1/3
1	x_1	16/3	1	−5/3	0	1/3	1/3*
	$z_j - c_j$	10	0	0	0	1	0

equation (2.39) to obtain the family of optimal non-basic feasible solutions

$$x_1^* = \tfrac{16}{3} + \tfrac{5}{3}\phi,$$
$$x_2^* = \phi$$
$$x_3^* = \tfrac{14}{3} + \tfrac{1}{3}\phi,$$

for $0 < \phi < \infty$. The solution becomes unbounded as $\phi \to \infty$, though $z = z^* = 10$ for all ϕ.

The only alternative optimal *basic* feasible solution is obtained by interchanging x_5 and x_1, as shown by the pivot in Tableau 3. The usual simplex transformation rules give Tableau 4.

Tableau 4 (Example 2.4)

	c′		1	−2	1	0	0
$\mathbf{c}_B$	Basic Variables		x_1	x_2	x_3	x_4	x_5
1	x_3	10	1	−2	1	1	0
0	x_5	16	3	−5	0	1	1
	$z_j - c_j$	10	0	0	0	1	0

Tableau 4 gives the optimal solution

$$x_1^* = 0, \quad x_2^* = 0, \quad x_3^* = 10; \quad z^* = 10.$$

It also indicates alternative optima, since $z_j - c_j = 0$ for the non-basic variables x_1 and x_2. However, an interchange of x_1 and x_5, following the usual simplex rules, merely reproduces Tableau 3. On the other hand, since $\beta_{12} < 0$ and $\beta_{22} < 0$, we obtain from equation (2.39) another family of optimal non-basic feasible solutions

$$x_2^* = \phi,$$
$$x_3^* = 10 + 2\phi,$$
$$x_5^* = 16 + 5\phi,$$

for $0 < \phi < \infty$. Again, the solution becomes unbounded as $\phi \to \infty$, though $z = z^* = 10$ for all ϕ.

No further alternative optimum is indicated by Tableau 4. We conclude that all the alternative optima have been found, apart from convex combinations of those already found.

2.8.2 No Feasible Solution

A linear programming problem with constraints $\mathbf{Ax} = \mathbf{b}$ (which include slack and surplus variables but exclude artificial variables) has no feasible solution in two cases:

(i) There are one or more solutions, but none is feasible.

(ii) There is no solution because the original *equality* constraints (containing only main variables) are inconsistent.

Careful interpretation of the optimal simplex tableau enables us to distinguish between these two cases. It first becomes apparent that there is no feasible solution when we find that the optimal tableau at the end of the calculation in the M-method, or the final optimal tableau of phase 1 in the two-phase method, contains one or more non-degenerate artificial basic variables. All that has happened is that an optimal solution has been found for the augmented problem, and no further legitimate simplex transformation is possible.

Simplex transformations which break the simplex rules are usually required in order to distinguish between cases (i) and (ii). Suppose that we are given an optimal tableau containing one or more non-degenerate artificial basic variables x_{Bi}, $i = 1, \ldots, h$, and suppose further that $\beta_{ij} \neq 0$ for some i, $i = 1, \ldots, h$, and some j for which x_j is non-artificial and therefore non-basic. Then one of the artificial variables x_{Bi} for which $\beta_{ij} \neq 0$ is replaced as a basic variable by x_j, though the new basic solution may not be feasible. This procedure—replacing an artificial variable by a non-artificial variable as long as some $\beta_{ij} \neq 0$—is repeated as often as possible. Ultimately we arrive at one of two situations corresponding to cases (i) and (ii) above. Either (i) all the artificial variables have become non-basic, and the basic solution so obtained is not feasible (if it were feasible, it could be obtained by legitimate simplex transformations), or (ii) $\beta_{ij} = 0$ for all artificial basic variables x_{Bi} and all j for which x_j is non-artificial.

In case (i) we have obtained a basic non-feasible solution. In case (ii) any column vector $\mathbf{a}_j$ of $\mathbf{A}$ can be expressed as a linear combination of the non-artificial basis vectors, because of equation (2.23); but the requirements vector $\mathbf{b}$ cannot be expressed as a linear combination of these vectors, since the basis matrix contains at least one artificial vector. Hence the constraints $\mathbf{Ax} = \mathbf{b}$ are inconsistent or, equivalently, the original equality constraints (containing only main variables) are inconsistent.

Considering case (i) in more detail, it is often important to make the distinction between basic non-feasible solutions of $\mathbf{Ax} = \mathbf{b}$ that satisfy the original *inequality* constraints (among the mixed constraints $\mathbf{A}_0\mathbf{x}_0 \leqslant, =, \geqslant \mathbf{b}$) and those that do not. The former are solutions in which the slack and surplus variables remain non-negative; in this case, the original inequality constraints are consistent. The latter are those for which at least one slack or surplus variable takes a strictly negative value; if every basic non-feasible solution is of this type, then the original inequality constraints are inconsistent.

When the augmented equations have an unbounded solution containing at least one non-degenerate artificial variable, the original problem has either no feasible solution or an unbounded solution. These cases are relatively unimportant, and are not discussed in detail; we confine ourselves to illustrating them in Examples 2.7 and 2.8.

***Example* 2.5**

$$\text{Maximize } z = 2x_1 + x_2 + x_3,$$

subject to

$$2x_1 - 3x_2 - 5x_3 \geqslant 2,$$
$$-x_1 + x_2 - x_3 \geqslant 4,$$
$$x_1, x_2, x_3 \geqslant 0.$$

Solution

Subtract surplus variables x_4, x_5 and add artificial variables x_6, x_7.

Tableau 1 (Example 2.5)

	$\mathbf{c}'$		2	1	1	0	0	$-M$	$-M$
$\mathbf{c}_B$	Basic Variables		x_1	x_2	x_3	x_4	x_5	x_6	x_7
$-M$	x_6	2	2*	-3	-5	-1	0	1	0
$-M$	x_7	4	-1	1	-1	0	-1	0	1
	$z_j - c_j$	0	-2	-1	-1	0	0	0	0
		-6	-1	2	6	1	1	0	0

Tableau 2 is optimal, since the signs of the $z_j - c_j$ are determined solely by the coefficients of M in the last row. However, the artificial variable x_7 is a non-degenerate basic variable, and so the original problem has no feasible solution.

The artificial variable x_7 is made non-basic, choosing arbitrarily the pivot $\beta_{22} = -1/2$ of Tableau 2, to give Tableau 3.

Tableau 2 (Example 2.5)

	c′		2	1	1	0	0	$-M$
$\mathbf{c}_B$	Basic Variables		x_1	x_2	x_3	x_4	x_5	x_7
2	x_1	1	1	$-3/2$	$-5/2$	$-1/2$	0	0
$-M$	x_7	5	0	$-1/2$*	$-7/2$	$-1/2$	-1	1
	$z_j - c_j$	2	0	-4	-6	-1	0	0
		-5	0	1/2	7/2	1/2	1	0

Tableau 3 (Example 2.5)

	c′		2	1	1	0	0
$\mathbf{c}_B$	Basic Variables		x_1	x_2	x_3	x_4	x_5
2	x_1	-14	1	0	8	1	3
1	x_2	-10	0	1	7	1	2
	$z_j - c_j$	-38	0	0	22	3	8

Tableau 3 gives the basic non-feasible solution

$$x_1 = -14,\ x_2 = -10;\ z = -38.$$

This example therefore corresponds to case (i), and we can also infer that the original inequality constraints are consistent (because both the surplus variables are non-negative; in fact, they are both zero). Tableau 3 is not optimal, although $z_j - c_j \geqslant 0$ for all j. This apparent contradiction occurs because of the non-feasible solution: the simplex transformation rules have been violated in the construction of the tableau. Actually, the original problem has three other basic non-feasible solutions in which both surplus variables take non-negative values, and each of these solutions gives a greater value for z.

Example 2.6

$$\text{Maximize } z = 3x_1 + 2x_2 + x_3,$$

subject to

$$\begin{aligned} 5x_1 - 2x_2 + x_3 &\leqslant 6, \\ 2x_1 - x_2 - x_3 &\leqslant 4, \\ 9x_1 - 4x_2 - x_3 &\geqslant 15, \\ x_1, x_2, x_3 &\geqslant 0, \end{aligned}$$

Solution

Add slack variables x_4, x_5, subtract a surplus variable x_6, and add an artificial variable x_7.

Tableau 1 (Example 2.6)

	$\mathbf{c}'$		3	2	1	0	0	0	$-M$
$\mathbf{c}_B$	Basic Variables		x_1	x_2	x_3	x_4	x_5	x_6	x_7
0	x_4	6	5*	-2	1	1	0	0	0
0	x_5	4	2	-1	-1	0	1	0	0
$-M$	x_7	15	9	-4	-1	0	0	-1	1
	$z_j - c_j$	0	-3	-2	-1	0	0	0	0
		-15	-9	4	1	0	0	1	0

Tableau 2 (Example 2.6)

	$\mathbf{c}'$		3	2	1	0	0	0	$-M$
$\mathbf{c}_B$	Basic Variables		x_1	x_2	x_3	x_4	x_5	x_6	x_7
3	x_1	6/5	1	$-2/5$	1/5	1/5	0	0	0
0	x_5	8/5	0	$-1/5$	$-7/5$	$-2/5$	1	0	0
$-M$	x_7	21/5	0	$-2/5$*	$-14/5$	$-9/5$	0	-1	1
	$z_j - c_j$	18/5	0	$-16/5$	$-2/5$	3/5	0	0	0
		$-21/5$	0	2/5	14/5	9/5	0	1	0

Tableau 2 is optimal, but contains the artificial variable x_7 as a non-degenerate basic variable; hence the original problem has no feasible solution. To make x_7 non-basic, we choose the pivot $\beta_{32} = -2/5$ in Tableau 2, giving Tableau 3. Other possible choices of pivot are β_{33}, β_{34} and β_{36}.

Tableau 3 (Example 2.6)

	$\mathbf{c}'$		3	2	1	0	0	0
$\mathbf{c}_B$	Basic Variables		x_1	x_2	x_3	x_4	x_5	x_6
3	x_1	-3	1	0	3	2	0	1
0	x_5	$-1/2$	0	0	0	1/2	1	1/2
2	x_2	$-21/2$	0	1	7	9/2	0	5/2
	$z_j - c_j$	-30	0	0	22	15	0	8

The basic non-feasible solution of Tableau 3 corresponds to case (i), page 45. There are, of course, many other basic non-feasible solutions. In fact, it can be shown (without an excessive amount of computation) that every basic solution that can be derived from Tableau 3 by successive tableau transformations must contain at least one slack or surplus variable with a strictly negative value. This means that the original inequality constraints are inconsistent.

***Example** 2.7*

$$\text{Minimize } z = x_1 - 2x_2 + 3x_3 - 4x_4,$$

subject to

$$\begin{aligned} 3x_1 - 2x_2 + x_3 - x_4 &= 6, \\ x_1 - 5x_2 - x_3 + 4x_4 &= 2, \\ 5x_1 + x_2 + 3x_3 - 6x_4 &= 5, \\ x_1, x_2, x_3, x_4 &\geqslant 0. \end{aligned}$$

Solution

Add artificial variables x_5, x_6, x_7.

Tableau 3 is interesting for two reasons: the x_2 column shows an unbounded solution, and $\beta_{1j} = 0, j = 1, 2, 3, 4$, in the row of the artificial variable $x_{B1} = x_5$. The unbounded solution is

$$x_1 = \tfrac{16}{13} + \phi, \quad x_2 = \phi, \quad x_3 = 0, \quad x_4 = \tfrac{5}{26} + \phi, \quad (x_5 = \tfrac{5}{2}); \quad z = \tfrac{6}{13} - 5\phi,$$

with ϕ arbitrarily large. This solution satisfies the constraint

$$3x_1 - 2x_2 + x_3 - x_4 + x_5 = 6,$$

and also satisfies the second and third of the original constraints. But x_5 cannot be

Tableau 1 (Example 2.7)

	$\mathbf{c}'$		1	-2	3	-4	M	M	M
$\mathbf{c}_B$	Basic Variables		x_1	x_2	x_3	x_4	x_5	x_6	x_7
M	x_5	6	3	-2	1	-1	1	0	0
M	x_6	2	1	-5	-1	4	0	1	0
M	x_7	5	5*	1	3	-6	0	0	1
	$z_j - c_j$	0	-1	2	-3	4	0	0	0
		13	9	-6	3	-3	0	0	0

Tableau 2 (Example 2.7)

	$\mathbf{c}'$		1	−2	3	−4	M	M
$\mathbf{c}_B$	Basic Variables		x_1	x_2	x_3	x_4	x_5	x_6
M	x_5	3	0	−13/5	−4/5	13/5	1	0
M	x_6	1	0	−26/5	−8/5	26/5*	0	1
1	x_1	1	1	1/5	3/5	−6/5	0	0
	$z_j - c_j$	1	0	11/5	−12/5	14/5	0	0
		4	0	−39/5	−12/5	39/5	0	0

Tableau 3 (Example 2.7)

	$\mathbf{c}'$		1	−2	3	−4	M
$\mathbf{c}_B$	Basic Variables		x_1	x_2	x_3	x_4	x_5
M	x_5	5/2	0	0	0	0	1
−4	x_4	5/26	0	−1	−4/13	1	0
1	x_1	16/13	1	−1	3/13	0	0
	$z_j - c_j$	6/13	0	5	−20/13	0	0
		5/2	0	0	0	0	0

made non-basic, because $\beta_{1j} = 0, j = 1, 2, 3, 4$. Hence the original constraints are inconsistent, illustrating case (ii) for an 'unbounded' tableau.

It is hardly necessary to point out that, since all the original constraints are equations, their inconsistency may also be deduced from the fact that rank $(\mathbf{A}) \neq$ rank $(\mathbf{A}, \mathbf{b})$.

In contrast to the result of Example 2.7, the next example shows that if the augmented problem has an unbounded solution, then the original problem may have an unbounded solution rather than no feasible solution.

Example 2.8

$$\text{Maximize } z = x_1 + x_2 + x_3,$$

subject to

$$\begin{aligned} x_1 + x_3 &= 5, \\ -x_1 - 4x_2 + 2x_3 &\leqslant 6, \\ -x_1 - 3x_2 + 3x_3 &\leqslant 7, \\ x_1, x_2, x_3 &\geqslant 0. \end{aligned}$$

Solution

Add an artificial variable x_4 and slack variables x_5, x_6.

Tableau 1 (Example 2.8)

	c′		1	1	1	$-M$	0	0
$\mathbf{c}_B$	Basic Variables		x_1	x_2	x_3	x_4	x_5	x_6
$-M$	x_4	5	1*	0	1	1	0	0
0	x_5	6	-1	-4	2	0	1	0
0	x_6	7	-1	-3	3	0	0	1
	$z_j - c_j$	0	-1	-1	-1	0	0	0
		-5	-1	0	-1	0	0	0

Tableau 1 contains the artificial variable x_4 as a basic variable, and the x_2 column indicates an unbounded solution. Following the general principle of making an artificial variable non-basic—within the simplex rules, if possible—we obtain Tableau 2 by means of a legitimate simplex transformation.

Tableau 2 (Example 2.8)

	c′		1	1	1	0	0
$\mathbf{c}_B$	Basic Variables		x_1	x_2	x_3	x_5	x_6
1	x_1	5	1	0	1	0	0
0	x_5	11	0	-4	3	1	0
0	x_6	12	0	-3	4	0	1
	$z_j - c_j$	5	0	-1	0	0	0

Tableau 2 shows that the original problem has the unbounded solution

$$x_1 = 5, \quad x_2 = \phi, \quad x_3 = 0; \quad z = 5 + \phi; \quad \phi \text{ arbitrarily large.}$$

It is also possible to make the artificial variable x_4 non-basic by means of a transformation which breaks the simplex rules, using the pivot β_{13} in Tableau 1. This leads to another unbounded solution of the original problem, viz.

$$x_1 = 0, \quad x_2 = \phi, \quad x_3 = 5; \quad z = 5 + \phi; \quad \phi \text{ arbitrarily large.}$$

2.8.3 Redundant Constraints

Suppose that an optimal basic feasible solution of the general linear programming problem (2.10) contains some degenerate artificial basic variables. If any

β_{ij} is non-zero (x_{Bi} artificial and degenerate, x_j non-basic), then x_j can replace x_{Bi} as a basic variable. Since $x_{Bi} = 0$, the new and old basic feasible solutions are identical and the value of z is unchanged, i.e. the new solution is still optimal. If it is possible to repeat this procedure until all the degenerate artificial basic variables have become non-basic, then a degenerate optimal basic feasible solution exists and there is no redundancy.

The above procedure cannot be continued, however, when $\beta_{ij} = 0$ for all i corresponding to the remaining degenerate artificial basic variables x_{Bi}, and for all j corresponding to non-basic x_j. Suppose that there are k such variables x_{Bi}. Then any column vector $\mathbf{a}_j$ of $\mathbf{A}$ can be expressed as a linear combination of the $(m-k)$ non-artificial basic vectors, i.e. rank $(\mathbf{A}) = m-k$, and this means that k of the original *equality* constraints (containing only main variables) are redundant. This argument applies equally to the M-method and to the situation at the end of phase 1 of the two-phase method.

The k redundant constraints are those for which $\beta_{ij} = 0$ for the k values of i corresponding to the k degenerate artificial basic variables, and for all j corresponding to non-basic x_j. This can be proved as follows.

Let $\mathbf{e}_{a1}, \ldots, \mathbf{e}_{ak}$ be the unit column vectors corresponding to the k degenerate artificial basic variables x_{Bi}, $i = a1, \ldots, ak$. Denote the ith row of $\mathbf{A}$ by $\mathbf{A}_i$, and denote the ith row of the matrix $(\mathbf{A}, \mathbf{e}_{a1}, \ldots, \mathbf{e}_{ak})$ by $(\mathbf{A}_i, 0, 0, \ldots, 0)$ when $i \neq a1, \ldots, ak$, and by $(\mathbf{A}_i, 0, \ldots, 0, 1, 0, \ldots, 0)$ when $i = a1, \ldots, ak$, with the 1 appearing in the appropriate position. Since rank $(\mathbf{A}) = m-k$, any $(m-k+1)$, or more, rows of $\mathbf{A}$ are linearly dependent. In particular, there exist γ_i, $i = 1, \ldots, m$, *not all zero*, such that

$$\sum_{\substack{i=1 \\ i \neq a1, \ldots, ak}}^{m} \gamma_i \mathbf{A}_i + \gamma_{a1} \mathbf{A}_{a1} + \ldots + \gamma_{ak} \mathbf{A}_{ak} = \mathbf{0}. \tag{2.62}$$

On the other hand, since the rank of the basis matrix is m, we also have

$$\text{rank}\,(\mathbf{A}, \mathbf{e}_{a1}, \ldots, \mathbf{e}_{ak}) = m,$$

so that the m rows of this matrix are linearly independent. This means that in the equation

$$\sum_{\substack{i=1 \\ i \neq a1, \ldots, ak}}^{m} \eta_i (\mathbf{A}_i, 0, 0, \ldots, 0) + \eta_{a1} (\mathbf{A}_{a1}, 1, 0, \ldots, 0) + \eta_{a2} (\mathbf{A}_{a2}, 0, 1, 0, \ldots, 0)$$
$$+ \ldots + \eta_{ak} (\mathbf{A}_{ak}, 0, \ldots, 0, 1) = \mathbf{0}, \tag{2.63}$$

the η_i, $i = 1, \ldots, m$, are *all zero.* [In equation (2.63), the last k row vectors on the left-hand side have been arranged in a natural order; this can always be done without loss of generality.]

If $\gamma_{a1} = \ldots = \gamma_{ak} = 0$, then the N-component equation (2.62) and the first N components of (2.63) are contradictory, as the italics show. Thus at least one of the coefficients $\gamma_{a1}, \ldots, \gamma_{ak}$ is non-zero, which means, from equation (2.62), that the corresponding row of **A** can be expressed as a linear combination of the remaining rows of **A**. Consequently, the constraint associated with this row is redundant. Omitting this row from **A**, the above argument can be repeated and another redundant constraint identified. Proceeding in this way all the redundant constraints can be recognized, thus completing the proof.

It should be emphasized that by a 'redundant constraint' we mean an equality constraint that can be expressed as a linear combination of other equality constraints. In particular, we have not considered the case when one constraint 'dominates' another. For example, if $x_1, x_2, x_3 \geqslant 0$, then the constraint

$$8x_1 + 6x_2 + 3x_3 \leqslant 8$$

dominates the constraint

$$6x_1 + 3x_2 + x_3 \leqslant 12,$$

because the former implies the latter. The latter is usually said to be redundant, since it can be ignored without altering the problem. However, in the simplex method no special provision need be made for this type of redundancy, although dominated constraints should be ignored *ab initio* if they are recognized.

Example 2.9

$$\text{Minimize } z = x_1 + x_2 - x_3 + x_4,$$

subject to

$$\begin{aligned} x_1 - 6x_2 + 2x_3 + x_4 &= 5, \\ 3x_1 + x_2 + 5x_3 + 2x_4 &= 13, \\ 7x_1 + 15x_2 + 11x_3 + 4x_4 &= 29, \\ x_1, x_2, x_3, x_4 &\geqslant 0. \end{aligned}$$

Solution

Add artificial variables x_5, x_6, x_7.

Tableau 1 (Example 2.9)

	$\mathbf{c}'$		1	1	−1	1	M	M	M
$\mathbf{c}_B$	Basic Variables		x_1	x_2	x_3	x_4	x_5	x_6	x_7
M	x_5	5	1	−6	2*	1	1	0	0
M	x_6	13	3	1	5	2	0	1	0
M	x_7	29	7	15	11	4	0	0	1
	$z_j - c_j$	0	−1	−1	1	−1	0	0	0
		47	11	10	18	7	0	0	0

In Tableau 2 the pivot can be either β_{22} or β_{32}; we choose β_{22}.

Tableau 3 shows that the constraint associated with the artificial variable x_7 is redundant, since $\beta_{3j} = 0$ for all j corresponding to *non-basic* x_j. Of course, we must also have $\beta_{32} = \beta_{33} = 0$, corresponding to the *basic* variables x_2 and x_3. As soon as a constraint has shown itself to be redundant, the row and column of the corresponding artificial variable may be deleted from the tableau. This gives Tableau 3a. In the present example, however, the identification of a redundant constraint happens to coincide with the end of the simplex calculations, since Tableau 3a is optimal.

Tableau 2 (Example 2.9)

	$\mathbf{c}'$		1	1	−1	1	M	M
$\mathbf{c}_B$	Basic Variables		x_1	x_2	x_3	x_4	x_6	x_7
−1	x_3	5/2	1/2	−3	1	1/2	0	0
M	x_6	1/2	1/2	16*	0	−1/2	1	0
M	x_7	3/2	3/2	48	0	−3/2	0	1
	$z_j - c_j$	−5/2	−3/2	2	0	−3/2	0	0
		2	2	64	0	−2	0	0

Tableau 3 (Example 2.9)

	$\mathbf{c}'$		1	1	−1	1	M
$\mathbf{c}_B$	Basic Variables		x_1	x_2	x_3	x_4	x_7
−1	x_3	83/32	19/32	0	1	13/32	0
1	x_2	1/32	1/32	1	0	−1/32	0
M	x_7	0	0	0	0	0	1
	$z_j - c_j$	−41/16	−25/16	0	0	−23/16	0
		0	0	0	0	0	0

Tableau 3a (Example 2.9)

	$\mathbf{c}'$		1	1	−1	1
$\mathbf{c}_B$	Basic Variables		x_1	x_2	x_3	x_4
−1	x_3	83/32	19/32	0	1	13/32
1	x_2	1/32	1/32	1	0	−1/32
	$z_j - c_j$	−41/16	−25/16	0	0	−23/16

2.9 Geometrical Interpretation of the Simplex Method

The purpose of this section is to extend the geometrical interpretation of the simplex method from two dimensions, as given in Chapter 1, to the general case of n dimensions. Many of the algebraic results obtained previously are intuitively obvious when explained geometrically. In particular we shall prove Theorem 2.8, which, for the general linear programming problem, relates optimal feasible solutions to optimal basic feasible solutions. This theorem is of crucial importance for the simplex method.

A column vector $\mathbf{x}$ is regarded as a point in an n-dimensional Euclidean space, its coordinates being $(x_1, \ldots, x_n)$. The following definitions are required.

1. The *line* through the points $\mathbf{x}_1$ and $\mathbf{x}_2$ is the set of points

$$R = \{\mathbf{r} : \mathbf{r} = \lambda \mathbf{x}_1 + (1 - \lambda)\mathbf{x}_2, \text{ all real } \lambda\}. \tag{2.64}$$

2. The *line segment* joining the points $\mathbf{x}_1$ and $\mathbf{x}_2$ is the set of points R given by equation (2.64) with λ restricted to $0 \leqslant \lambda \leqslant 1$.

3. A set X is *convex* if the line segment joining any two points in the set lies entirely in the set.

4. An *extreme point* of a convex set is a point $\mathbf{x}$ in the set such that $\mathbf{x}$ cannot be represented in the form

$$\mathbf{x} = \lambda \mathbf{x}_1 + (1 - \lambda)\mathbf{x}_2, \quad 0 < \lambda < 1,$$

for any $\mathbf{x}_1$ and $\mathbf{x}_2$ $(\neq \mathbf{x}_1)$ belonging to the set.
(An extreme point of a convex set in an n-dimensional Euclidean space is analogous to a corner of a two-dimensional convex polygon.)

5. A *hyperplane* is a set of points

$$X = \{\mathbf{x} : \mathbf{c}'\mathbf{x} = z\}, \tag{2.65}$$

where $\mathbf{c}$ $(\neq \mathbf{0})$ and z are constants.
(Note that equation (2.65) is linear in $x_1, \ldots, x_n$: a hyperplane in an n-dimensional Euclidean space may therefore be regarded as a surface analogous to a plane in a three-dimensional Euclidean space.)

6. A *closed half-space* is a set of points

$$X_{\mathrm{L}} = \{\mathbf{x} : \mathbf{c}'\mathbf{x} \leqslant z\} \quad \text{or} \quad X_{\mathrm{G}} = \{\mathbf{x} : \mathbf{c}'\mathbf{x} \geqslant z\},$$

where $\mathbf{c}$ $(\neq \mathbf{0})$ and z are constants.

7. Let $\mathbf{x}_b$ be a boundary point of a convex set X. Then

$$\mathbf{c}'\mathbf{x} = z$$

is called a *supporting hyperplane* to X at $\mathbf{x}_b$ if $\mathbf{c}'\mathbf{x}_b = z$ and if all of X lies in one closed half-space defined by the hyperplane, i.e. if

$$\mathbf{c}'\mathbf{x} \leqslant z \text{ for all } \mathbf{x} \in X, \text{ or } \mathbf{c}'\mathbf{x} \geqslant z \text{ for all } \mathbf{x} \in X.$$

■ Theorem 2.4

In the general linear programming problem the set of points representing all the feasible solutions is a closed convex set.

Proof

The set of points representing all the feasible solutions is determined by (1.2) and (1.3); each of these equations and inequalities represents either a hyperplane (which is a closed set) or a closed half-space. From the above definitions, both a hyperplane and a closed half-space are convex sets; also the intersection of two convex sets is a convex set. (Let the two convex sets be S_1, S_2; consider the line segment joining any two points $\mathbf{x}_1, \mathbf{x}_2$ in $S_1 \cap S_2$, and apply the definition of convexity to S_1, S_2 and $S_1 \cap S_2$.) Furthermore, the intersection of two closed sets is a closed set. It follows by mathematical induction that the intersection of a finite number of closed convex sets is a closed convex set, and the theorem is proved.

We now see how the two-dimensional graphical method of Chapter 1 is extended to n dimensions. The value of the objective function at any point $\mathbf{x}$ is given by z in the equation of the hyperplane (2.65). This hyperplane is moved parallel to itself (i.e. $\mathbf{c}$ remains constant and z varies) over the closed convex set of feasible solutions until z is made as large (or as small) as possible, while the hyperplane and the closed convex set of feasible solutions still have at least one point $\mathbf{x}^*$ in common. From now on, we shall assume that the constraints are written in the form

$$\mathbf{A}\mathbf{x} = \mathbf{b}, \quad \mathbf{x} = [x_1, \ldots, x_N]. \tag{2.66}$$

Theorem 2.4 still applies; we shall denote the closed convex set of feasible solutions by F.

■ Theorem 2.5

Every basic feasible solution satisfying the constraint equations (2.66) corresponds to an extreme point of F, and conversely.

Proof

The proof of the first part of the theorem is by contradiction. Suppose that there is a basic feasible solution $\mathbf{x}^{BF}$ which does not correspond to an extreme point of F. Then there exist feasible solutions $\mathbf{x}^{F1}$ and $\mathbf{x}^{F2}$ $(\neq \mathbf{x}^{F1})$ such that

$$\mathbf{x}^{BF} = \lambda \mathbf{x}^{F1} + (1-\lambda)\mathbf{x}^{F2}, \quad 0 < \lambda < 1. \tag{2.67}$$

Assume that

$$\left.\begin{aligned} x_j^{BF} &> 0, \quad j = 1, \ldots, m, \\ &= 0, \quad j = m+1, \ldots, N. \end{aligned}\right\} \tag{2.68}$$

Then the equation

$$\sum_{j=1}^{m} x_j \mathbf{a}_j = \mathbf{b} \tag{2.69}$$

has the *unique* solution $x_j = x_j^{BF}$, $j = 1, \ldots, m$, by the definition of a basic solution (Section 2.2). From (2.67) and 2.68),

$$0 = \lambda x_j^{F1} + (1-\lambda)x_j^{F2}, \quad j = m+1, \ldots, N,$$

giving

$$x_j^{F1} = x_j^{F2} = 0, \quad j = m+1, \ldots, N,$$

since $0 < \lambda < 1$. Hence equation (2.69) determines the coordinates x_j^{F1} and x_j^{F2}, $j = 1, \ldots, m$, as well as the coordinates $x_j^{BF}, j = 1, \ldots, m$, which contradicts the uniqueness of its solution. This completes the proof of the first part of the theorem.

To prove the converse, let $\mathbf{x}^*$ be an extreme point of F. The vector $\mathbf{a}_j$ can be associated with the component x_j^* of $\mathbf{x}^*$, as shown by equation (2.69). We shall prove that the vectors $\mathbf{a}_j$ associated with the strictly positive components of $\mathbf{x}^*$ are linearly independent. Since rank $(\mathbf{A}) = m$, it will follow that there are not more than m of these strictly positive components, and therefore that $\mathbf{x}^*$ corresponds to a basic feasible solution of $\mathbf{Ax} = \mathbf{b}$.

Again the proof is by contradiction. Let the first k components of $\mathbf{x}^*$ be strictly positive, and assume that the $\mathbf{a}_j$ corresponding to these components are linearly dependent. Then there exist μ_j, not all zero, such that

$$\sum_{j=1}^{k} \mu_j \mathbf{a}_j = \mathbf{0}. \tag{2.70}$$

Considering only the non-zero μ_j, choose ε such that

$$0 < \varepsilon < \min_j \frac{x_j^*}{|\mu_j|} \quad (\text{all } j \text{ for which } \mu_j \neq 0). \tag{2.71}$$

Then

$$\begin{aligned} x_j^* \pm \varepsilon\mu_j &\geqslant x_j^* - \varepsilon|\mu_j| \\ &= |\mu_j|\left(\frac{x_j^*}{|\mu_j|} - \varepsilon\right) \\ &\geqslant |\mu_j|\left(\min_j \frac{x_j^*}{|\mu_j|} - \varepsilon\right) \\ &> 0, \end{aligned} \tag{2.72}$$

using (2.71). The inequality(2.72) is valid for all $j, j = 1, \ldots, k$, independently of whether μ_j is zero or non-zero, since $x_j^* > 0$ for these k values of j.

Define the N-component vector

$$\boldsymbol{\mu} = (\mu_1, \ldots, \mu_k, 0, \ldots, 0),$$

and let

$$\mathbf{x}_1 = \mathbf{x}^* + \varepsilon\boldsymbol{\mu}, \quad \mathbf{x}_2 = \mathbf{x}^* - \varepsilon\boldsymbol{\mu}. \tag{2.73}$$

Then, from (2.70) and (2.72), we have

$$\mathbf{A}\boldsymbol{\mu} = \mathbf{0}, \quad \mathbf{x}_1 \geqslant \mathbf{0}, \quad \mathbf{x}_2 \geqslant \mathbf{0}. \tag{2.74}$$

From (2.73) and (2.74),

$$\mathbf{A}\mathbf{x}_1 = \mathbf{A}\mathbf{x}^* + \varepsilon\mathbf{A}\boldsymbol{\mu} = \mathbf{A}\mathbf{x}^* = \mathbf{b}.$$

Similarly,

$$\mathbf{A}\mathbf{x}_2 = \mathbf{b}.$$

Hence $\mathbf{x}_1$ and $\mathbf{x}_2$ are feasible solutions different from $\mathbf{x}^*$, and from (2.73) we have

$$\mathbf{x}^* = \tfrac{1}{2}(\mathbf{x}_1 + \mathbf{x}_2),$$

which contradicts the fact that $\mathbf{x}^*$ is an extreme point of F. This completes the proof of the theorem.

Corollary

The number of extreme points of F is finite and not greater than ${}_N C_m$, the number of basic solutions of $\mathbf{A}\mathbf{x} = \mathbf{b}$.

Theorem 2.5 is the n-dimensional analogue of the two-dimensional result that a basic feasible solution corresponds to a corner of the polygon of feasible solutions. There is a one-to-one correspondence between *non-degenerate* basic feasible solutions and extreme points of F. On the other hand, more than one *degenerate* basic feasible solution may correspond to the same extreme point of F. The perturbation method of the next section may be interpreted geometrically as follows. A carefully chosen small perturbation of the requirements vector $\mathbf{b}$ produces a small distortion of F. This causes the several degenerate basic feasible solutions associated with an extreme point of F to be perturbed, and hence separated, so that each of these solutions corresponds to a unique extreme point of the distorted F.

■ **Theorem 2.6**

If an optimal solution of the general linear programming problem exists, then it can occur only at a boundary point of F.

Proof

An optimal solution $\mathbf{x}^*$ lies on an optimal hyperplane; let the equation of this hyperplane be $\mathbf{c}'\mathbf{x} = z$, and assume that one of its points $\mathbf{x}_0$ is an interior point of F. Choose $\varepsilon > 0$ such that if $|\mathbf{x} - \mathbf{x}_0| < \varepsilon$, then $\mathbf{x}$ belongs to F. Suppose that the linear programming problem is a maximizing problem. The point

$$\mathbf{x}_1 = \mathbf{x}_0 + \frac{\varepsilon}{2}\hat{\mathbf{c}},$$

where $\hat{\mathbf{c}}$ is the unit vector $\mathbf{c}/|\mathbf{c}|$, belongs to F, since $|\mathbf{x}_1 - \mathbf{x}_0| < \varepsilon$.
But

$$\begin{aligned} \mathbf{c}'\mathbf{x}_1 &= \mathbf{c}'\mathbf{x}_0 + \frac{\varepsilon}{2}|\mathbf{c}| \\ &= z + \frac{\varepsilon}{2}|\mathbf{c}| \\ &> z, \end{aligned}$$

which contradicts the fact that z is the maximum value of the objective function. (A similar contradiction may be obtained for a minimizing problem.)

The assumption that $\mathbf{x}_0$ is an interior point of F is therefore false, and it follows that any point which lies on the optimal hyperplane and which also belongs to F must be a boundary point of F.

Corollary

If $\mathbf{x}^*$ is an optimal solution, and if $\mathbf{c}'\mathbf{x}^* = z$, then $\mathbf{c}'\mathbf{x} = z$ is a supporting hyperplane to F at $\mathbf{x}^*$.

Proof

The proof follows immediately from the definition of a supporting hyperplane: the theorem states that $\mathbf{x}^*$ is a boundary point of F; $\mathbf{c}'\mathbf{x} \leqslant z$ for all $\mathbf{x} \in F$, since $\mathbf{x}^*$ is an optimal solution (of a maximizing problem); and $\mathbf{x}^*$ lies on the hyperplane $\mathbf{c}'\mathbf{x} = z$.

■ **Theorem 2.7**

A closed convex set F which is bounded from below, i.e. $\mathbf{x} \in F \Rightarrow \mathbf{x} \geqslant \mathbf{x}_l$, where $\mathbf{x}_l$ is some fixed vector, has at least one extreme point in every supporting hyperplane.

Proof

Let H be the supporting hyperplane to F at $\mathbf{x}_0$ with equation $\mathbf{c}'\mathbf{x} = z$. Let $G = F \cap H$. Then G is a closed, non-empty, convex set, bounded from below. (G is closed because it is the intersection of two closed sets, non-empty because it contains the point $\mathbf{x}_0$, convex because it is the intersection of two convex sets, and bounded from below because $\mathbf{g} \in G \Rightarrow \mathbf{g} \in F$, and F is bounded from below.) The remainder of the proof consists of two parts: to show that (i) any extreme point of G is also an extreme point of F, and that (ii) G has at least one extreme point.

First, let $\mathbf{g} \in G$. Then $\mathbf{g} \in H$ and $\mathbf{c}'\mathbf{g} = z$. Suppose that $\mathbf{g}$ is not an extreme point of F. We shall prove that $\mathbf{g}$ is not an extreme point of G; the required result (i) will then follow. We have

$$\mathbf{g} = \lambda \mathbf{x}_1 + (1-\lambda)\mathbf{x}_2, \quad 0 < \lambda < 1, \tag{2.75}$$

where $\mathbf{x}_1$ and $\mathbf{x}_2$ $(\neq \mathbf{x}_1) \in F$. Therefore

$$z = \mathbf{c}'\mathbf{g} = \lambda \mathbf{c}'\mathbf{x}_1 + (1-\lambda)\mathbf{c}'\mathbf{x}_2. \tag{2.76}$$

But since $\mathbf{c}'\mathbf{x} = z$ is a supporting hyperplane to F,

$$\left.\begin{aligned} &\mathbf{c}'\mathbf{x}_1 \leqslant z \text{ and } \mathbf{c}'\mathbf{x}_2 \leqslant z, \\ \text{or} \quad &\mathbf{c}'\mathbf{x}_1 \geqslant z \text{ and } \mathbf{c}'\mathbf{x}_2 \geqslant z. \end{aligned}\right\} \tag{2.77}$$

From (2.76) and (2.77),

$$\mathbf{c}'\mathbf{x}_1 = z \quad \text{and} \quad \mathbf{c}'\mathbf{x}_2 = z,$$

i.e.

$$\mathbf{x}_1, \mathbf{x}_2 \in G.$$

Hence, from (2.75), $\mathbf{g}$ is not an extreme point of G, which completes the proof of (i).

Next, we will show that G has at least one extreme point by actually constructing such a point. Choose the point in G with the algebraically smallest first component—at least one such point exists, since G is closed and bounded from below. In the case of a tie, choose the point with the smallest first and second components; and in the case of a further tie, choose the point with the smallest first, second and third components. Proceed in this way until a unique point $\mathbf{g}^*$ is obtained. Then $\mathbf{g}^*$ is an extreme point of G. For if not, then

$$\mathbf{g}^* = \lambda \mathbf{g}_1 + (1-\lambda)\mathbf{g}_2, \quad 0 < \lambda < 1, \quad \mathbf{g}_1, \mathbf{g}_2 (\neq \mathbf{g}_1) \in G. \tag{2.78}$$

Suppose that $\mathbf{g}^*$ was determined *uniquely* when the jth component g_j was minimized. Then, from (2.78),

$$g_i^* = \lambda g_{1i} + (1-\lambda) g_{2i} \leqslant g_{1i}, \quad i = 1, \ldots, j-1, \tag{2.79}$$

and

$$g_i^* = \lambda g_{1i} + (1-\lambda) g_{2i} \leqslant g_{2i}, \quad i = 1, \ldots, j-1, \tag{2.80}$$

since $g_i{}^*$ is the smallest ith component, $i = 1, \ldots, j-1$. Now (2.79) and (2.80) imply

$$g_i{}^* = g_{1i} = g_{2i}, \quad i = 1, \ldots, j-1,$$

and these are the smallest ith components. Thus $\mathbf{g}^*$ is first distinguished from $\mathbf{g}_1$ and $\mathbf{g}_2$ by comparison of the jth components. But the jth component of (2.78) is

$$g_j{}^* = \lambda g_{1j} + (1-\lambda)g_{2j} \geqslant \min\{g_{1j}, g_{2j}\},$$

which contradicts the assumption that $g_j{}^*$ is the unique minimum jth component. For if

$$g_j{}^* > \min\{g_{1j}, g_{2j}\},$$

then it is not the *minimum* jth component, and if

$$g_j{}^* = \min\{g_{1j}, g_{2j}\},$$

then it is not the *unique* minimum jth component. This completes the proof of (ii) and of the theorem.

A result which is fundamental for the simplex method is obtained by combining Theorem 2.5, the corollary to Theorem 2.6, and Theorem 2.7. Let F be the closed convex set of feasible solutions of the general linear programming problem

$$\left.\begin{array}{ll} & \text{Maximize } z = \mathbf{c}'\mathbf{x}, \\ \text{subject to} & \mathbf{A}\mathbf{x} = \mathbf{b} \quad \text{and} \quad \mathbf{x} \geqslant \mathbf{0}. \end{array}\right\} \tag{2.81}$$

The non-negativity restrictions ensure that the set F is bounded from below, and hence that it satisfies Theorem 2.7. Combining the above results, we obtain Theorem 2.8.

■ Theorem 2.8

If the linear programming problem (2.81) has an optimal, and therefore feasible, solution, then at least one basic feasible solution of (2.81) is optimal.

Theorem 2.8 is an extension of the two-dimensional result that if an optimal solution exists then at least one corner of the polygon of feasible solutions represents an optimal solution. It holds for both degenerate and non-degenerate solutions. As explained at the end of Section 2.2, the major importance of Theorem 2.8 lies in the fact that, apart from the elimination of cycling, it completes the proof that the simplex method may be used to solve the *general* linear programming problem. There remains the outstanding theoretical question of how to amend the simplex method, as described so far, in order to eliminate cycling. This is the subject of the next section.

For further details of the geometrical aspects of the simplex method, the reader is referred to Hadley [20].

*2.10 The Perturbation Method for Avoiding Degeneracy

We have already seen, in Section 2.4, that cycling can occur only when degeneracy is present. The purpose of this section is to explain the perturbation method for avoiding degeneracy. The description of the method is similar to that given by Dantzig [9]. Obviously if degeneracy is avoided then so is cycling, and the last loophole in the simplex method is closed.

Suppose that the problem is given in the form

$$\left.\begin{array}{ll} & \text{Maximize } z = \mathbf{c}'\mathbf{x}, \\ \text{subject to} & \mathbf{A}_1\mathbf{x} = \mathbf{b}, \quad \mathbf{x} \geqslant \mathbf{0}, \end{array}\right\} \tag{2.82}$$

where the matrix $\mathbf{A}_1$ (of order $m \times N_1$) includes column vectors corresponding to any artificial variables that may be necessary, as well as the usual column vectors corresponding to main, slack and surplus variables, cf. (2.10). Consider the perturbed problem

$$\left.\begin{array}{ll} & \text{Maximize } z = \mathbf{c}'\mathbf{x}, \\ \text{subject to} & \mathbf{A}_1\mathbf{x} = \mathbf{b}+\boldsymbol{\varepsilon}, \quad \mathbf{x} \geqslant \mathbf{0}, \quad \varepsilon > 0, \end{array}\right\} \tag{2.83}$$

where the components of $\boldsymbol{\varepsilon}$ are the first m powers of ε:

$$\boldsymbol{\varepsilon} = [\varepsilon, \varepsilon^2, \ldots, \varepsilon^m],$$

and $0 < \varepsilon < \varepsilon_0$ for some fixed ε_0. Solutions of problems (2.82) and (2.83) will be denoted by $\mathbf{x}$ and $\mathbf{x}(\varepsilon)$, respectively.

A basic solution of the constraints (2.83) is

$$\begin{aligned} \mathbf{x}_B(\varepsilon) &= \mathbf{B}^{-1}(\mathbf{b}+\boldsymbol{\varepsilon}) \\ &= \mathbf{x}_B + \mathbf{B}^{-1}\boldsymbol{\varepsilon}, \end{aligned} \tag{2.84}$$

where $\mathbf{B}$ is a basis matrix consisting of m linearly independent columns of $\mathbf{A}_1$. From equation (2.84), we see that

$$x_{Bi}(\varepsilon) > 0, \quad 0 < \varepsilon < \varepsilon_0,$$

provided that

$$\left.\begin{array}{ll} & \text{(i) } x_{Bi} > 0 \quad \text{with } \varepsilon_0 \text{ sufficiently small}, \\ \text{or} & \text{(ii) } x_{Bi} = 0 \quad \text{and } [\mathbf{B}^{-1}\boldsymbol{\varepsilon}]_i > 0. \end{array}\right\} \tag{2.85}$$

Assume that one or other of the conditions (2.85) is satisfied for each i,

* Sections marked with an asterisk may be omitted on a first reading.

$i=1, \ldots, m$, so that the basic solution $\mathbf{x}_B(\varepsilon)$ of (2.84) is non-degenerate. Assume further that ε_0 is chosen sufficiently small for this solution to remain feasible as $\varepsilon \to 0$.

Now apply the simplex algorithm to the perturbed problem (2.83), with the aim not only of improving the given non-degenerate basic feasible solution $\mathbf{x}_B(\varepsilon)$ of (2.84), but also of ensuring that the new basic feasible solution $\bar{\mathbf{x}}_B(\varepsilon)$ is non-degenerate. The variable $x_k(\varepsilon)$ which becomes basic is the same variable x_k which becomes basic in the unperturbed problem, since the $z_j - c_j$ are unaffected by the perturbation in $\mathbf{b}$:

$$z_j - c_j = \mathbf{c}_B' \boldsymbol{\beta}_j - c_j,$$

and both the c_j and the $\boldsymbol{\beta}_j$ remain unchanged. The variable $x_{Br}(\varepsilon)$ becomes non-basic, where r is chosen by the rule, cf. (2.32):

$$\frac{x_{Br}(\varepsilon)}{\beta_{rk}} = \min_{i=1,\ldots,m} \left\{ \frac{x_{Bi} + [\mathbf{B}^{-1}\boldsymbol{\varepsilon}]_i}{\beta_{ik}} : \beta_{ik} > 0 \right\}. \tag{2.86}$$

As $\varepsilon \to 0$, it may happen that different values for r are obtained from equation (2.86). However, this possibility can be excluded by making ε_0 smaller, if necessary.

Denote the elements of $\mathbf{B}^{-1}$ by $\{d_{is}\}$. Then

$$[\mathbf{B}^{-1}\boldsymbol{\varepsilon}]_i = d_{i1}\varepsilon + d_{i2}\varepsilon^2 + \ldots + d_{im}\varepsilon^m, \tag{2.87}$$

and the condition $[\mathbf{B}^{-1}\boldsymbol{\varepsilon}]_i > 0$ of (2.85) is clearly satisfied if

$$\left.\begin{aligned} d_{is} = 0, \quad s = 1, \ldots, k-1, \\ d_{ik} > 0, \quad k \leqslant m, \\ 0 < \varepsilon < \varepsilon_0, \quad \text{with } \varepsilon_0 \text{ sufficiently small}, \end{aligned}\right\} \tag{2.88}$$

i.e. if the leading term in the polynomial (2.87) is strictly positive, and if ε is sufficiently small. Conditions (2.88) are therefore sufficient to ensure that the basic variable $x_{Bi}(\varepsilon)$ is non-degenerate. Also, substituting the polynomial expression for $[\mathbf{B}^{-1}\boldsymbol{\varepsilon}]_i$ from equation (2.87) into equation (2.86), we obtain

$$\frac{x_{Br}(\varepsilon)}{\beta_{rk}} = \min_{i=1,\ldots,m} \left\{ \frac{x_{Bi} + d_{i1}\varepsilon + d_{i2}\varepsilon^2 + \ldots + d_{im}\varepsilon^m}{\beta_{ik}} : \beta_{ik} > 0 \right\}. \tag{2.89}$$

A unique value for r in the present simplex iteration is obtained from equation (2.89) as follows.

1. Ignore the terms in ε, and determine r from

$$\frac{x_{Br}}{\beta_{rk}} = \min_{i=1,\ldots,m} \left\{ \frac{x_{Bi}}{\beta_{ik}} : \beta_{ik} > 0 \right\}. \tag{2.90}$$

If this minimum gives a unique value for r, then proceed with the simplex transformation in the usual way. From equations (2.29a) and (2.29b), and using equations (2.84) and (2.87), the new values of the basic variables are found to be

$$\bar{x}_{Bi}(\varepsilon) = x_{Bi}(\varepsilon) - \frac{\beta_{ik}}{\beta_{rk}} x_{Br}(\varepsilon)$$

$$= \left(x_{Bi} + \sum_{s=1}^{m} d_{is}\varepsilon^s \right) - \frac{\beta_{ik}}{\beta_{rk}} \left(x_{Br} + \sum_{s=1}^{m} d_{rs}\varepsilon^s \right)$$

$$= \left(x_{Bi} - \frac{\beta_{ik}}{\beta_{rk}} x_{Br} \right) + \sum_{s=1}^{m} \left(d_{is} - \frac{\beta_{ik}}{\beta_{rk}} d_{rs} \right) \varepsilon^s, \quad i = 1, \ldots, m, \quad i \neq r, \tag{2.91a}$$

and

$$\bar{x}_{Br}(\varepsilon) = \frac{x_{Br}(\varepsilon)}{\beta_{rk}} = \frac{x_{Br} + \sum_{s=1}^{m} d_{rs}\varepsilon^s}{\beta_{rk}}. \tag{2.91b}$$

The old basic solution $\mathbf{x}_B(\varepsilon)$ is non-degenerate, since it satisfies conditions (2.85). Hence equations (2.91a) and (2.91b) show that the new basic solution $\bar{\mathbf{x}}_B(\varepsilon)$ is also non-degenerate, because of the choice of r and the smallness of ε.

2. If the minimum in equation (2.90) occurs for more than one value of i, then, using only these tied values of i, determine r by comparing the coefficients of ε in the polynomials of equation (2.89):

$$\frac{d_{r1}}{\beta_{rk}} = \min_i \left\{ \frac{d_{i1}}{\beta_{ik}} : i \text{ tied in (2.90)} \right\}. \tag{2.92}$$

Note that in equation (2.92), unlike equation (2.90), there is no restriction on the sign of β_{ik}, and in fact the ratios being compared may take either sign. If the minimum in equation (2.92) gives a unique value for r, then proceed with the simplex transformation in the usual way. If the calculation reaches this stage, then equations (2.91a) are replaced by

$$\bar{x}_{Bi}(\varepsilon) = \left(x_{Bi} - \frac{\beta_{ik}}{\beta_{rk}} x_{Br} \right) + \sum_{s=1}^{m} \left(d_{is} - \frac{\beta_{ik}}{\beta_{rk}} d_{rs} \right) \varepsilon^s, \quad i \text{ not tied in (2.90)}, \ i \neq r, \tag{2.93a}$$

$$= \sum_{s=1}^{m} \left(d_{is} - \frac{\beta_{ik}}{\beta_{rk}} d_{rs} \right) \varepsilon^s, \ i \text{ tied in (2.90)}, \tag{2.93b}$$

while $\bar{x}_{Br}(\varepsilon)$ is again given by equation (2.91b). The basic solution given by equations (2.93a), (2.93b) and (2.91b) is again non-degenerate, since the leading terms in the polynomial expressions for $\bar{x}_{Bi}(\varepsilon)$, $i = 1, \ldots, m$, are all strictly positive, cf. (2.88). In particular, the leading term in (2.93b) is strictly positive, because r is *uniquely* determined from equation (2.92).

3. If the minimum in equation (2.92) occurs for more than one value of i, then,

using only these tied values of i, determine r by comparing the coefficients of ε^2 in the polynomials of equation (2.89):

$$\frac{d_{r2}}{\beta_{rk}} = \min_i \left\{ \frac{d_{i2}}{\beta_{ik}} : i \text{ tied in (2.92)} \right\}. \tag{2.94}$$

Again, the minimum in equation (2.94) may or may not yield a unique value for r. If r is uniquely determined at this stage, then the $\bar{x}_{Bi}(\varepsilon)$ (expressed as polynomials in ε) have leading terms which are constants, of order ε, and of order ε^2. Furthermore, all these leading terms are strictly positive, by reasoning similar to that given above, and so $\bar{\mathbf{x}}_B(\varepsilon)$ is non-degenerate. If r is not uniquely determined at this stage, then the coefficients of ε^3 in the polynomials of equation (2.89) are compared for the values of i that are tied in equation (2.94).

The above process continues until a unique value of r is obtained—this must happen eventually, for otherwise two rows of the non-singular matrix $\mathbf{B}^{-1}$ would be proportional to each other, which is impossible. Thus the variable $x_{Br}(\varepsilon)$ to become non-basic is uniquely determined, and the new basic solution $\bar{\mathbf{x}}_B(\varepsilon)$ is non-degenerate. From the usual simplex transformation formula (2.35), the new value of the objective function is

$$\bar{z}(\varepsilon) = z(\varepsilon) - \frac{x_{Br}(\varepsilon)}{\beta_{rk}}(z_k - c_k) > z(\varepsilon),$$

since $z_k - c_k < 0$ for the non-optimal solution $\mathbf{x}_B(\varepsilon)$, and both $x_{Br}(\varepsilon)$ and β_{rk} are strictly positive.

We have proved that if a basic feasible solution $\mathbf{x}_B(\varepsilon)$ is non-degenerate and non-optimal, then a new basic feasible solution $\bar{\mathbf{x}}_B(\varepsilon)$ can be found which is also non-degenerate, and which improves the value of the objective function. But the initial basis matrix $\mathbf{B}$ for problem (2.82) can always be chosen to be the unit matrix, and in this case the initial basic solution $\mathbf{x}_B(\varepsilon)$ of the perturbed problem (2.83) is feasible and non-degenerate, since conditions (2.85) are satisfied by this solution. It follows by mathematical induction that the usual simplex procedure, modified only by choosing r according to the above rules, gives a sequence of non-degenerate basic feasible solutions of problem (2.83), leading to an optimal solution. In particular, cycling is avoided. The required optimal solution of problem (2.82) is then obtained immediately by setting $\varepsilon = 0$.

The computational procedure for the avoidance of degeneracy is much simpler than the preceding theoretical development would suggest, for although ε must be sufficiently small, the numerical value of ε is never required. This means that, computationally, ε can be ignored, provided that r is chosen by the rules given above. The only remaining problem is to locate the elements of the successive $m \times m$ matrices $\mathbf{B}^{-1} = \{d_{is}\}$ in the simplex tableaux. If the revised simplex method is used, then these elements are immediately available in the revised simplex tableau (see Section 3.7). If the standard simplex method is used, and if the initial basis matrix is $\mathbf{B} = \mathbf{I} = \mathbf{B}^{-1}$, then the columns in the initial and subsequent tableaux headed by the *initial* basic variables always comprise $\mathbf{B}^{-1}$, where $\mathbf{B}$ is the current basis matrix. For the column headed by x_j contains the vector β_j, where, from equation (2.24),

$$\beta_j = \mathbf{B}^{-1}\mathbf{a}_j,$$

in which $\mathbf{a}_j$ is the jth column of $\mathbf{A}_1$. The result follows because the *initial* basis vectors $\mathbf{a}_j$ comprise the unit basis matrix. Thus every d_{is} is a β_{ij}. Specifically, if the *initial* basic variables are denoted by $x_u, x_v, x_w, \ldots$, then

$$d_{i1} = \beta_{iu},\ d_{i2} = \beta_{iv},\ d_{i3} = \beta_{iw}, \ldots.$$

For the purpose of relating the d_{is} to the β_{ij}, it is convenient, though not essential, to take the initial basic variables in numerical order. Note that if any artificial variables appear in the initial tableau their columns must be retained in subsequent tableaux.

The following summary outlines the steps for the determination of a unique value of r. The variable x_k becomes basic, and the variable x_{Br} becomes non-basic, in the current simplex iteration.

Summary

Denote the basic variables in the initial basic feasible solution (with unit basis matrix) by x_u, x_v, x_w, ...

1. Find i such that x_{Bi}/β_{ik} is a minimum, with $\beta_{ik} > 0$. If i is determined uniquely, call it r.
2. If i is not determined uniquely in step 1, then, from among the tied values of i in step 1, find i such that β_{iu}/β_{ik} is a minimum. If i is determined uniquely in this step, call it r.
3. If i is not determined uniquely in step 2, then, from among the tied values of i in step 2, find i such that β_{iv}/β_{ik} is a minimum. If i is determined uniquely in this step, call it r.
4. Repeat this procedure until a unique value of r is found, as it must be eventually. Then the variable x_{Br} becomes non-basic, and the simplex calculations proceed normally.

Example 2.10. *Illustration of Cycling*

Beale [3] constructed an example of cycling in the dual simplex method. The dual problem, which follows, provides an example of cycling in the standard simplex method.

$$\text{Maximize } z = \tfrac{3}{4}x_1 - 20x_2 + \tfrac{1}{2}x_3 - 6x_4,$$

subject to

$$\begin{aligned} \tfrac{1}{4}x_1 - 8x_2 - x_3 + 9x_4 + x_5 &= 0, \\ \tfrac{1}{2}x_1 - 12x_2 - \tfrac{1}{2}x_3 + 3x_4 + x_6 &= 0, \\ x_3 + x_7 &= 1, \\ x_j \geqslant 0,\ j &= 1, \ldots, 7. \end{aligned}$$

Table 2.2 shows that cycling can occur if the perturbation method is not used. Note that the initial basic feasible solution contains two degenerate variables.

Table 2.2 An Example of Cycling

	Basic Variables	
Tableau	Standard simplex method	Perturbation method
1	x_5, x_6, x_7	x_5, x_6, x_7
2	x_1, x_6, x_7	x_5, x_1, x_7
3	x_1, x_2, x_7	x_5, x_1, x_3
4	x_3, x_2, x_7	
5	x_3, x_4, x_7	
6	x_5, x_4, x_7	
7	x_5, x_6, x_7	

The details of the calculations are left as an exercise: it is interesting to repeat the perturbation calculations with the initial basic variables taken in a different order. The optimal solution is

$$\mathbf{x}^* = [1, 0, 1, 0, \tfrac{3}{4}, 0, 0];\ z^* = \tfrac{5}{4}.$$

Exercises

1. A farmer has 100 acres of land which can be used for growing wheat, barley, oats, sugar beet or grass. Of the 100 acres, 10 are suitable for any crop, a further 50 are suitable for any crop except sugar beet, and the remainder is suitable only for grass. Any part of the land may also lie fallow.

The farmer may, in addition, keep cows, pigs and hens. The cows require half an acre of grassland each; each pig eats £4 worth of meal per year; and each hen eats £1 worth of corn per year. The available space for pigs and hens (in addition to the 100 acres) is 10 000 square feet: a pig requires 30 square feet, and a hen requires 15 square feet of space.

The farmer wishes to work for not more than 2 000 hours in any year. The cost of additional labour is 50p per hour up to 2 200 hours in any year, and 75p per hour for any overtime hours. Costs and profits for the crops and livestock are as follows.

	Wheat	Barley	Oats	Sugar beet	Grass
Cost (£) of seed, fertilizer, etc., per acre	6	4	3	8	5
Selling price (£) of produce of one acre	45	40	35	100	0
Labour requirements (hours) per acre per year	12	13	14	20	5

	Cows	Pigs	Hens
Cost (£) per head	75	2	1
Profit (£) per head per year from sale of milk, eggs, etc.	200	0	2
Selling price (£) per head after one year	70	8	1
Labour requirements (hours) per head per year	100	25	20

Set up this problem as a linear programming problem, the objective being to maximize the farmer's net annual profit.

2. Find all the basic solutions of the simultaneous equations

$$\begin{aligned} x_1 - 2x_2 + 3x_3 - 2x_4 &= 2, \\ 3x_1 - 3x_2 + 7x_3 &= 7, \\ 6x_2 - x_3 + 3x_4 &= 1. \end{aligned}$$

Hence obtain the most general solution of these equations.

3. A complete check on the tableau arithmetic is obtained by adding an extra column on the right of each tableau. In the initial tableau for any problem, the entries in the extra column are the row sums, $\sigma_1, \ldots, \sigma_{m+1}$, including all the elements in the rows except the prices. Subsequently, the entries in a σ column (as the check column is called) are transformed by the usual tableau transformation equations, viz. (2.58a) and (2.58b). Each tableau is checked by ensuring that the entries in the σ column are the row sums.

Explain how the check works. Does it still work when artificial variables are present?

Solve the linear programming problems 4–23 by the simplex method. Assume that the objective functions have to be optimized subject to the given constraints, and that all the variables satisfy non-negativity restrictions.

4.
$$\text{Maximize } z = 5x_1 + 3x_2 + 4x_3.$$
$$\begin{aligned} 3x_1 + 6x_2 + 2x_3 &\leqslant 12, \\ x_1 + 2x_2 + 2x_3 &\leqslant 8, \\ 4x_1 + 2x_2 + 4x_3 &\leqslant 17. \end{aligned}$$

5.
$$\text{Minimize } z = 7x_1 - 5x_2 - 6x_3 - x_4.$$
$$\begin{aligned} x_1 - x_2 + x_3 - x_4 &\leqslant 10, \\ 2x_1 + 5x_2 + 8x_3 + 11x_4 &\leqslant 20. \end{aligned}$$

6.
$$\text{Maximize } z = x_1 + 12x_2 + 3x_3.$$
$$\begin{aligned} 4x_1 + 2x_2 - 3x_3 &\leqslant -4, \\ 6x_1 - 5x_2 + 2x_3 &\geqslant 15, \\ 3x_1 + 2x_2 + x_3 &\leqslant 15. \end{aligned}$$

7a.
$$\text{Minimize } z = x_1 + x_2 + x_3.$$

7b.
$$\text{Maximize } z = x_1 + x_2 + x_3.$$
$$\begin{aligned} 6x_1 - 2x_2 + x_3 &\geqslant 1, \\ 2x_1 - 5x_2 - x_3 &\geqslant 12, \\ x_1 + x_2 + x_3 &\geqslant -5. \end{aligned}$$

8.
$$\text{Maximize } z = x_1 + 8x_2 + x_3.$$
$$\begin{aligned} 3x_1 + 5x_2 + 2x_3 &\leqslant 15, \\ x_1 + 8x_2 + x_3 &\leqslant 8. \end{aligned}$$

9.
$$\text{Minimize } z = x_1 + 3x_2 + 3x_3 + x_4.$$
$$\begin{aligned} 2x_1 + 5x_2 - 3x_3 + x_4 &= 2, \\ 3x_1 - 2x_2 + 6x_3 - x_4 &= 1, \\ 7x_1 + 5x_2 \qquad + x_4 &= 5. \end{aligned}$$

10.
$$\text{Maximize } z = x_1 + x_2 + x_3 + x_4 + x_5.$$
$$\begin{aligned} 3x_1 - x_2 + 2x_3 - x_4 + x_5 &\leqslant 0, \\ 6x_1 - 2x_2 + x_3 - 3x_4 + 4x_5 &\geqslant 4. \end{aligned}$$

11.
$$\text{Maximize } z = 3x_1 + x_2.$$
$$\begin{aligned} x_1 - 4x_2 + 2x_3 &\geqslant 12, \\ 2x_1 + x_2 + x_3 &\geqslant 10, \\ x_1 - x_2 + x_3 &\leqslant 7. \end{aligned}$$

12.
$$\begin{aligned} \text{Minimize } z &= 8x_1 + 6x_2 + 9x_3.\\ 22x_1 + x_2 + 8x_3 &= 40,\\ 10x_1 + x_2 + 4x_3 &= 20,\\ 4x_1 + x_2 + 2x_3 &= 10. \end{aligned}$$

13.
$$\begin{aligned} \text{Maximize } z &= 4x_1 + 2x_2 + 5x_3.\\ 3x_1 - 6x_2 - 2x_3 &\geqslant 12,\\ 2x_1 - 3x_2 + x_3 &\leqslant -8,\\ 4x_1 + 5x_2 - x_3 &\leqslant 4. \end{aligned}$$

14.
$$\begin{aligned} \text{Maximize } z &= 2x_1 - x_2 + 3x_3 - x_4.\\ 3x_1 - 2x_2 + x_3 - 2x_4 &\leqslant 9,\\ 2x_1 + x_2 - 3x_3 &\geqslant 2,\\ x_2 - x_3 + x_4 &\leqslant -6. \end{aligned}$$

15.
$$\begin{aligned} \text{Maximize } z &= 3x_1 - x_2 - x_3 - 14x_4,\\ x_2 + x_3 + 2x_4 &\geqslant 3,\\ x_1 + 2x_2 + x_3 &= 9,\\ 2x_1 + 2x_2 + x_3 - 4x_4 &\leqslant 10. \end{aligned}$$

16.
$$\begin{aligned} \text{Minimize } z &= x_1 + 2x_2 - 3x_3,\\ x_1 + x_2 + x_3 &\geqslant 4,\\ 4x_1 + 3x_2 + 2x_3 &\leqslant 10. \end{aligned}$$

17.
$$\begin{aligned} \text{Minimize } z &= 3x_1 + 4x_2 + x_3,\\ 5x_1 - 2x_2 + x_3 &\geqslant 2,\\ 6x_1 + x_2 - 5x_3 &\geqslant 5,\\ -x_1 + 4x_2 - 7x_3 &\geqslant 6. \end{aligned}$$

18.
$$\begin{aligned} \text{Maximize } z &= 2x_1 - 4x_2 + x_3,\\ 4x_1 + 5x_2 - x_3 &\leqslant 13,\\ 5x_1 - 2x_2 + x_3 &\leqslant -1,\\ 3x_1 + x_2 + 2x_3 &\leqslant 16. \end{aligned}$$

19. $$\text{Minimize } z = 2x_1 + 3x_2 + x_3,$$

$$\begin{aligned} 6x_1 - 2x_2 + x_3 &\geq 3, \\ 3x_1 + x_2 - 4x_3 &\geq 6, \\ x_1 + x_2 + x_3 &\leq 9, \\ x_1 - x_2 - x_3 &\leq 12. \end{aligned}$$

20. $$\text{Maximize } z = x_1 + 4x_2 + 3x_3,$$

$$\begin{aligned} 2x_1 - x_2 + 5x_3 &= 40, \\ x_1 + 2x_2 - 3x_3 &\geq 9, \\ 3x_1 + x_2 + 2x_3 &\leq 30. \end{aligned}$$

21. $$\text{Minimize } z = x_1 - 2x_2 - 3x_3,$$

$$\begin{aligned} x_1 + x_2 + x_3 &\geq 10, \\ x_1 - x_2 + x_3 &\leq 10, \\ x_1 + x_2 - x_3 &\leq 10. \end{aligned}$$

22. $$\text{Maximize } z = x_1 - 2x_2 - 3x_3 + x_4,$$

$$\begin{aligned} x_1 + 2x_2 + 2x_3 - 2x_4 &\geq 12, \\ x_1 + 2x_2 + x_3 - 2x_4 &\leq 18, \\ 3x_1 + 6x_2 + 2x_3 - 4x_4 &= 24. \end{aligned}$$

23. $$\text{Maximize } z = 3x_1 + 2x_2 + x_3,$$

$$\begin{aligned} 2x_1 + x_2 + x_3 &\leq 2, \\ 3x_1 + 4x_2 + 2x_3 &\geq 8. \end{aligned}$$

24. $$\text{Maximize } z = 3x_1 - x_2 - 4x_3,$$

subject to

$$\begin{aligned} x_1 + x_2 - x_3 &\leq 4, \\ |x_1 - x_2| &\leq 2, \\ x_1, x_2 \geq 0, |x_3| &\geq 1. \end{aligned}$$

25. Consider the problem:

$$\text{Maximize } z = -x_1 - 2x_2 - 3x_3,$$

subject to

$$\begin{aligned} x_1 + 2x_2 + x_3 &\geq 4, \\ 2x_1 + x_2 + x_3 &\geq 5, \\ 2x_1 + 3x_2 + 2x_3 &\geq 6, \\ x_1, x_2, x_3 &\geq 0. \end{aligned}$$

Introduce surplus variables. By multiplying two of the resulting equations by -1 and adding the third to each in turn, find an equivalent system of equations for which a basic feasible solution can be found by introducing only one artificial variable. Now use the simplex method to find every optimal solution.

26. At least 15 m of material 36 cm wide and at least 20 m of material 30 cm wide are to be cut from a roll of material 120 cm wide. Any excess material cut from the roll is wasted. Show that the minimization of the area of material wasted can be formulated as a linear programming problem, and solve this problem by the simplex method.

27. In a legitimate simplex transformation, the variable x_k becomes basic and the variable $x_{Br} = x_l$ becomes non-basic. Show that in the next transformation, assumed legitimate, x_l cannot become basic though x_k may become non-basic. **Hint.** Consider the appropriate entries in successive simplex tableaux.

28. When an initial basic *non-feasible* solution of a linear programming problem can be found, the use of artificial variables can be avoided by proceeding as follows. Find the most negative x_{Bi}; call it x_{Bh}. Next, find

$$\beta_{hk} = \min_{j=1,\ldots,N} \left\{ \beta_{hj} \colon \beta_{hj} < 0 \right\}.$$

Then x_k becomes basic. Choose x_{Br} to become non-basic using

$$\frac{x_{Br}}{\beta_{rk}} = \min_{i=1,\ldots,m} \left\{ \frac{x_{Bi}}{\beta_{ik}} \colon x_{Bi} > 0, \beta_{ik} > 0 \right\},$$

a formula which should be compared with equation (2.32). Carry out the usual tableau transformation, except that there is no need to evaluate the $z_j - c_j$ row. Repeat this procedure until a basic feasible solution appears.

(a) Use this method to find a basic feasible solution for Exercise 6.

(b) Explain why the method produces a basic feasible solution (if one exists).

(c) What happens if $\beta_{hj} \geqslant 0$ for all j?

In using this method, the initial tableau must be constructed carefully. The constraint equations $\mathbf{Ax} = \mathbf{b}$ should be rewritten so that each basic variable appears in one, and only one, equation, and with a coefficient of $+1$. The entries in the tableau may then be written down in the usual way.

29. In a standard simplex tableau, the elements (apart from the prices) are described by the matrix

$$\mathbf{M} = \{\beta_{ij}\}, \ i = 1, \ldots, m+1, j = 0, 1, \ldots, N.$$

Show that a simplex transformation of the tableau is equivalent to premultiplication of **M** by a matrix of the form

$$\begin{pmatrix}
1 & 0 & \cdots & 0 & -\alpha_1 & 0 & \cdots & 0 \\
0 & 1 & 0 \cdots & 0 & -\alpha_2 & 0 & \cdots & 0 \\
\cdot & \cdot & \cdot & \cdot & \cdot & \cdot & \cdot & \cdot \\
0 & & \cdots & 0\ 1 & -\alpha_{r-1} & 0 & \cdots & 0 \\
0 & & \cdots & 0 & -\alpha_r & 0 & \cdots & 0 \\
0 & & \cdots & 0 & -\alpha_{r+1} & 1\ 0 & \cdots & 0 \\
\cdot & \cdot & \cdot & \cdot & \cdot & \cdot & \cdot & \cdot \\
0 & & \cdots & 0 & -\alpha_{m+1} & 0 & \cdots & 0\ 1
\end{pmatrix}$$

Find expressions for the α_i.

30. A basic feasible solution of a linear programming problem contains only one degenerate variable. Show that this solution cannot belong to a cycle of solutions.

3

Duality and the Revised Simplex Method

3.1 Introduction

In two-dimensional Euclidean geometry the following statements are true:

(a) two points define a line,

(b) two lines define a point.

These two statements are completely symmetrical: they cannot be used to distinguish points from lines. Thus for every theorem concerned only with points and lines there must be another theorem with the words 'point' and 'line' interchanged. Of course, a few other words and phrases must be changed at the same time in order to preserve our intuitive notions of points and lines. For example, 'the point of intersection of two lines' becomes 'the line joining two points', and 'the locus of the point P' becomes 'the envelope of the line p'.

We say that points and lines are *dual elements* in two-dimensional Euclidean geometry, and that a theorem on points and lines has a *dual theorem* associated with it. A famous example is Pascal's Mystic Hexagram theorem, whose dual is Brianchon's theorem.

Pascal's Theorem. If a hexagon is inscribed in a conic, then the points of intersection of the three pairs of opposite sides are collinear.

Brianchon's Theorem. If a hexagon is circumscribed about a conic, then the lines joining the three pairs of opposite vertices are concurrent.

Historically, François Viète (1540–1603), better known as Vieta, was the first person to make use of the principle of duality, in connection with the properties of the polar triangle of a given spherical triangle. Duality now appears in many branches of pure and applied mathematics, including geometry in any number of dimensions, electrical network theory, mechanics and economics.

In October 1947, John von Neumann pointed out that linear programming was closely related to the theory of games, and thence showed that every linear programming problem has a dual problem associated with it. Specifically, if the *primal* problem is

$$\left.\begin{aligned} &\text{Maximize } z = \mathbf{c}'\mathbf{x}, \\ \text{subject to} \quad &\mathbf{Px} \leqslant \mathbf{b} \quad \text{and} \quad \mathbf{x} \geqslant \mathbf{0}, \end{aligned}\right\} \tag{3.1}$$

then the corresponding *dual* problem is

$$\left.\begin{aligned} &\text{Minimize } w = \mathbf{b}'\mathbf{y}, \\ \text{subject to} \quad & \\ &\mathbf{P}'\mathbf{y} \geqslant \mathbf{c} \quad \text{and} \quad \mathbf{y} \geqslant \mathbf{0}. \end{aligned}\right\} \tag{3.2}$$

It is convenient to regard (3.1) and (3.2), which have inequality constraints, as the standard formulations of the primal and dual problems, respectively. In Chapters 1 and 2, problem (3.1) was written in the form

$$\left.\begin{aligned} &\text{Maximize } z = \mathbf{c}_0{}'\mathbf{x}_0, \\ \text{subject to} \quad & \\ &\mathbf{A}_0\mathbf{x}_0 \leqslant \mathbf{b} \quad \text{and} \quad \mathbf{x}_0 \geqslant \mathbf{0}. \end{aligned}\right\}$$

The present slight changes in notation are introduced for simplicity, and also to avoid confusion with the standard formulation of the constraints in the general linear programming problem (2.10) when duality is not being considered.

Either (3.1) or (3.2) may be regarded as the primal problem, and the other is then the dual problem. This result is usually stated as 'the dual of the dual is the primal', and is proved as follows. The minimizing problem (3.2) can be written as a maximizing problem:

$$\left.\begin{aligned} &\text{Maximize } \bar{w} = -\mathbf{b}'\mathbf{y}, \\ \text{subject to} \quad & \\ &-\mathbf{P}'\mathbf{y} \leqslant -\mathbf{c} \quad \text{and} \quad \mathbf{y} \geqslant \mathbf{0}, \end{aligned}\right\} \tag{3.3}$$

where $\bar{w} = -w$ and hence $[\bar{w}]_{\max} = -[w]_{\min}$. Now (3.3) is in the same form as (3.1) and its dual is therefore

$$\begin{aligned} &\text{Minimize } \bar{z} = -\mathbf{c}'\mathbf{x}, \\ \text{subject to} \quad & \\ &-\mathbf{P}\mathbf{x} \geqslant -\mathbf{b} \quad \text{and} \quad \mathbf{x} \geqslant \mathbf{0}, \end{aligned}$$

i.e.

$$\left.\begin{aligned} &\text{Maximize } z = \mathbf{c}'\mathbf{x}, \\ \text{subject to} \quad & \\ &\mathbf{P}\mathbf{x} \leqslant \mathbf{b} \quad \text{and} \quad \mathbf{x} \geqslant \mathbf{0}, \end{aligned}\right\} \tag{3.4}$$

where $z = -\bar{z}$ and hence $[z]_{\max} = -[\bar{z}]_{\min}$. Problem (3.4) is precisely the primal problem (3.1). The primal problem and the dual problem are often called simply the 'primal' and 'dual', respectively.

Before writing down the dual of a given linear programming problem, it is necessary to adjust the constraints so that all the inequalities are in the same direction. The following example illustrates this point, and also shows how to deal with equality constraints in the primal.

Example 3.1

Find the dual of the following linear programming problem.

$$\left.\begin{aligned} &\text{Maximize } z = 10x_1 + x_2 + 4x_3 + 7x_4, \\ &\text{subject to} \\ &3x_1 - 2x_2 + 7x_3 - 6x_4 \leqslant 5, \\ &8x_1 + 4x_2 - 11x_3 + x_4 \geqslant 12, \\ &9x_1 + 15x_2 + 14x_3 + 10x_4 = 13, \\ &x_1, x_2, x_3, x_4 \geqslant 0. \end{aligned}\right\} \quad (3.5)$$

Solution

Multiply the $\geqslant$ constraint throughout by -1, replace the equality constraint by the two inequality constraints

$$9x_1 + 15x_2 + 14x_3 + 10x_4 \leqslant 13,$$
$$9x_1 + 15x_2 + 14x_3 + 10x_4 \geqslant 13,$$

and multiply the second of these throughout by -1. Then problem (3.5) is in the standard form of the primal:

$$\left.\begin{aligned} &\text{Maximize } z = 10x_1 + x_2 + 4x_3 + 7x_4, \\ &\text{subject to} \\ &3x_1 - 2x_2 + 7x_3 - 6x_4 \leqslant 5, \\ &-8x_1 - 4x_2 + 11x_3 - x_4 \leqslant -12, \\ &9x_1 + 15x_2 + 14x_3 + 10x_4 \leqslant 13, \\ &-9x_1 - 15x_2 - 14x_3 - 10x_4 \leqslant -13, \\ &x_1, x_2, x_3, x_4 \geqslant 0. \end{aligned}\right\} \quad (3.6)$$

The dual of (3.6), and therefore of (3.5), is

$$\left.\begin{aligned} &\text{Minimize } w = 5y_1 - 12y_2 + 13y_3' - 13y_3'', \\ &\text{subject to} \\ &3y_1 - 8y_2 + 9y_3' - 9y_3'' \geqslant 10, \\ &-2y_1 - 4y_2 + 15y_3' - 15y_3'' \geqslant 1, \\ &7y_1 + 11y_2 + 14y_3' - 14y_3'' \geqslant 4, \\ &-6y_1 - y_2 + 10y_3' - 10y_3'' \geqslant 7, \\ &y_1, y_2, y_3', y_3'' \geqslant 0. \end{aligned}\right\} \quad (3.7)$$

The dual variables y_3' and y_3'' always appear together in the form $y_3' - y_3''$. If we write $y_3 \equiv y_3' - y_3''$, then the dual problem (3.7) is simplified, and the only effect of the equality in the third primal constraint is to make y_3 unrestricted in sign. Thus the dual of (3.5) is, finally,

$$\left.\begin{array}{c}\text{Minimize } w = 5y_1 - 12y_2 + 13y_3,\\ \text{subject to}\\ 3y_1 - 8y_2 + 9y_3 \geqslant 10,\\ -2y_1 - 4y_2 + 15y_3 \geqslant 1,\\ 7y_1 + 11y_2 + 14y_3 \geqslant 4,\\ -6y_1 - y_2 + 10y_3 \geqslant 7,\\ y_1, y_2 \geqslant 0,\ y_3 \text{ unrestricted in sign.}\end{array}\right\} \tag{3.8}$$

By an obvious generalization from the result of Example 3.1, and from that fact that we may regard problem (3.5) as the dual of problem (3.8), we obtain Theorem 3.1.

■ **Theorem 3.1**

(i) An equality constraint in the primal corresponds to a dual variable which is unrestricted in sign.

(ii) A primal variable which is unrestricted in sign corresponds to an equality constraint in the dual.

It is important to notice that an equality constraint in the primal does *not* correspond to an equality constraint in the dual. In particular, if the primal problem is

$$\text{Maximize } z = \mathbf{c}'\mathbf{x},$$

subject to

$$\mathbf{Px} = \mathbf{b} \quad \text{and} \quad \mathbf{x} \geqslant \mathbf{0},$$

in which every constraint is an equation, then the dual problem is

$$\text{Minimize } w = \mathbf{b}'\mathbf{y},$$

subject to

$$\mathbf{P}'\mathbf{y} \geqslant \mathbf{c}, \text{ with } \mathbf{y} \text{ unrestricted in sign,}$$

in which every dual constraint is of the usual $\geqslant$ type. Having obtained these preliminary results, we are now in a position to prove some important theorems concerning duality.

3.2 Theorems on Duality

All the results which we shall obtain in this section are directly concerned with the values of the objective functions for the primal and dual problems, viz.

$$z = \mathbf{c}'\mathbf{x} \quad \text{and} \quad w = \mathbf{b}'\mathbf{y}.$$

The most important of these results is Theorem 3.4, the *Fundamental Theorem of Duality*.

■ **Theorem 3.2**

For any feasible solutions $\mathbf{x}$ and $\mathbf{y}$ of problems (3.1) and (3.2), respectively,

$$z = \mathbf{c}'\mathbf{x} \leqslant \mathbf{b}'\mathbf{y} = w. \tag{3.9}$$

Proof

Since $\mathbf{y} \geqslant \mathbf{0}$ and $\mathbf{Px} \leqslant \mathbf{b}$,

$$\mathbf{y}'\mathbf{Px} \leqslant \mathbf{y}'\mathbf{b}. \tag{3.10}$$

Also, since $\mathbf{x} \geqslant \mathbf{0}$ and $\mathbf{P}'\mathbf{y} \geqslant \mathbf{c}$,

$$\mathbf{x}'\mathbf{P}'\mathbf{y} \geqslant \mathbf{x}'\mathbf{c}. \tag{3.11}$$

Combining (3.10) and (3.11), we obtain

$$\mathbf{c}'\mathbf{x} \leqslant \mathbf{y}'\mathbf{Px} \leqslant \mathbf{b}'\mathbf{y}. \tag{3.12}$$

■ **Theorem 3.3**

If $\mathbf{x}_{F1}$ and $\mathbf{y}_{F1}$ are feasible solutions of problems (3.1) and (3.2), respectively, such that

$$z = \mathbf{c}'\mathbf{x}_{F1} = \mathbf{b}'\mathbf{y}_{F1} = w,$$

then $\mathbf{x}_{F1}$ and $\mathbf{y}_{F1}$ are optimal solutions of their respective problems.

Proof

Let $\mathbf{x}_F$ be *any* feasible solution of problem (3.1). Then, by Theorem 3.2 and the present hypothesis,

$$\mathbf{c}'\mathbf{x}_F \leqslant \mathbf{b}'\mathbf{y}_{F1} = \mathbf{c}'\mathbf{x}_{F1},$$

which shows that $\mathbf{x}_{F1}$ is optimal for the maximizing problem (3.1).

Similarly, let $\mathbf{y}_F$ be any feasible solution of problem (3.2). Then

$$\mathbf{b}'\mathbf{y}_F \geqslant \mathbf{c}'\mathbf{x}_{F1} = \mathbf{b}'\mathbf{y}_{F1},$$

which shows that $\mathbf{y}_{F1}$ is optimal for the minimizing problem (3.2).

■ **Theorem 3.4** The Fundamental Theorem of Duality

If one of the problems (3.1), (3.2) has an optimal solution then so has the other. Furthermore, the optimal values of the objective functions for the two problems are equal, i.e.

$$\max z = \min w.$$

Proof

Since either (3.1) or (3.2) may be regarded as the primal problem, it is sufficient to prove that if (3.1) has an optimal solution then so has (3.2).

Assume that $\mathbf{P}$ is an $m \times n$ matrix. When solving problem (3.1) by the simplex method, the constraints become

$$\mathbf{P}\mathbf{x} + \mathbf{x}_s = \mathbf{b}, \tag{3.13}$$

where $\mathbf{x}_s = [x_{n+1}, \ldots, x_{n+m}]$ is the column vector of slack variables. Let $\mathbf{x}_B$ be the given optimal basic feasible solution of equation (3.13); the assumption that $\mathbf{x}_B$ is a *basic* feasible solution may be made without loss of generality because of Theorem 2.8. In the usual notation the first n optimality conditions for problem (3.1), corresponding to the n main variables, are

$$z_j - c_j \geqslant 0, \quad j = 1, \ldots, n. \tag{3.14}$$

But

$$z_j = \mathbf{c}_B' \boldsymbol{\beta}_j \quad \text{and} \quad \mathbf{p}_j = \mathbf{B}\boldsymbol{\beta}_j, \quad j = 1, \ldots, n, \tag{3.15}$$

where $\mathbf{p}_j$ is the jth column of $\mathbf{P}$, and $\mathbf{B}$ is the basis matrix for the optimal solution. Hence (3.14) becomes

$$\mathbf{c}_B' \mathbf{B}^{-1} \mathbf{p}_j - c_j \geqslant 0, \quad j = 1, \ldots, n. \tag{3.16}$$

The n inequalities (3.16) can be collected together to give

$$\mathbf{c}_B' \mathbf{B}^{-1} \mathbf{P} \geqslant \mathbf{c}'. \tag{3.17}$$

Now choose $\mathbf{y}$ such that

$$\mathbf{y}' = \mathbf{c}_B' \mathbf{B}^{-1}. \tag{3.18}$$

Then (3.17) can be written

$$\mathbf{P}'\mathbf{y} \geqslant \mathbf{c},$$

showing that $\mathbf{y}$, defined by (3.18), is a solution of problem (3.2).

We still have to show that $\mathbf{y}$ is feasible and optimal. To show that $\mathbf{y}$ is feasible consider the last m optimality conditions for problem (3.1), corresponding to the m slack variables $x_{n+1}, \ldots, x_{n+m}$:

$$z_j - c_j \geqslant 0, \quad j = n+i, \ i = 1, \ldots, m.$$

Since $c_j = 0$, these become

$$z_j = \mathbf{c}_B' \mathbf{B}^{-1} \mathbf{e}_i \geqslant 0, \quad j = n+i, \ i = 1, \ldots, m, \tag{3.19}$$

where $\mathbf{e}_i$ is the unit column vector with 1 as its ith component. Collecting together the m inequalities (3.19), we obtain

$$\mathbf{c}_B' \mathbf{B}^{-1} \mathbf{I}_m \geqslant \mathbf{0}, \quad \text{or} \quad \mathbf{c}_B' \mathbf{B}^{-1} \geqslant \mathbf{0},$$

i.e.

$$\mathbf{y}' \geqslant \mathbf{0}.$$

Thus $\mathbf{y}$ is a feasible solution of problem (3.2).

To show that $\mathbf{y}$ is optimal we use Theorem 3.3. Since $\mathbf{x}_B$ is optimal,

$$\max z = \mathbf{c}_B'\mathbf{x}_B = \mathbf{c}_B'\mathbf{B}^{-1}\mathbf{b} = \mathbf{y}'\mathbf{b} = w.$$

Thus $\mathbf{x}_B$ and $\mathbf{y}$ are feasible solutions of problems (3.1) and (3.2) respectively, such that $z = w$. It follows from Theorem 3.3 that $\mathbf{y}$ is optimal for problem (3.2), and hence that

$$\max z = \min w.$$

■ Theorem 3.5

If one of the problems (3.1), (3.2) has an unbounded solution with an unbounded value of the objective function, then the other has no feasible solution.

Proof

Since either (3.1) or (3.2) may be regarded as the primal problem, it is sufficient to prove that if (3.1) has an unbounded solution with an unbounded value of z then (3.2) has no feasible solution.

Theorem 3.2 states that

$$z = \mathbf{c}'\mathbf{x} \leqslant \mathbf{b}'\mathbf{y} = w, \tag{3.20}$$

where $\mathbf{x}$ is any feasible solution of (3.1) and $\mathbf{y}$ is any feasible solution of (3.2). Suppose $z \to \infty$. Then $w \to \infty$, and there is no vector $\mathbf{y}$ with finite components satisfying (3.20). Also we cannot claim that problem (3.2) has an unbounded solution with an unbounded value of w, for this would imply $w \to -\infty$ (not $+\infty$). Hence problem (3.2) has no feasible solution.

N.B. (i) The converse of Theorem 3.5 is false, i.e. it is *not* true that if one of the problems (3.1), (3.2) has no feasible solution then the other always has an unbounded solution with an unbounded value of the objective function. This may be shown by the following example.

Primal	*Dual*
Maximize $z = x_1 + x_2$,	Minimize $w = y_1 - 2y_2$,
subject to	subject to
$x_1 - x_2 \leqslant 1$,	$y_1 - y_2 \geqslant 1$,
$-x_1 + x_2 \leqslant -2$,	$-y_1 + y_2 \geqslant 1$,
$x_1, x_2 \geqslant 0$.	$y_1, y_2 \geqslant 0$.
(No feasible solution)	(No feasible solution)

N.B. (ii) The following example shows that the words 'with an unbounded value of the objective function' are essential in the statement of Theorem 3.5.

Primal	*Dual*
Minimize $w = x_1 - 3x_2$,	Maximize $z = y_1 - 3y_2$,
subject to	subject to
$x_1 - x_2 \geqslant 1$,	$y_1 + y_2 \leqslant 1$,
$x_1 - 3x_2 \geqslant -3$,	$-y_1 - 3y_2 \leqslant -3$,
$x_1, x_2 \geqslant 0$.	$y_1, y_2 \geqslant 0$.
(Alternative optima, including unbounded solution, with $w = -3$)	(Unique feasible solution: $y_1 = 0$, $y_2 = 1$; $z = -3$)

3.3 Relationships between Optimal Primal and Dual Tableaux

Theorem 3.4 indicates that, if we wish to find the optimal value of the objective function for any given linear programming problem, we can either solve the problem directly or solve its dual. In this section we shall show that, given any optimal primal tableau, the optimal dual tableau can be written down almost immediately. It turns out that, apart from certain changes in sign, the entries in the optimal dual tableau are merely a rearrangement of those in the optimal primal tableau. Unless otherwise stated, all the quantities referred to in this section are those appearing in the optimal tableaux.

The major results of the present section are contained in the following two theorems, the second of which is a variant of the first.

■ **Theorem 3.6** The Complementary Slackness Principle

For any pair of optimal solutions **x**, **y** of problems (3.1), (3.2), respectively,

(i) $y_i x_{n+i} = 0, \quad i = 1, \ldots, m,$

(ii) $x_j y_{m+j} = 0, \quad j = 1, \ldots, n.$

Proof

(i) Take the scalar product of equation (3.13) with **y**′, to give

$$\mathbf{y}'\mathbf{P}\mathbf{x} + \mathbf{y}'\mathbf{x}_s = \mathbf{y}'\mathbf{b}. \tag{3.21}$$

Since the solutions **x**, **y** of problems (3.1), (3.2), respectively, are both optimal, Theorem 3.4 gives $z = w$, and equation (3.12) then becomes

$$\mathbf{c}'\mathbf{x} = \mathbf{y}'\mathbf{P}\mathbf{x} = \mathbf{b}'\mathbf{y}. \tag{3.22}$$

From equations (3.21) and (3.22), we deduce

$$\mathbf{y}'\mathbf{x}_s = 0,$$

i.e.

$$y_i x_{n+i} = 0, \quad i = 1, \ldots, m, \tag{3.23}$$

since $y_i \geqslant 0$ and $x_{n+i} \geqslant 0$, $i = 1, \ldots, m$.

(ii) Introducing surplus variables, represented by the vector $\mathbf{y}_s$, the constraints of problem (3.2) become

$$\mathbf{P}'\mathbf{y} - \mathbf{y}_s = \mathbf{c}.$$

Take the scalar product of this equation with $\mathbf{x}'$, to give

$$\mathbf{x}'\mathbf{P}'\mathbf{y} - \mathbf{x}'\mathbf{y}_s = \mathbf{x}'\mathbf{c}. \tag{3.24}$$

From equations (3.22) and (3.24), we deduce

$$\mathbf{x}'\mathbf{y}_s = 0,$$

i.e.

$$x_j y_{m+j} = 0, \quad j = 1, \ldots, n, \tag{3.25}$$

since $x_j \geqslant 0$ and $y_{m+j} \geqslant 0, \quad j = 1, \ldots, n.$

It should be emphasized that Theorem 3.6 applies to any pair of optimal solutions, whether or not they are both basic. Theorem 3.6 has several variants; the most useful of these for the purpose of finding relationships between optimal primal and dual tableaux is the following theorem, which is limited to optimal *basic* solutions.

■ **Theorem 3.7.** The Complementary Slackness Principle for Basic Solutions.

Let $\mathbf{x}$ and $\mathbf{y}$ be any pair of optimal basic solutions of problems (3.1) and (3.2), respectively. Then

(i) the main dual variable y_i is basic if and only if the slack primal variable x_{n+i} is non-basic;

(ii) the surplus dual variable y_{m+j} is basic if and only if the main primal variable x_j is non-basic.

Proof

Assume that each of the optimal basic solutions is non-degenerate and that neither problem has an alternative optimum.

(i) Since x_{n+i} is a slack variable, its price is zero. Hence

$$z_{n+i} - c_{n+i} = z_{n+i} = \mathbf{c}_B{}'\mathbf{B}^{-1}\mathbf{e}_i = \mathbf{y}'\mathbf{e}_i = y_i, \tag{3.26}$$

where we have used (3.19) and (3.18).

Suppose that x_{n+i} is non-basic. Then $z_{n+i} - c_{n+i} > 0$, because of the optimality conditions (Section 2.4) and the assumption that problem (3.1) has no alternative optimum. Hence (3.26) gives $y_i > 0$, i.e. y_i is basic.

Now suppose that x_{n+i} is basic. Then $z_{n+i} - c_{n+i} = 0$, from the proof of Theorem 2.3. Hence (3.26) gives $y_i = 0$, i.e. y_i is non-basic, since we have assumed that the solution $\mathbf{y}$ is non-degenerate.

(ii) Since y_{m+j} is a surplus variable its price is zero. Hence

$$w_{m+j} - b_{m+j} = w_{m+j} = \mathbf{b}_B' \hat{\mathbf{B}}^{-1}(-\mathbf{e}_j) = \mathbf{x}'(-\mathbf{e}_j) = -x_j, \qquad (3.27)$$

using a term-by-term analogue of equations (3.26), where $\hat{\mathbf{B}}$ is the dual basis matrix.

Suppose that y_{m+j} is basic. Then $w_{m+j} - b_{m+j} = 0$. Hence (3.27) gives $x_j = 0$, i.e. x_j is non-basic, since we have assumed that the solution $\mathbf{x}$ is non-degenerate.

Now suppose that y_{m+j} is non-basic. Then $w_{m+j} - b_{m+j} < 0$, because of the optimality conditions (for a minimizing problem) and the assumption that problem (3.2) has no alternative optimum. Hence (3.27) gives $x_j > 0$, i.e. x_j is basic.

To complete the proof of the theorem we have to show that the assumptions of non-degeneracy and of no alternative optimum are unnecessary. We have already seen (Section 2.10) that a degenerate solution may be regarded as the limiting case of a non-degenerate solution in which the values of one or more non-degenerate variables tend to zero. Then from equations (3.26) and (3.27) the corresponding quantities $z_{n+i} - c_{n+i}$ and $w_{m+j} - b_{m+j}$ also tend to zero. It follows that the assumptions with which we began the proof merely define the limiting cases of the theorem, in which one of the problems (3.1), (3.2) has a degenerate optimal solution and the other has alternative optima.

It is worth noting that Theorem 3.7 can also be proved by using the result

$$z_j - c_j = \mathbf{c}_B' \mathbf{B}^{-1} \mathbf{p}_j - c_j = \mathbf{y}' \mathbf{p}_j - c_j = y_{m+j} \qquad (3.28)$$

and its term-by-term analogue

$$w_i - b_i = \mathbf{b}_B' \hat{\mathbf{B}}^{-1} \hat{\mathbf{p}}_i - b_i = \mathbf{x}' \hat{\mathbf{p}}_i - b_i = -x_{n+i}, \qquad (3.29)$$

where $\hat{\mathbf{p}}_i$ (a column vector) represents the ith row of $\mathbf{P}$, i.e. the ith column of $\mathbf{P}'$. The last equations in (3.28) and (3.29) are obtained from the jth dual constraint in problem (3.2) and the ith primal constraint in problem (3.1), respectively. The proof of Theorem 3.7 by means of equations (3.28) and (3.29) is closely similar to that given above, in which equations (3.26) and (3.27) were used.

In the present section we shall confine our attention to pairs of optimal basic feasible solutions. Theorems 3.6 and 3.7 group the primal and dual variables in pairs according to their type (basic, non-basic; main, slack or surplus). Each pair consists of a basic and a non-basic variable, and also of a main variable and a slack or surplus variable. Table 3.1 shows the pairing of variables suggested by Theorems 3.6 and 3.7; we shall say that the variables x_{n+i} and y_i are *complementary*, and we shall write

$$x_{n+i} \sim y_i;$$

and likewise

$$x_j \sim y_{m+j}.$$

Table 3.1 Complementary Variables

Primal	*Dual*
Basic slack	Non-basic main
Non-basic slack	Basic main
Basic main	Non-basic surplus
Non-basic main	Basic surplus

As an example of the use of Table 3.1, suppose that **P** is a 3×5 matrix, i.e. $m = 3$, $n = 5$. The primal variables are

$$x_1, x_2, x_3, x_4, x_5; \ x_6, x_7, x_8,$$

of which x_1, x_2, x_3, x_4, x_5 are main and x_6, x_7, x_8 slack. It is convenient to write the dual variables in the order

$$y_4, y_5, y_6, y_7, y_8; \ y_1, y_2, y_3,$$

where y_4, y_5, y_6, y_7, y_8 are surplus and y_1, y_2, y_3 main. Then

$$x_1 \sim y_4, \quad x_2 \sim y_5, \ldots, x_8 \sim y_3.$$

Hence, if x_2, x_3, x_7 are basic variables in the primal, then y_5, y_6, y_2 are non-basic variables in the dual, and the dual basic variables are y_1, y_3, y_4, y_7, y_8.

The general forms of the two optimal tableaux are displayed for reference in Tables 3.2 and 3.3; the notation is self-explanatory.

We now consider in detail how to construct the optimal dual tableau from the optimal primal tableau.

1. Theorem 3.7 shows that the dual basic variables are complementary to the primal non-basic variables:

$$y_i \sim x_{n+i} \quad \text{and} \quad y_{m+j} \sim x_j.$$

2. Equation (3.26) shows that the values of the basic main dual variables y_i, $i = l+1, \ldots, m$, appear in the $z_j - c_j$ row of the primal tableau in the columns headed by the non-basic slack primal variables x_{n+i}, $i = l+1, \ldots, m$. Therefore from Table 3.2 we find

$$y_i = \beta_{m+1,n+i}, \quad i = l+1, \ldots, m. \tag{3.30}$$

3. Equation (3.28) shows that the values of the basic surplus dual variables y_{m+j}, $j = k+1, \ldots, n$, appear in the $z_j - c_j$ row of the primal tableau in the columns headed by the non-basic main primal variables x_j, $j = k+1, \ldots, n$. Therefore from Table 3.2 we find

$$y_{m+j} = \beta_{m+1,j}, \quad j = k+1, \ldots, n. \tag{3.31}$$

4. The values of the objective functions w and z are equal, by Theorem 3.4.

Table 3.2 Optimal Primal Tableau

		$\mathbf{c}'$		$c_1 \ldots c_k$	$c_{k+1} \ldots c_n$	$\mathbf{0}'$	$\mathbf{0}'$
	$\mathbf{c}_B$	Basic Variables		$x_1 \ldots x_k$	$x_{k+1} \ldots x_n$	$x_{n+1} \ldots x_{n+l}$	$x_{n+l+1} \ldots x_{n+m}$
↑ Main	$c_{B1} = c_1$	$x_{B1} = x_1$	β_{10}		$\beta_{1,k+1} \ldots \beta_{1n}$		$\beta_{1,n+l+1} \ldots \beta_{1,n+m}$
	$\vdots$	$\vdots$	$\vdots$	$\mathbf{I}$	$\vdots\ \mathbf{B}_1\ \vdots$	$\mathbf{O}$	$\vdots\ \mathbf{B}_2\ \vdots$
k ↓	$c_{Bk} = c_k$	$x_{Bk} = x_k$	β_{k0}		$\beta_{k,k+1} \ldots \beta_{kn}$		$\beta_{k,n+l+1} \ldots \beta_{k,n+m}$
↑ Slack		$x_{B,k+1} = x_{n+1}$	$\beta_{k+1,0}$		$\beta_{k+1,k+1} \ldots \beta_{k+1,n}$		$\beta_{k+1,n+l+1} \ldots \beta_{k+1,n+m}$
	$\mathbf{0}$	$\vdots$	$\vdots$	$\mathbf{O}$	$\vdots\ \mathbf{B}_3\ \vdots$	$\mathbf{I}$	$\vdots\ \mathbf{B}_4\ \vdots$
$l = m-k$ ↓		$x_{Bm} = x_{n+l}$	β_{m0}		$\beta_{m,k+1} \ldots \beta_{mn}$		$\beta_{m,n+l+1} \ldots \beta_{m,n+m}$
		$z_j - c_j$	$z = \beta_{m+1,0}$	$\mathbf{0}'$	$\beta_{m+1,k+1} \ldots \beta_{m+1,n}$	$\mathbf{0}'$	$\beta_{m+1,n+l+1} \ldots \beta_{m+1,n+m}$
				←Main	→	←Slack	→
				←Basic→	←Non-basic→	←Basic→	←Non-basic→
				k	$n-k$	$l = m-k$	$m-l=k$

Maximize $z = \mathbf{c}'\mathbf{x}$, subject to $\mathbf{Px} \leqslant \mathbf{b}$ and $\mathbf{x} \geqslant \mathbf{0}$.

Table 3.3 Optimal Dual Tableau

		$\mathbf{b}'$		$b_1 \ldots b_l$	$b_{l+1} \ldots b_m$	$\mathbf{0}'$	$\mathbf{0}'$
	$\mathbf{b}_B$	Basic Variables		$y_1 \ldots y_l$	$y_{l+1} \ldots y_m$	$y_{m+1} \ldots y_{m+k}$	$y_{m+k+1} \ldots y_{m+n}$
↑ Main $k = m - l$ ↓	$b_{B1} = b_{l+1}$ . . . $b_{Bk} = b_m$	$y_{B1} = y_{l+1}$ . . . $y_{Bk} = y_m$	$\beta_{m+1,n+l+1}$ . . . $\beta_{m+1,n+m}$	$-\beta_{k+1,n+l+1} \cdots -\beta_{m,n+l+1}$. $-\mathbf{B}_4'$. $-\beta_{k+1,n+m} \cdots -\beta_{m,n+m}$	$\mathbf{I}$	$-\beta_{1,n+l+1} \cdots -\beta_{k,n+l+1}$. $-\mathbf{B}_2'$. $-\beta_{1,n+m} \cdots -\beta_{k,n+m}$	$\mathbf{O}$
↑ Surplus $n - k$ ↓	$\mathbf{0}$	$y_{B,k+1} = y_{m+k+1}$ . . . $y_{Bn} = y_{m+n}$	$\beta_{m+1,k+1}$ . . . $\beta_{m+1,n}$	$-\beta_{k+1,k+1} \cdots -\beta_{m,k+1}$. $-\mathbf{B}_3'$. $-\beta_{k+1,n} \cdots -\beta_{mn}$	$\mathbf{O}$	$-\beta_{1,k+1} \cdots -\beta_{k,k+1}$. $-\mathbf{B}_1'$. $-\beta_{1n} \ldots -\beta_{kn}$	$\mathbf{I}$
		$w_i - b_i$	$w = z = \beta_{m+1,0}$	$-\beta_{k+1,0} \cdots -\beta_{m0}$	$\mathbf{0}'$	$-\beta_{10} \ldots -\beta_{k0}$	$\mathbf{0}'$
				← Main →		← Surplus →	
				← Non-basic → $l = m - k$	← Basic → $m - l = k$	← Non-basic → k	← Basic → $n - k$

Minimize $z = \mathbf{b}'\mathbf{y}$, subject to $\mathbf{P}'\mathbf{y} \geqslant \mathbf{c}$ and $\mathbf{y} \geqslant \mathbf{0}$.

5. The entries in the $w_i - b_i$ row of the dual tableau corresponding to non-basic variables y_i are found by using equations (3.29) and (3.27), to give respectively

$$w_i - b_i = -x_{n+i}, \quad i = 1, \ldots, l,$$

and

$$w_{m+j} - b_{m+j} = -x_j, \quad j = 1, \ldots, k.$$

Thus, using Table 3.2, we find

$$w_i - b_i = -\beta_{k+i,0}, \quad i = 1, \ldots, l, \quad \text{where } k + l = m, \tag{3.32}$$

and

$$w_{m+j} - b_{m+j} = -\beta_{j0}, \quad j = 1, \ldots, k. \tag{3.33}$$

All the entries in the last row of the dual tableau (except possibly w) are non-positive since the dual is a minimizing problem.

6. The positions of the unit and zero matrices in the dual tableau are known as soon as the names of the dual basic variables are known. It remains to prove that the sub-matrices $\mathbf{B}_1$, $\mathbf{B}_2$, $\mathbf{B}_3$, $\mathbf{B}_4$ in the primal tableau, Table 3.2, become $-\mathbf{B}_1'$, $-\mathbf{B}_2'$, $-\mathbf{B}_3'$, $-\mathbf{B}_4'$ respectively in the rather curious positions shown in the dual tableau, Table 3.3. A complete proof of this result requires a somewhat lengthy analysis of the structure of the basis matrices for the primal and dual problems. However, the result is made plausible by the following argument.

Suppose that we are given the primal and dual problems (3.1) and (3.2), and that we arrive at the optimal primal and dual tableaux in the following way. Add slack variables to the primal constraints and, in the initial primal tableau, set each slack variable equal to the right-hand side of the constraint equation in which it appears. (This initial basic solution may not be feasible.) Subtract surplus variables from the dual constraints and, in the initial dual tableau, set each surplus variable equal to -1 times the right-hand side of the constraint equation in which it appears.

Consider the initial primal and dual sub-tableaux formed by omitting (i) the unit and zero elements associated with the basic variables, (ii) the columns containing the values of the basic variables and (iii) the $z_j - c_j$ and $w_i - b_i$ rows. Because of the way in which the initial tableaux have been constructed, the initial dual sub-tableau is the negative transpose of the initial primal sub-tableau. If the two initial tableaux are optimal, then we already have the desired result, due allowance being made for the order in which the constraints and variables are arranged in the standard layout of the optimal tableaux.

If the two initial tableaux are not optimal, then we perform a sequence of simplex transformations on the primal tableaux, arriving eventually at the optimal primal tableau. Now, apart from the elements in the pivotal rows and columns, the rules of tableaux transformation are such that if *any* tableau and its transpose are transformed using identical pivots (i.e. pivot and its transpose, respectively), then the new tableaux are also transposes of each other. Furthermore, the elements derived from the pivotal row and non-basic columns of a tableau, apart from the 1 into which the pivot itself is transformed, also appear (with changed signs) in the tableau derived from its transpose—in the column corresponding to the variable that has just become non-basic. Thus, excluding only the unit and zero elements associated with the basic variables, and allowing for tableau layout, the new tableaux are still transposes of each other, except for discrepancies in sign between a row of one and a column of the other.

Returning to the present problem, it follows that if simplex transformations are carried out on the dual tableaux, always using pivots corresponding to those used for the primal transformations (i.e. *negative* transposes of the primal pivots), then the primal and dual sub-tableaux, defined by the omission of elements (i), (ii), and (iii) above, retain the negative transpose property at corresponding stages (allowing for layout), since the discrepancies in sign at each stage now disappear. (Consider the effect on a new sub-tableau of a change of sign in every element of the old sub-tableau.) Finally, both tableaux are optimal and have the properties shown in Tables 3.2 and 3.3.

7. Having shown how to derive the optimal dual tableau from the optimal primal tableau, we now see that it is not strictly necessary to use the standard forms (Tables 3.2 and 3.3) of the tableaux for this purpose; the optimal dual tableau may be constructed almost immediately from the optimal primal tableau by using the properties of complementary variables.

For example, consider the column headed by y_{m+1} in the optimal dual tableau, Table 3.3. This column may be completed in isolation; for $y_{m+1} \sim x_1$, which determines $-\beta_{10}$ as the last element in the column. Also, the remaining elements in the column appear (with changed signs) in the x_1 row of the optimal primal tableau. To determine the order in which they appear, we use an obvious extension of the notation introduced on page 83.

$$(y_{l+1}, \ldots, y_m) \sim (x_{n+l+1}, \ldots, x_{n+m})$$

and

$$(y_{m+k+1}, \ldots, y_{m+n}) \sim (x_{k+1}, \ldots, x_n).$$

Thus the elements $\beta_{1,n+l+1}, \ldots, \beta_{1,n+m}$ in the optimal primal tableau, which appear in the columns headed by the non-basic variables $x_{n+l+1}, \ldots, x_{n+m}$, also appear (with changed signs) in the optimal dual tableau in the rows corresponding to the complementary basic variables $y_{l+1}, \ldots, y_m$, respectively. A similar rule applies to the elements $\beta_{1,k+1}, \ldots, \beta_{1n}$ in the optimal primal tableau. Any column in the optimal dual tableau may be completed by this method. Alternatively, the optimal dual tableau may be constructed row by row. In this case a dual row, which corresponds to a dual basic variable, is associated with the primal column headed by the non-basic complementary variable.

There is no difficulty in constructing the optimal primal (maximizing) tableau from the optimal dual (minimizing) tableau. We conclude this section with an example which illustrates the procedure.

Example 3.2

Solve the dual of the following linear programming problem, and thence construct the optimal primal tableau.

$$\text{Maximize } z = x_1 + x_2 + x_3,$$

subject to

$$\begin{aligned} x_1 - x_2 + 2x_3 &\leqslant 4, \\ 2x_1 + x_2 - x_3 &\leqslant 6, \\ 4x_1 - x_2 - x_3 &\leqslant 8, \\ 8x_1 + x_2 + x_3 &\leqslant 10, \\ x_1, x_2, x_3 &\geqslant 0. \end{aligned}$$

Solution

The dual problem is

$$\text{Minimize } w = 4y_1 + 6y_2 + 8y_3 + 10y_4,$$

subject to

$$\begin{aligned} y_1 + 2y_2 + 4y_3 + 8y_4 &\geqslant 1, \\ -y_1 + y_2 - y_3 + y_4 &\geqslant 1, \\ 2y_1 - y_2 - y_3 + y_4 &\geqslant 1, \\ y_1, y_2, y_3, y_4 &\geqslant 0. \end{aligned}$$

Introducing surplus variables y_5, y_6, y_7, the dual constraints become

$$\begin{aligned} y_1 + 2y_2 + 4y_3 + 8y_4 - y_5 &= 1, \\ -y_1 + y_2 - y_3 + y_4 - y_6 &= 1, \\ 2y_1 - y_2 - y_3 + y_4 - y_7 &= 1. \end{aligned}$$

A fairly obvious basic feasible solution is $y_4 = 1$, $y_5 = 7$, with all other variables zero. Let y_6 be the third basic variable (chosen at random). Using the third constraint to eliminate y_4 from the first two, we obtain two constraint equations containing isolated basic variables with coefficients of $+1$, which replace the first two constraints above:

$$\begin{aligned} 15y_1 - 10y_2 - 12y_3 + y_5 - 8y_7 &= 7, \\ 3y_1 - 2y_2 + y_6 - y_7 &= 0. \end{aligned}$$

This procedure avoids the use of artificial variables. The initial and subsequent dual tableaux can now be completed; the problem is solved as a minimizing problem.

Tableau 1 (Example 3.2)

	$\mathbf{b}'$		4	6	8	10	0	0	0
$\mathbf{b}_B$	Basic Variables		y_1	y_2	y_3	y_4	y_5	y_6	y_7
10	y_4	1	2	-1	-1	1	0	0	-1
0	y_5	7	15	-10	-12	0	1	0	-8
0	y_6	0	3*	-2	0	0	0	1	-1
	$w_i - b_i$	10	16	-16	-18	0	0	0	-10

Tableau 2 (Example 3.2)

	$\mathbf{b}'$		4	6	8	10	0	0	0
$\mathbf{b}_B$	Basic Variables		y_1	y_2	y_3	y_4	y_5	y_6	y_7
10	y_4	1	0	1/3	-1	1	0	$-2/3$	$-1/3$
0	y_5	7	0	0	-12	0	1	-5	-3
4	y_1	0	1	$-2/3$	0	0	0	1/3	$-1/3$
	$w_i - b_i$	10	0	$-16/3$	-18	0	0	$-16/3$	$-14/3$

Tableau 2 is optimal. Construction of the optimal primal tableau begins by pairing off the complementary variables:

$$(x_1, x_2, x_3; x_4, x_5, x_6, x_7) \sim (y_5, y_6, y_7; y_1, y_2, y_3, y_4).$$

The basic dual variables are y_5, y_1, y_4. Hence the basic primal variables are x_2, x_3, x_5, x_6. The values of these variables are 16/3, 14/3, 16/3, 18, respectively: they appear (with changed signs) in Tableau 2 in the $w_i - b_i$ row and in the columns headed by the complementary variables y_6, y_7, y_2, y_3, respectively. Similarly, the entries in the $z_j - c_j$ row of the primal tableau corresponding to non-basic variables x_j are the values of the complementary basic dual variables (without change of sign).

The x_1, x_4 and x_7 columns of the optimal primal tableau are completed from the y_5, y_1 and y_4 rows respectively of the optimal dual tableau, remembering that the signs of all the elements must be changed, and that the rows of the optimal primal tableau (associated with basic primal variables) correspond to the columns of the optimal dual tableau headed by the complementary non-basic dual variables, i.e. we use

$$(x_2, x_3, x_5, x_6) \sim (y_6, y_7, y_2, y_3)$$

Optimal Primal Tableau (Example 3.2)

	$\mathbf{c}'$		1	1	1	0	0	0	0
$\mathbf{c}_B$	Basic Variables		x_1	x_2	x_3	x_4	x_5	x_6	x_7
1	x_2	16/3	5	1	0	−1/3	0	0	2/3
1	x_3	14/3	3	0	1	1/3	0	0	1/3
0	x_5	16/3	0	0	0	2/3	1	0	−1/3
0	x_6	18	12	0	0	0	0	1	1
	$z_j - c_j$	10	7	0	0	0	0	0	1

to determine the order in which the elements appear in the columns of the optimal primal tableau.

Incidentally, since x_4 is a non-basic variable in the optimal primal tableau, and $z_4 - c_4 = 0$, the primal problem has alternative optima. In the optimal dual tableau the complementary basic variable y_1 is degenerate. This result illustrates the limiting case that was mentioned at the end of the proof of Theorem 3.7.

*3.4 The Dual Simplex Method: Theory

It is always desirable to try to reduce the number of simplex iterations that are used in solving a linear programming problem. The standard simplex method, described in Chapter 2, requires an initial basic feasible solution. Unfortunately, a considerable amount of preliminary computation (e.g. the elimination of artificial variables) is sometimes necessary if there is no obvious basic feasible solution.

Many variants of the simplex method have been developed for the case when an initial basic *non-feasible* solution is available. Probably the best-known of these is the *dual simplex method*, due to C. E. Lemke [29]. The fundamental idea behind the method is that the choice of basic and non-basic variables to be exchanged in each transformation of the primal tableau is determined by criteria applied to the current dual tableau. However, the computation is carried out on primal tableaux only. The major change in the rules for tableau transformation is that in the dual simplex method we decide first which variable becomes non-basic, and then decide which variable becomes basic. Once these variables have been chosen, the usual simplex transformation equations are used. We now give the detailed derivation of the rules for the dual simplex method.

Suppose that the primal problem is

$$\left.\begin{aligned} &\text{Maximize } z = \mathbf{c}'\mathbf{x}, \\ \text{subject to} \quad & \\ &\mathbf{A}\mathbf{x} = \mathbf{b} \quad \text{and} \quad \mathbf{x} \geqslant 0, \end{aligned}\right\} \tag{3.34}$$

where, as usual, the matrix $\mathbf{A}$ is of order $m \times N$. Then the dual problem is

$$\left.\begin{aligned} &\text{Minimize } w = \mathbf{b}'\mathbf{y}, \\ \text{subject to} \\ &\mathbf{A}'\mathbf{y} \geqslant \mathbf{c}, \text{ with } \mathbf{y} \text{ unrestricted in sign.} \end{aligned}\right\} \tag{3.35}$$

From (3.34) and (3.35),

$$\mathbf{c}'\mathbf{x} \leqslant \mathbf{y}'\mathbf{A}\mathbf{x} = \mathbf{y}'\mathbf{b}. \tag{3.36}$$

Now suppose that it is possible to find a basis matrix $\mathbf{B}$, consisting of m linearly independent columns of $\mathbf{A}$, such that a basic solution $\mathbf{y}_B$ of the dual problem (3.35) is given by

$$\mathbf{B}'\mathbf{y}_B = \mathbf{c}_B. \tag{3.37}$$

The importance of equation (3.37) lies in the fact that the major aim of the present analysis is to obtain a new solution of the dual problem, still in the form of equation (3.37), but giving a smaller value for the dual objective function.

The dual constraints (3.35) can be written in the form

$$\mathbf{y}'\mathbf{A} \geqslant \mathbf{c}',$$

or

$$\mathbf{y}'\mathbf{a}_j \geqslant c_j, \quad j = 1, \ldots, N. \tag{3.38}$$

For the basic solution $\mathbf{y} = \mathbf{y}_B = (\mathbf{B}')^{-1}\mathbf{c}_B$, (3.38) becomes

$$\left.\begin{aligned} \mathbf{c}_B'\mathbf{B}^{-1}\mathbf{a}_j &\geqslant c_j, \\ \text{i.e.} \qquad z_j - c_j &\geqslant 0, \end{aligned}\right\} \quad j = 1, \ldots, N, \tag{3.39}$$

since $\mathbf{a}_j = \mathbf{B}\boldsymbol{\beta}_j$ and $z_j = \mathbf{c}_B'\boldsymbol{\beta}_j$, these being equations (2.24) and (2.36), respectively. The inequalities (3.39) are precisely the optimality conditions for the primal problem.

Next, consider the basic solution $\mathbf{x}_B$ of the primal problem (3.34) given by $\mathbf{B}\mathbf{x}_B = \mathbf{b}$. If

$$\mathbf{x}_B = \mathbf{B}^{-1}\mathbf{b} \geqslant \mathbf{0}, \tag{3.40}$$

then $\mathbf{x}_B$ and $\mathbf{y}_B$ are optimal solutions of the primal and dual problems, respectively, since

$$z = \mathbf{c}_B'\mathbf{x}_B = \mathbf{c}_B'\mathbf{B}^{-1}\mathbf{b} = \mathbf{y}_B'\mathbf{b} = w, \tag{3.41}$$

using equation (3.37) and Theorem 3.3. It follows that if $\mathbf{y}_B$ in equation (3.37) is not optimal, then at least one component of $\mathbf{x}_B$ in equation (3.40) is strictly negative. In this case, suppose $x_{Br} < 0$, and consider a new solution $\bar{\mathbf{y}}_B$ of the dual problem, given by

$$\bar{\mathbf{y}}_B' = \mathbf{y}_B' - \phi(\mathbf{B}^{-1})_r, \tag{3.42}$$

where ϕ is a scalar, and $(\mathbf{B}^{-1})_r$ is the rth row of $\mathbf{B}^{-1}$. Then from equation (3.40) we have

$$x_{Br} = (\mathbf{B}^{-1})_r \mathbf{b},$$

and using equation (3.42) we find

$$\bar{w} = \bar{\mathbf{y}}_B{}'\mathbf{b} = \mathbf{y}_B{}'\mathbf{b} - \phi(\mathbf{B}^{-1})_r \mathbf{b} = w - \phi x_{Br}. \tag{3.43}$$

The value of w for the minimizing problem (3.35) will therefore be improved if (i) $\bar{\mathbf{y}}_B{}'$ satisfies the constraints of problem (3.35), and (ii) $\phi < 0$, since $x_{Br} < 0$. But if $\mathbf{b}_i$ is the ith column of $\mathbf{B}$, then

$$\bar{\mathbf{y}}_B{}'\mathbf{b}_i = \mathbf{y}_B{}'\mathbf{b}_i - \phi(\mathbf{B}^{-1})_r \mathbf{b}_i = c_{Bi} - \phi\delta_{ri},$$

where δ_{ri} is the Kronecker symbol, defined by

$$\begin{aligned} \delta_{ri} &= 1, \quad i = r, \\ &= 0, \quad i \neq r. \end{aligned}$$

Therefore

$$\left.\begin{aligned} \bar{\mathbf{y}}_B{}'\mathbf{b}_i &= c_{Bi}, \quad i = 1, \ldots, m, \quad i \neq r, \\ \bar{\mathbf{y}}_B{}'\mathbf{b}_r &= c_{Br} - \phi \geqslant c_{Br} \quad \text{if } \phi \leqslant 0. \end{aligned}\right\} \tag{3.44}$$

This shows that the constraints of problem (3.35) are satisfied by $\bar{\mathbf{y}}_B$ for the columns of $\mathbf{A}$ (i.e. rows of $\mathbf{A}'$) comprising the basis matrix $\mathbf{B}$. For the columns $\mathbf{a}_j$ of $\mathbf{A}$ not in $\mathbf{B}$, equation (3.42) gives

$$\bar{\mathbf{y}}_B{}'\mathbf{a}_j = \mathbf{y}_B{}'\mathbf{a}_j - \phi(\mathbf{B}^{-1})_r \mathbf{a}_j, \tag{3.45}$$

and from equation (3.38), with $\mathbf{y} = \mathbf{y}_B$, we have

$$\mathbf{y}_B{}'\mathbf{a}_j \geqslant c_j. \tag{3.46}$$

Suppose that $(\mathbf{B}^{-1})_r \mathbf{a}_j \geqslant 0$ for every $\mathbf{a}_j$ not in $\mathbf{B}$. Then it follows from (3.45) and (3.46) that

$$\bar{\mathbf{y}}_B{}'\mathbf{a}_j \geqslant c_j \quad \text{for all } \phi \leqslant 0.$$

Thus the dual constraints are satisfied, but equation (3.43) shows that $\bar{w} \to -\infty$ as $\phi \to \infty$, i.e. the dual problem has an unbounded solution with an unbounded value of the objective function. By Theorem 3.5 the primal problem has no feasible solution in this case, which is therefore of little or no interest.

Suppose, on the contrary, that $(\mathbf{B}^{-1})_r \mathbf{a}_j < 0$ for at least one $\mathbf{a}_j$ not in $\mathbf{B}$. From equation (2.24) we have

$$\mathbf{B}^{-1}\mathbf{a}_j = \boldsymbol{\beta}_j,$$

and the rth component of this equation gives

$$(\mathbf{B}^{-1})_r \mathbf{a}_j = \beta_{rj} < 0.$$

Hence equation (3.45) becomes

$$\bar{\mathbf{y}}_B'\mathbf{a}_j = \mathbf{y}_B'\mathbf{a}_j - \phi\beta_{rj}, \tag{3.47}$$

and we require

$$\bar{\mathbf{y}}_B'\mathbf{a}_j \geqslant c_j$$

in order that $\bar{\mathbf{y}}_B$ should satisfy the dual constraints. From equation (3.47) this implies

$$\mathbf{y}_B'\mathbf{a}_j - \phi\beta_{rj} \geqslant c_j, \tag{3.48}$$

or

$$\phi \geqslant \frac{\mathbf{y}_B'\mathbf{a}_j - c_j}{\beta_{rj}}. \tag{3.49}$$

Combining this condition on ϕ with the obvious requirement from equation (3.43) that ϕ must be as negative as possible in order to decrease w as much as possible, we take

$$\phi = \max_{j=1,\ldots,N}\left\{\frac{\mathbf{y}_B'\mathbf{a}_j - c_j}{\beta_{rj}}:\ \beta_{rj} < 0\right\}, \tag{3.50}$$

i.e.

$$\phi = \max_{j=1,\ldots,N}\left\{\frac{z_j - c_j}{\beta_{rj}}:\ \beta_{rj} < 0\right\}. \tag{3.51}$$

If we write

$$\phi = \frac{z_k - c_k}{\beta_{rk}} = \max_{j=1,\ldots,N}\left\{\frac{z_j - c_j}{\beta_{rj}}:\ \beta_{rj} < 0\right\}, \tag{3.52}$$

then the new solution $\bar{\mathbf{y}}_B$ of the dual problem satisfies

$$\left.\begin{aligned}\bar{\mathbf{y}}_B'\mathbf{a}_j &\geqslant c_j, \quad j \neq k,\\ \bar{\mathbf{y}}_B'\mathbf{a}_k &= c_k,\end{aligned}\right\} \tag{3.53}$$

for the columns $\mathbf{a}_j$ of **A** not in **B**, and satisfies (3.44) for the columns of **A** which comprise **B**.

From (3.39) and (3.51) we must have $\phi \leqslant 0$. Then from equation (3.43) we obtain

$$\begin{aligned}\bar{w} &< w \quad \text{if } \phi < 0,\\ &= w \quad \text{if } \phi = 0.\end{aligned}$$

The new solution $\bar{\mathbf{y}}_B$ of (3.53) is obtained, in effect, by decreasing w until one of the dual constraints becomes an equation:

$$\bar{\mathbf{y}}_B'\mathbf{a}_k = c_k.$$

We are now in a position to deduce the rules for the dual simplex method. Our aim is to reach the optimal primal solution, and we know from equation (3.40) that this is attained when all the primal basic variables are non-negative. Suppose we choose β_{rk} as pivot in the primal tableau. This element, and the tableau transformation associated with it, have the following desirable properties:

(i) $\beta_{rk} \neq 0$; in fact, $\beta_{rk} < 0$ from equation (3.52).

(ii) The negative-valued basic variable x_{Br} becomes non-basic, i.e. takes the value zero.

(iii) The vector $\mathbf{a}_k$ replaces $\mathbf{a}_r$ in $\mathbf{B}$ and, since $\mathbf{a}_k$ corresponds to the dual equality constraint of (3.53), a new equation (3.37) can be assumed and the whole procedure repeated if necessary.

Ultimately w must attain its minimum by the usual simplex process. Theorem 3.4 then tells us that the optimal primal solution has been reached.

There is one final choice to be made. If $x_{Bi} < 0$ for more than one value of i, then w could be improved by taking x_{Br} to be any one of these x_{Bi}. In an attempt to speed up the procedure in this case, we choose x_{Br} to be the most negative x_{Bi}. Thus the rules for solving the *maximizing* problem (3.34) by the dual simplex method are:

1. Find an initial basic solution with $z_j - c_j \geqslant 0$ for all j, $j = 1, \ldots, N$.

2(a). If $x_{Bi} \geqslant 0$ for all i, $i = 1, \ldots, m$, then the solution is optimal.

2(b). If $x_{Bi} < 0$ for at least one value of i, then the variable x_{Br} becomes non-basic, where

$$x_{Br} = \min_{i=1,\ldots,m} \{x_{Bi} : x_{Bi} < 0\}. \tag{3.54}$$

3. When 2(b) holds, the variable x_k becomes basic, where k is chosen by the rule

$$\frac{z_k - c_k}{\beta_{rk}} = \max_{j=1,\ldots,N} \left\{ \frac{z_j - c_j}{\beta_{rj}} : \beta_{rj} < 0 \right\}. \tag{3.55}$$

If r is not determined uniquely by (3.54) then one of the values of r is chosen arbitrarily; similarly for k and (3.55). It is shown in the next section that if $\beta_{rj} \geqslant 0$ for all j, then there is no feasible solution.

It is possible to use the dual simplex method to solve a minimizing problem directly, by making appropriate changes to rules 1 and 3 above; rules 2(a) and 2(b) remain unchanged. Specifically, if the given problem is the *minimizing* problem

$$\text{Minimize } z = \mathbf{c}'\mathbf{x},$$

subject to

$$\mathbf{A}\mathbf{x} = \mathbf{b} \quad \text{and} \quad \mathbf{x} \geqslant \mathbf{0},$$

then the rules for the dual simplex method are:

1. Find an initial basic solution with $z_j - c_j \leqslant 0$ for all j, $j = 1, \ldots, N$.

2(a). If $x_{Bi} \geqslant 0$ for all i, $i = 1, \ldots, m$, then the solution is optimal.

2(b). If $x_{Bi} < 0$ for at least one value of i, then the variable x_{Br} becomes non-basic, where

$$x_{Br} = \min_{i=1,\ldots,m} \{x_{Bi} : x_{Bi} < 0\}.$$

3. When 2(b) holds, the variable x_k becomes basic, where k is chosen by the rule

$$\frac{z_k - c_k}{\beta_{rk}} = \min_{j=1,\ldots,N} \left\{ \frac{z_j - c_j}{\beta_{rj}} : \beta_{rj} < 0 \right\}. \tag{3.56}$$

Statements similar to those following equation (3.55) also apply here.

An interesting property of the dual simplex method, and one which affords a check on the computation, is that $z = w$ at each stage of the calculation, from equation (3.41). Thus, for a maximizing problem, z will steadily *decrease* to its optimal value.

In conclusion, we note that if the primal problem has an unbounded solution with an unbounded value of z, then the dual problem has no feasible solution, by Theorem 3.5. This in turn means that (for a maximizing problem) there is no primal basic solution with $z_j - c_j \geqslant 0$, $j = 1, \ldots, N$, as may be seen from equations (3.26) and (3.28). That is, the conditions (3.39) cannot be satisfied. Similarly, for a minimizing problem, there is no primal basic solution with $z_j - c_j \leqslant 0$, $j = 1, \ldots, N$. Thus the fact that the initial step in the dual simplex method cannot be carried out indicates an unbounded solution with an unbounded value of the objective function.

*3.5 The Dual Simplex Method: Discussion

It is not possible to say precisely when the standard simplex method should be abandoned in favour of the dual simplex method. An essential requirement for the latter is that the optimality conditions (3.39) are satisfied in the initial primal tableau. (In this section we shall consider only the maximizing problem; similar remarks apply to the minimizing problem.) Satisfying these conditions may entail more work than solving the problem by some other method. There is one special case, however, when the optimality conditions are satisfied automatically: if every basic variable is either a slack or surplus variable (and therefore has a zero price), and if $c_j \leqslant 0$ for all j, then $z_j - c_j = -c_j \geqslant 0$ for all j. As an extension of this special case, the dual simplex method may be used to obtain a basic feasible solution of a problem whose objective function contains both positive and negative prices by the device of replacing any positive price $c_j > 0$ by $c_j' = 0$. This substitution ensures that $z_j - c_j \geqslant 0$ for all j, but the basic feasible solution so obtained will not, in general, be optimal. However, starting with this basic feasible solution and replacing the zero c_j' by the correct positive c_j, the standard simplex method (in effect, phase 2 of the two-phase method) may be used to complete the calculation. The details of this procedure are illustrated in Example 3.3 below.

As a general rule, if an initial basic feasible solution can be found without introducing artificial variables, then there is no advantage to be gained in using the dual simplex method. The use of the dual simplex method is normally an alternative to the use of artificial variables. However, it is also possible to have artificial variables among the primal basic variables in the dual simplex method. As usual, they are disregarded once they have become non-basic. The calculations cannot terminate as long as non-degenerate artificial variables are present: eventually all the artificial variables are eliminated, or one of the special cases of Section 2.8—2.8.2 or 2.8.3—is indicated. If one of the basic variables is an artificial variable with a strictly positive value, and if all the remaining basic variables have non-negative values, then the dual simplex method can be continued by the device of changing the sign of the artificial variable, writing $-x_4'$ instead of x_4, for example. The sign of the price of the artificial variable must also, of course, be changed. Further details of this technique may be found in reference [9].

If $\beta_{rj} \geqslant 0$ for all j in (3.55) or (3.56), then the primal problem has no feasible solution. For the rth row in the primal tableau represents the equality constraint

$$\beta_{r1}x_1 + \ldots + \beta_{rN}x_N = \text{current value of } x_{Br},$$

which is inconsistent with the non-negativity restrictions $x_j \geqslant 0, j = 1, \ldots, N$, since the current value of x_{Br} is strictly negative—see rules 2(b) in Section 3.4.

As shown by Lemke [29], degeneracy can be avoided in the dual simplex method by using a perturbation of the dual problem. Results similar to those of Section 2.10 are obtained—additional rules are found for selecting the variable to become basic whenever k is not determined uniquely by equation (3.55) or equation (3.56). The additional rules for the *maximizing* problem are:

1. If k is not determined uniquely by equation (3.55), then, from among the tied values of j, find j such that β_{1j}/β_{rj} is a maximum. If j is determined uniquely in this step, call it k.
2. If j is not determined uniquely in step 1, then, from among the tied values of j in step 1, find j such that β_{2j}/β_{rj} is a maximum. If j is determined uniquely in this step, call it k; and so on.

Similar rules hold for the minimizing problem: start with equation (3.56), next find the minimum of the ratios β_{1j}/β_{rj}, etc.

Example 3.3

Solve the following linear programming problem without using artificial variables.

$$\text{Minimize } z = 6x_1 - 3x_2 + x_3,$$

subject to

$$\begin{aligned} 4x_1 + 5x_2 - 6x_3 &\geqslant 7, \\ 2x_1 + 4x_2 - 3x_3 &\geqslant 4, \\ x_1 - 3x_2 + 2x_3 &\geqslant 6, \\ x_1, x_2, x_3 &\geqslant 0. \end{aligned}$$

Solution

Subtract surplus variables x_4, x_5, x_6, and then multiply all the constraints throughout by -1 in order to give coefficients of $+1$ to the surplus variables (and thereby avoid errors in writing down the initial tableau). Change to a maximizing problem:

$$\text{Maximize } (-z) = -6x_1 + 3x_2 - x_3.$$

First, we shall obtain a basic feasible solution of this problem using the dual simplex method. To do this we ignore the positive price $(+3)$ in the objective function. The initial tableau can now be written down: it is convenient in these calculations to use the ordinary tableau notation, even though, at this stage, neither z nor $-z$ is being maximized.

Tableau 1 (Example 3.3)

	$\mathbf{c}'$		-6	0	-1	0	0	0
$\mathbf{c}_B$	Basic Variables		x_1	x_2	x_3	x_4	x_5	x_6
0	x_4	-7	-4	-5^*	6	1	0	0
0	x_5	-4	-2	-4	3	0	1	0
0	x_6	-6	-1	3	-2	0	0	1
	$z_j - c_j$	0	6	0	1	0	0	0

The pivot is chosen by rules 2(b) and 3 of Section 3.4.

Tableau 2 (Example 3.3)

	$\mathbf{c}'$		-6	0	-1	0	0	0
$\mathbf{c}_B$	Basic Variables		x_1	x_2	x_3	x_4	x_5	x_6
0	x_2	7/5	4/5	1	$-6/5$	$-1/5$	0	0
0	x_5	8/5	6/5	0	$-9/5$	$-4/5$	1	0
0	x_6	$-51/5$	$-17/5^*$	0	8/5	3/5	0	1
	$z_j - c_j$	0	6	0	1	0	0	0

Tableau 5 yields a basic feasible solution which satisfies the given constraints. At this point we revert to the problem of maximizing $-z = -6x_1 + 3x_2 - x_3$. This stage of the calculation begins with Tableau 5a, an amended version of Tableau 5, which takes account of the correct price of x_2. The only adjustments to

Tableau 3 (Example 3.3)

	$\mathbf{c}'$		-6	0	-1	0	0	0
$\mathbf{c}_B$	Basic Variables		x_1	x_2	x_3	x_4	x_5	x_6
0	x_2	-1	0	1	$-14/17$	$-1/17$	0	$4/17$
0	x_5	-2	0	0	$-21/17$	$-10/17$*	1	$6/17$
-6	x_1	3	1	0	$-8/17$	$-3/17$	0	$-5/17$
	$z_j - c_j$	-18	0	0	$65/17$	$18/17$	0	$30/17$

Tableau 4 (Example 3.3)

	$\mathbf{c}'$		-6	0	-1	0	0	0
$\mathbf{c}_B$	Basic Variables		x_1	x_2	x_3	x_4	x_5	x_6
0	x_2	$-4/5$	0	1	$-7/10$*	0	$-1/10$	$1/5$
0	x_4	$17/5$	0	0	$21/10$	1	$-17/10$	$-3/5$
-6	x_1	$18/5$	1	0	$-1/10$	0	$-3/10$	$-2/5$
	$z_j - c_j$	$-108/5$	0	0	$8/5$	0	$9/5$	$12/5$

Tableau 5 (Example 3.3)

	$\mathbf{c}'$		-6	0	-1	0	0	0
$\mathbf{c}_B$	Basic Variables		x_1	x_2	x_3	x_4	x_5	x_6
-1	x_3	$8/7$	0	$-10/7$	1	0	$1/7$	$-2/7$
0	x_4	1	0	3	0	1	-2	0
-6	x_1	$26/7$	1	$-1/7$	0	0	$-2/7$	$-3/7$
	$z_j - c_j$	$-164/7$	0	$16/7$	0	0	$11/7$	$20/7$

Tableau 5a (Example 3.3)

	$\mathbf{c}'$		-6	3	-1	0	0	0
$\mathbf{c}_B$	Basic Variables		x_1	x_2	x_3	x_4	x_5	x_6
-1	x_3	$8/7$	0	$-10/7$	1	0	$1/7$	$-2/7$
0	x_4	1	0	3*	0	1	-2	0
-6	x_1	$26/7$	1	$-1/7$	0	0	$-2/7$	$-3/7$
	$z_j - c_j$	$-164/7$	0	$-5/7$	0	0	$11/7$	$20/7$

Tableau 5 are to c_2 and $z_2 - c_2$, the latter being obtained from the usual formula

$$z_2 - c_2 = \mathbf{c}_B{}'\beta_2 - c_2.$$

Now $z_2 - c_2$ is negative, so that the basic feasible solution of Tableau 5a does not satisfy the optimality conditions for a maximizing problem. Proceeding by the standard simplex method, we obtain Tableau 6, which is optimal.

Remembering that the original problem is a minimizing problem (which we have solved as a maximizing problem), the required solution is

$$(x_1{}^*, x_2{}^*, x_3{}^*) = (79/21, 1/3, 34/21); \quad z^* = 487/21.$$

Tableau 6 (Example 3.3)

	$\mathbf{c}'$		-6	3	-1	0	0	0
$\mathbf{c}_B$	Basic Variables		x_1	x_2	x_3	x_4	x_5	x_6
-1	x_3	34/21	0	0	1	10/21	$-17/21$	$-2/7$
3	x_2	1/3	0	1	0	1/3	$-2/3$	0
-6	x_1	79/21	1	0	0	1/21	$-8/21$	$-3/7$
	$z_j - c_j$	$-487/21$	0	0	0	5/21	23/21	20/7

Example 3.4

Solve the following linear programming problem by the dual simplex method.

$$\text{Minimize } z = 2x_1 + 3x_2 + x_3 + 2x_4,$$

subject to

$$2x_1 + 4x_2 + x_3 + 5x_4 \geqslant 12,$$
$$x_1 + 3x_2 - x_3 + 6x_4 \geqslant 4,$$
$$2x_1 + 5x_2 + 3x_3 + 7x_4 \geqslant 21,$$
$$x_1, x_2, x_3, x_4 \geqslant 0.$$

Solution

Subtract surplus variables x_5, x_6, x_7, and start with the basic non-feasible solution

$$x_5 = -12, \quad x_6 = -4, \quad x_7 = -21.$$

Tableau 2 is optimal.

Although the dual simplex method is of limited usefulness, it should always be considered as a possible method of solution when the alternative is the introduction of artificial variables, as Example 3.4 shows.

Tableau 1 (Example 3.4)

	c′		2	3	1	2	0	0	0
$\mathbf{c}_B$	Basic Variables		x_1	x_2	x_3	x_4	x_5	x_6	x_7
0	x_5	−12	−2	−4	−1	−5	1	0	0
0	x_6	−4	−1	−3	1	−6	0	1	0
0	x_7	−21	−2	−5	−3	−7*	0	0	1
	$z_j - c_j$	0	−2	−3	−1	−2	0	0	0

Tableau 2 (Example 3.4)

	c′		2	3	1	2	0	0	0
$\mathbf{c}_B$	Basic Variables		x_1	x_2	x_3	x_4	x_5	x_6	x_7
0	x_5	3	−4/7	−3/7	8/7	0	1	0	−5/7
0	x_6	14	5/7	9/7	25/7	0	0	1	−6/7
2	x_4	3	2/7	5/7	3/7	1	0	0	−1/7
	$z_j - c_j$	6	−10/7	−11/7	−1/7	0	0	0	−2/7

More generally, the question often arises as to whether to solve a problem directly, or to solve its dual. There are three important cases when duality can be used with advantage:

(i) There are more constraints than variables. The dual basis matrix is then smaller than the primal basis matrix.

(ii) The dual constraints are all of the $\leqslant$ type. A basic feasible solution for the dual problem can then be written down immediately.

(iii) It is required to add a further constraint to a problem already solved.

The additional primal constraint becomes merely a further variable in the dual problem, with a value of zero at the time it is added, i.e. a non-basic variable. The calculation is continued by attaching a column for the new variable to the optimal dual tableau, which will then become non-optimal, in general. When the new optimal dual tableau is attained, it is converted into an optimal primal tableau. Alternatively, the additional constraint can be added directly to the optimal primal tableau, and the dual simplex method used to obtain the new optimal solution.

Of these two techniques, the second is generally preferable, since it involves less manipulation than the first. The following example is solved by the second method.

Example 3.5

$$\text{Minimize } z = 2x_1 + 3x_2 + 4x_3 + 5x_4,$$

subject to

$$x_1 - x_2 + x_3 - x_4 \geqslant 10,$$
$$x_1 - 2x_2 + 3x_3 - 4x_4 \geqslant 6,$$
$$3x_1 - 4x_2 + 5x_3 - 6x_4 \geqslant 15,$$
$$x_1, x_2, x_3, x_4 \geqslant 0.$$

The additional constraint

$$x_1 + 2x_2 + 3x_3 - 4x_4 \leqslant 8$$

is added to the set of constraints for this problem. Solve the new problem, starting with the optimal tableau for the original problem.

Solution

The original problem is easily solved by the dual simplex method, which leads to the following optimal tableau. The variables x_5, x_6, x_7 are surplus variables associated with the three original constraints, in order.

Optimal Tableau—Original Problem (Example 3.5)

	$\mathbf{c}'$		2	3	4	5	0	0	0
$\mathbf{c}_B$	Basic Variables		x_1	x_2	x_3	x_4	x_5	x_6	x_7
0	x_7	15	0	1	-2	3	-3	0	1
0	x_6	4	0	1	-2	3	-1	1	0
2	x_1	10	1	-1	1	-1	-1	0	0
	$z_j - c_j$	20	0	-5	-2	-7	-2	0	0

An essential preliminary step is to check whether or not the additional constraint is satisfied by the current optimal solution. If it is, there is no further problem: the current optimal solution remains optimal in the presence of the additional constraint. In the present example, the additional constraint is not satisfied by the current optimal solution; a new optimal solution must therefore be found.

The additional constraint is expressed in terms of the non-basic variables x_2, x_3, x_4, x_5 and its own basic slack variable x_8. Eliminating x_1 between the first constraint

$$x_1 - x_2 + x_3 - x_4 - x_5 = 10$$

and the additional constraint

$$x_1 + 2x_2 + 3x_3 - 4x_4 + x_8 = 8,$$

we obtain

$$3x_2 + 2x_3 - 3x_4 + x_5 + x_8 = -2.$$

This constraint is used to construct a new row in the optimal tableau. An x_8 column must also be added. Thus we arrive at the amended tableau.

Amended Tableau—New Row and Column Added (Example 3.5)

	$\mathbf{c}'$		2	3	4	5	0	0	0	0
$\mathbf{c}_B$	Basic Variables		x_1	x_2	x_3	x_4	x_5	x_6	x_7	x_8
0	x_7	15	0	1	-2	3	-3	0	1	0
0	x_6	4	0	1	-2	3	-1	1	0	0
2	x_1	10	1	-1	1	-1	-1	0	0	0
0	x_8	-2	0	3	2	-3^*	1	0	0	1
	$z_j - c_j$	20	0	-5	-2	-7	-2	0	0	0

The solution represented by the amended tableau is no longer feasible, since $x_8 = -2$. However, only one iteration of the dual simplex method is required to produce the final optimal tableau.

Final Optimal Tableau—Additional Constraint Included (Example 3.5)

	$\mathbf{c}'$		2	3	4	5	0	0	0	0
$\mathbf{c}_B$	Basic Variables		x_1	x_2	x_3	x_4	x_5	x_6	x_7	x_8
0	x_7	13	0	4	0	0	-2	0	1	1
0	x_6	2	0	4	0	0	0	1	0	1
2	x_1	32/3	1	-2	1/3	0	$-4/3$	0	0	$-1/3$
5	x_4	2/3	0	-1	$-2/3$	1	$-1/3$	0	0	$-1/3$
	$z_j - c_j$	74/3	0	-12	$-20/3$	0	$-13/3$	0	0	$-7/3$

A more general discussion of the effects of changes in the initial data of a linear programming problem on the optimal solution is given in Section 3.8.

*3.6 Economic Interpretation of Duality

It is interesting to investigate the economic implications of duality. Although we have proved algebraically that optimal solutions of the primal and dual problems are closely related, and that the optimal values of the two objective functions are equal, it is obvious that there must be some underlying reason for these apparently coincidental results. The simplest approach is to consider a specific example.

One of the classic examples of linear programming is the machine-shop problem. Suppose that there are m machines in a machine-shop, and that n products are being manufactured. Each product has to be processed on each machine, and the time taken by machine i on one unit of product j is p_{ij}. The maximum number of hours per week that machine i can be used is b_i. The profit on one unit of product j is c_j. It is required to find the production schedule that maximizes the total profit.

Let x_j be the number of units of product j that are produced each week, and let z be the total weekly profit. Then the problem can be expressed mathematically as follows:

$$\text{Maximize } z = \sum_{j=1}^{n} c_j x_j,$$

subject to the constraints

$$\sum_{j=1}^{n} p_{ij} x_j \leqslant b_i, \quad i = 1, \ldots, m,$$

and the non-negativity restrictions

$$x_j \geqslant 0, \quad j = 1, \ldots, n;$$

or, in matrix form,

$$\text{Maximize } z = \mathbf{c}'\mathbf{x},$$

subject to

$$\mathbf{Px} \leqslant \mathbf{b} \quad \text{and} \quad \mathbf{x} \geqslant \mathbf{0}.$$

This is precisely the standard primal problem (3.1). The dual problem is therefore (3.2):

$$\text{Minimize } w = \mathbf{b}'\mathbf{y},$$

subject to

$$\mathbf{P}'\mathbf{y} \geqslant \mathbf{c} \quad \text{and} \quad \mathbf{y} \geqslant \mathbf{0}.$$

What interpretation should be given to the dual variables y_i?

Consider the constraints in the dual problem. The dimensions of the coefficients p_{ji} are hours on machine i per unit of product j. Also, c_j is the profit per unit of product j. The dimensions of y_i are therefore profit per hour associated with machine i. It is found fruitful to interpret y_i as the *shadow cost* or *shadow price* of machine i. Using the shadow prices of machines $1, \ldots, m$, we can also define shadow prices of products $1, \ldots, n$; these are given by the left-hand sides of the dual constraints.

The quantity which is being minimized in the dual problem is

$$\sum_{i=1}^{m} b_i y_i = \sum_{i=1}^{m} [(\text{hours available per week})(\text{shadow price per hour})]_{\text{machine } i}$$

$$= \text{shadow price per week of all available machine time.}$$

The dual constraints ensure that the shadow price per unit of product j is greater than or equal to the profit per unit of product j. This apparent paradox emphasizes the fact that the shadow prices are fictitious prices—they are not the true costs of running the machines.

The shadow price of product j may be interpreted as follows. Consider a pair of optimal non-degenerate solutions of problems (3.1) and (3.2), and apply part of the complementary slackness principle: if the jth dual constraint is a strict inequality, then $x_j = 0$, and if it is an equality, then $x_j > 0$. In the first case the shadow price per unit of product j is greater than the profit per unit of product j, and product j is not manufactured—its manufacture would entail an uneconomic use of the available resources. In the second case, with equality between the shadow prices and the profits, there is no such uneconomic use of resources, and product j is manufactured. As the dual constraints make clear, the shadow price per unit of product j will never be less than the profit per unit of product j; if it were, an increase in production of product j until the profit and shadow price were equalized would result in an increase in profit.

The shadow price of machine i is, in a certain sense, a measure of the contribution from that machine to the total profit. In order to amplify this statement, consider the other half of the complementary slackness principle: if the ith primal constraint is a strict inequality then $y_i = 0$, and if it is an equality then $y_i > 0$. In the first case, machine i is *not* being fully utilized, and in the second case *is* being fully utilized, in the optimal solution. Since

$$w = \mathbf{b}'\mathbf{y} = \sum_{i=1}^{m} b_i y_i = z$$

in an optimal solution, representing the fact that the minimum shadow price of the total available resources is equal to the maximum profit, we can write formally

$$\frac{\partial z}{\partial b_i} = y_i, \tag{3.57}$$

where the use of a partial derivative implies that the y_i are kept constant during the differentiation.

Equation (3.57) leads to the following interpretation of the shadow prices y_i. Suppose that machine i is not being fully utilized in the optimal solution. Then if b_i is increased or decreased by a small amount, it is obvious that the optimal solution will be unchanged (provided that the 'slack' time is not fully taken up), and in particular the total profit z will be unchanged. In this case, the shadow price of machine i is zero, i.e.

$$\frac{\partial z}{\partial b_i} = y_i = 0, \tag{3.58}$$

in accordance with the complementary slackness principle. Now suppose, on the other hand, that machine i *is* being fully utilized in the optimal solution. If b_i is increased or decreased, then the total profit will increase or decrease, respectively, by a finite amount. In this case,

$$\frac{\partial z}{\partial b_i} = y_i > 0, \tag{3.59}$$

again in accordance with the complementary slackness principle. The change in profit can be found only by solving the new primal (or dual) problem. However, an indication of the change in total profit for small changes in b_i is given by a finite difference approximation to (3.59), namely

$$\Delta z = (\Delta b_i) y_i \neq 0. \tag{3.60}$$

We have seen that, ideally, the only products that are manufactured are those for which the shadow price is equal to the actual profit. It is also true that the greater the excess of the shadow price over the actual profit, the less economic it becomes to manufacture the product. This remark gives an indication of how to attain a near-optimal solution, which is often required in practice when there is some reason why an optimal solution is unacceptable.

We recognize from equation (3.57) that the shadow prices y_i are equivalent to the usual Lagrange multipliers of the classical theory of constrained maxima and minima [35]. A fuller discussion of shadow prices in an economic context is given in references [2], [9], [12], [15], and [16].

3.7 The Revised Simplex Method

The computational procedure for the standard simplex algorithm, described in Chapter 2, is somewhat inefficient, because many quantities which are not really needed are evaluated in each iteration. For example, if a variable x_k never becomes basic during the course of the calculation, then the transformations of the x_k column in the tableaux are not necessary. (Unfortunately we do not know *a priori* which variables, if any, will never become basic.) Furthermore, it is inefficient to transform the x_k column several times when x_k is going to become basic only once or twice. A more efficient algorithm, now known as the *revised simplex method*, was developed in 1953 by Dantzig and Orchard-Hays [11]. It is particularly suitable for solving large-scale problems on digital computers, since it requires much less storage space than the standard simplex algorithm, and often requires fewer arithmetical operations, especially when the original problem matrix contains a high proportion of zeros. Only essential quantities are computed. A feature of the revised simplex method, which it shares with the standard simplex method, is that once the primal problem has been solved the solution of the dual problem is immediately available. The basic theory of the method is the same as that of the standard simplex method which was given in Chapter 2; in particular, the variables that are exchanged in each iteration are chosen by the usual simplex rules of Section 2.5.

Consider first the case where there is no artificial variable in the initial basic feasible solution. Suppose that the given problem is

$$\left.\begin{array}{c}\text{Maximize } z = \mathbf{c}'\mathbf{x}, \\ \mathbf{A}\mathbf{x} = \mathbf{b} \quad \text{and} \quad \mathbf{x} \geqslant \mathbf{0},\end{array}\right\} \tag{3.61}$$

subject to

where $\mathbf{A}$, as usual, is an $m \times N$ matrix. (In the present section, we shall assume that every problem has been changed, if necessary, into a maximizing problem.) In the revised simplex method the equation $z = \mathbf{c}'\mathbf{x}$ is regarded as an additional constraint, with z being regarded as an additional variable. Thus we now have $(m+1)$ constraints in $(N+1)$ variables $z, x_1, \ldots, x_N$, which may be written in the partitioned form

$$\begin{pmatrix} 1 & -\mathbf{c}' \\ \mathbf{0} & \mathbf{A} \end{pmatrix}\begin{pmatrix} z \\ \mathbf{x} \end{pmatrix} = \begin{pmatrix} 0 \\ \mathbf{b} \end{pmatrix}. \tag{3.62}$$

We shall use the superscript R to denote quantities in the revised simplex method which are analogous to those used in the standard simplex method. Since the variable z must appear in every basic solution of the constraint equations (3.62), the corresponding column vector $\mathbf{e}_1 = [1, 0, \ldots, 0]$ must appear in every basis matrix $\mathbf{B}^R$ throughout the revised simplex calculations. Thus the $(m+1) \times (m+1)$ matrix $\mathbf{B}^R$ is of the form

$$\mathbf{B}^R = (\mathbf{e}_1, \mathbf{b}_1{}^R, \ldots, \mathbf{b}_m{}^R). \tag{3.63}$$

If the column vectors $\mathbf{b}_1, \ldots, \mathbf{b}_m$, whose components are the last m components of the vectors $\mathbf{b}_1{}^R, \ldots, \mathbf{b}_m{}^R$ respectively, form a basis matrix $\mathbf{B}$ for the constraints in (3.61), then we can write

$$\mathbf{B}^R = \begin{pmatrix} 1 & -\mathbf{c}_B{}' \\ \mathbf{0} & \mathbf{B} \end{pmatrix}. \tag{3.64}$$

In each iteration the equation

$$\mathbf{B}^R \mathbf{x}_B{}^R = \mathbf{b}^R,$$

where

$$\mathbf{x}_B{}^R = \begin{pmatrix} z \\ \mathbf{x}_B \end{pmatrix}, \quad \mathbf{b}^R = \begin{pmatrix} 0 \\ \mathbf{b} \end{pmatrix},$$

is solved to give a basic solution of equation (3.62):

$$\mathbf{x}_B{}^R = (\mathbf{B}^R)^{-1}\mathbf{b}^R. \tag{3.65}$$

At the next iteration we shall have

$$\bar{\mathbf{x}}_B{}^R = (\bar{\mathbf{B}}^R)^{-1}\mathbf{b}^R,$$

that is, we obtain the current solution by using the *current* inverse of the basis matrix with the requirements vector. The interesting problem arises of finding $(\bar{\mathbf{B}}^R)^{-1}$, given $(\mathbf{B}^R)^{-1}$, where $\mathbf{B}^R$ and $\bar{\mathbf{B}}^R$, being successive basis matrices, differ in one column only.

Returning to equation (3.64) and using the theory of partitioned matrices, we find

$$(\mathbf{B}^R)^{-1} = \begin{pmatrix} 1 & \mathbf{c}_B'\mathbf{B}^{-1} \\ \mathbf{0} & \mathbf{B}^{-1} \end{pmatrix}. \tag{3.66}$$

The first column of $(\mathbf{B}^R)^{-1}$ is the unit vector $\mathbf{e}_1$, and from equation (3.18) we see that the last m elements of the first row are the values of the main dual variables. From equation (2.24), and allowing for the additional constraint, we can write

$$\mathbf{a}_j^R = \mathbf{B}^R\boldsymbol{\beta}_j^R,$$

giving

$$\boldsymbol{\beta}_j^R = (\mathbf{B}^R)^{-1}\mathbf{a}_j^R \tag{3.67}$$

$$= \begin{pmatrix} 1 & \mathbf{c}_B'\mathbf{B}^{-1} \\ \mathbf{0} & \mathbf{B}^{-1} \end{pmatrix}\begin{pmatrix} -c_j \\ \mathbf{a}_j \end{pmatrix},$$

where we have obtained $(\mathbf{B}^R)^{-1}$ from equation (3.66), and $\mathbf{a}_j^R$ from column j of the matrix $\mathbf{A}^R$ on the left-hand side of equation (3.62): the columns of this matrix are numbered 0, 1, 2, . . . , N. Therefore

$$\boldsymbol{\beta}_j^R = \begin{pmatrix} -c_j + \mathbf{c}_B'\mathbf{B}^{-1}\mathbf{a}_j \\ \mathbf{B}^{-1}\mathbf{a}_j \end{pmatrix} = \begin{pmatrix} z_j - c_j \\ \boldsymbol{\beta}_j \end{pmatrix}, \tag{3.68}$$

from equations (2.24) and (2.36). Also, from equations (3.65) and (3.66), we have

$$\mathbf{x}_B^R = \begin{pmatrix} 1 & \mathbf{c}_B'\mathbf{B}^{-1} \\ \mathbf{0} & \mathbf{B}^{-1} \end{pmatrix}\begin{pmatrix} 0 \\ \mathbf{b} \end{pmatrix}$$

$$= \begin{pmatrix} \mathbf{c}_B'\mathbf{B}^{-1}\mathbf{b} \\ \mathbf{B}^{-1}\mathbf{b} \end{pmatrix}$$

$$= \begin{pmatrix} \mathbf{c}_B'\mathbf{x}_B \\ \mathbf{x}_B \end{pmatrix}$$

$$= \begin{pmatrix} z \\ \mathbf{x}_B \end{pmatrix}, \tag{3.69}$$

as expected.

We now consider the outstanding problem of how to transform $(\mathbf{B}^R)^{-1}$ in each iteration, knowing that a column of $\mathbf{B}^R$ has changed. The column vectors comprising $\mathbf{B}^R$ are $\mathbf{e}_1$, $\mathbf{b}_1^R$, . . . , $\mathbf{b}_m^R$, from equation (3.63). Suppose that $\mathbf{b}_r^R$ is replaced by $\mathbf{a}_k^R$, giving the new basis matrix $\overline{\mathbf{B}}^R$. Since the columns of $\mathbf{B}^R$ form a basis for Euclidean $(m+1)$-space E^{m+1}, we can write

$$\mathbf{a}_k^R = \beta_{0k}\mathbf{e}_1 + \beta_{1k}\mathbf{b}_1^R + \ldots + \beta_{rk}\mathbf{b}_r^R + \ldots + \beta_{mk}\mathbf{b}_m^R, \tag{3.70}$$

and if the columns of $\overline{\mathbf{B}}^R$ are to form a basis for E^{m+1} we must have $\beta_{rk} \neq 0$, by the lemma of Section 2.3, page 22. From equation (3.70) we obtain

$$\mathbf{b}_r^R = (\beta_{rk})^{-1}[-\beta_{0k}\mathbf{e}_1 - \beta_{1k}\mathbf{b}_1^R - \ldots - \beta_{r-1,k}\mathbf{b}_{r-1}^R + \mathbf{a}_k^R - \beta_{r+1,k}\mathbf{b}_{r+1}^R - \ldots - \beta_{mk}\mathbf{b}_m^R]. \tag{3.71}$$

Note that the vectors on the right-hand side of equation (3.71) are the columns of $\overline{\mathbf{B}}^R$. Thus equation (3.71) can be written

$$\mathbf{b}_r^R = \overline{\mathbf{B}}^R\mu, \tag{3.72}$$

where

$$\mu = (\beta_{rk})^{-1}[-\beta_{0k}, -\beta_{1k}, \ldots, -\beta_{r-1,k}, 1, -\beta_{r+1,k}, \ldots, -\beta_{mk}]. \tag{3.73}$$

For every column vector $\mathbf{b}_i^R$ of $\mathbf{B}^R$, except $\mathbf{b}_r^R$, we have

$$\mathbf{b}_i^R = \mathbf{B}^R\mathbf{e}_{i+1} = \overline{\mathbf{B}}^R\mathbf{e}_{i+1}, \quad i = 0, 1, \ldots, m, \quad i \neq r, \tag{3.74}$$

since the matrices $\mathbf{B}^R$ and $\overline{\mathbf{B}}^R$ differ only in the column denoted by $i = r$ [actually the $(r+1)$th column, since $i = 0, 1, \ldots, m$]. Collecting together the columns of $\mathbf{B}^R$ from equations (3.72) and (3.74), we obtain

$$\mathbf{B}^R = \overline{\mathbf{B}}^R\mathbf{E}, \tag{3.75}$$

where

$$\mathbf{E} = (\mathbf{e}_1, \ldots, \mathbf{e}_r, \mu, \mathbf{e}_{r+2}, \ldots, \mathbf{e}_{m+1}), \tag{3.76}$$

and so from equation (3.75),

$$(\overline{\mathbf{B}}^R)^{-1} = \mathbf{E}(\mathbf{B}^R)^{-1}, \tag{3.77}$$

which gives the required transformation law for $(\mathbf{B}^R)^{-1}$. The transformation law for $\mathbf{x}_B^R$ is obtained immediately from equations (3.77) and (3.65):

$$\overline{\mathbf{x}}_B^R = (\overline{\mathbf{B}}^R)^{-1}\mathbf{b}^R = \mathbf{E}(\mathbf{B}^R)^{-1}\mathbf{b}^R = \mathbf{E}\mathbf{x}_B^R. \tag{3.78}$$

The calculations of the revised simplex method are set out in the revised simplex tableau. The names of the basic variables appear in the first column,

Revised Simplex Tableau

Basic Variables	$\mathbf{d}_1$	$\mathbf{d}_2 \ldots \mathbf{d}_m$	$\mathbf{x}_B^R$	x_k
z	d_{01}	$d_{02} \ldots d_{0m}$	z	$z_k - c_k$
x_{B1}	d_{11}	$d_{12} \ldots d_{1m}$	x_{B1}	β_{1k}
$\vdots$	$\vdots$	$\vdots \quad \vdots$	$\vdots$	$\vdots$
x_{Bm}	d_{m1}	$d_{m2} \ldots d_{mm}$	x_{Bm}	β_{mk}

and their values in the penultimate column. The column vectors $\mathbf{d}_1, \ldots, \mathbf{d}_m$ are the last m columns of $(\mathbf{B}^R)^{-1}$; the first column of $(\mathbf{B}^R)^{-1}$ is always $\mathbf{d}_0 = \mathbf{e}_1$, and is omitted from every tableau. As already stated—immediately after equation (3.66)—the components of the row vector

$$(d_{01}, \ldots, d_{0m}) = \mathbf{c}_B' \mathbf{B}^{-1}$$

are the values of the main dual variables $y_1, \ldots, y_m$, respectively; also, from equation (3.66),

$$\mathbf{B}^{-1} = \begin{pmatrix} d_{11} & \ldots & d_{1m} \\ \vdots & & \vdots \\ d_{m1} & \ldots & d_{mm} \end{pmatrix}$$

The components of the column vector $\boldsymbol{\beta}_k{}^R$ appear in the last column of the tableau under the heading x_k. From equation (3.68), the first component of $\boldsymbol{\beta}_k{}^R$ is $z_k - c_k$; the remaining components are the usual linear dependence coefficients for $\mathbf{a}_k$ in terms of the basis vectors $\mathbf{b}_1, \ldots, \mathbf{b}_m$, where x_k is the variable that is about to become basic. Thus in contrast to the standard simplex tableau, in which *every* vector $\boldsymbol{\beta}_j$ appears, there is now only one $\boldsymbol{\beta}_j$ column.

It is interesting and profitable to consider the transformations (3.77) and (3.78) in more detail. Consider the (i, s)th component of equation (3.77) for $i = 0, 1, \ldots, m$, $s = 0, 1, \ldots, m$:

$$\bar{d}_{is} = (\text{row } i \text{ of } \mathbf{E})[\text{column } s \text{ of } (\mathbf{B}^R)^{-1}]$$

$$= \left(0, \ldots, 0, 1, 0, \ldots, 0, -\frac{\beta_{ik}}{\beta_{rk}}, 0, \ldots, 0\right)[d_{0s}, d_{1s}, \ldots, d_{ms}], \quad i \neq r,$$

where the 1 appears in the $(i+1)$th actual position, and $-\beta_{ik}/\beta_{rk}$ appears in the $(r+1)$th actual position, in the row vector. Therefore

$$\bar{d}_{is} = d_{is} - \frac{\beta_{ik}}{\beta_{rk}} d_{rs}, \quad i = 0, 1, \ldots, m, \quad i \neq r, \qquad s = 0, 1, \ldots, m. \tag{3.79a}$$

Also,

$$\bar{d}_{rs} = (\text{row } r \text{ of } \mathbf{E})[\text{column } s \text{ of } (\mathbf{B}^R)^{-1}]$$

$$= \left(0, \ldots, 0, \frac{1}{\beta_{rk}}, 0, \ldots, 0\right)[d_{0s}, d_{1s}, \ldots, d_{ms}], \quad s = 0, 1, \ldots, m,$$

where $1/\beta_{rk}$ appears in the $(r+1)$th actual position in the row vector. Therefore

$$\bar{d}_{rs} = \frac{d_{rs}}{\beta_{rk}}, \quad s = 0, 1, \ldots, m. \tag{3.79b}$$

Note that the values of $\bar{d}_{i0}$, $i = 0, 1, \ldots, m$, are not required in a tableau transformation. In fact, $\bar{d}_{i0} = \delta_{i0}$. Similarly, from equation (3.78),

$$\bar{x}_{Bi} = (\text{row } i \text{ of } \mathbf{E})\mathbf{x}_B{}^R, \quad i = 0, 1, \ldots, m.$$

$$= \left(0, \ldots, 0, 1, 0, \ldots, 0, -\frac{\beta_{ik}}{\beta_{rk}}, 0, \ldots, 0\right)[z, x_{B1}, \ldots, x_{Bm}], \quad i \neq r,$$

$$= x_{Bi} - \frac{\beta_{ik}}{\beta_{rk}} x_{Br}, \quad i = 0, 1, \ldots, m, \quad i \neq r, \ (x_{B0} \equiv z), \tag{3.80a}$$

and

$$\bar{x}_{Br} = (\text{row } r \text{ of } \mathbf{E})\mathbf{x}_B{}^R$$

$$= \left(0, \ldots, 0, \frac{1}{\beta_{rk}}, 0, \ldots, 0\right)[z, x_{B1}, \ldots, x_{Bm}]$$

$$= \frac{x_{Br}}{\beta_{rk}}. \tag{3.80b}$$

The transformation equations (3.79a), (3.79b), (3.80a) and (3.80b) are exactly the same as those for the β_{ij} in the standard simplex method, viz. (2.58a) and (2.58b).

The rules for the application of the revised simplex method to the *maximizing* problem (3.61), when no artificial variable is required, are therefore as follows.

1. Write down the matrix

$$\mathbf{A}^R = \begin{pmatrix} 1 & -\mathbf{c}' \\ \mathbf{0} & \mathbf{A} \end{pmatrix}.$$

The elements of $\mathbf{A}^R$ are denoted by a_{ij}, $i = 0, 1, \ldots, m$, $j = 0, 1, \ldots, N$. Find an initial basis matrix $\mathbf{B}^R$ (normally a unit matrix) and its inverse $(\mathbf{B}^R)^{-1}$.

2. Construct the initial tableau, except for the last column. The entries in the $\mathbf{d}_1, \ldots, \mathbf{d}_m$ columns of the tableau are the last m columns of $(\mathbf{B}^R)^{-1}$. Enter the initial values of $z, x_{B1}, \ldots, x_{Bm}$ in the $\mathbf{x}_B{}^R$ column.

3. Find the variable x_k to become basic, i.e. find

$$z_j - c_j = \sum_{s=1}^{m} d_{0s} a_{sj} - c_j = \sum_{s=0}^{m} d_{0s} a_{sj}, \tag{3.81}$$

for all j for which x_j is non-basic, and determine

$$z_k - c_k = \min_{j=1,\ldots,N} \{z_j - c_j : z_j - c_j < 0, \beta_{ij} > 0 \text{ for at least one } i, i = 1, \ldots m\}. \tag{3.82}$$

[Equation (3.82) is identical with equation (2.54).] Evaluate

$$\boldsymbol{\beta}_k = \mathbf{B}^{-1}\mathbf{a}_k. \tag{3.83}$$

Complete the tableau by inserting in the last column the values of $z_k - c_k$ and the components of $\boldsymbol{\beta}_k$.

4. Find the pivot β_{rk} in the last column of the tableau by the usual rule—equation (2.32):

$$\frac{x_{Br}}{\beta_{rk}} = \min_{i=1,\ldots,m} \left\{ \frac{x_{Bi}}{\beta_{ik}} : \beta_{ik} > 0 \right\}.$$

5. Use the transformation equations (3.79a), (3.79b), (3.80a) and (3.80b) to obtain all the entries in the new tableau, except those in the last column.

6. Repeat steps 3–5 until $z_j - c_j \geqslant 0$ for all j, or until the conditions for an unbounded solution appear—cf. 1(b) page 31.

N.B. When repeating step 3 it is not strictly necessary to evaluate $z_j - c_j$ for the variable which has just become non-basic, since this variable cannot become basic at the next iteration—see Exercise 27, Chapter 2. However, when using a computer it is probably simpler to evaluate this quantity than to arrange not to evaluate it. In the examples of this section we shall evaluate $z_j - c_j$ for *all* non-basic variables x_j.

As stated in Section 2.10, it is easy to avoid degeneracy (and therefore cycling) when the revised simplex method is used, since the required elements of the inverse basis matrix $\mathbf{B}^{-1}$ are immediately available from the revised simplex tableau. Hence equations of the type (2.92) and (2.94) can be applied directly whenever equation (2.90) (i.e. rule 4 above) does not determine r uniquely.

Example 3.6

Solve the following problem and its dual problem by the revised simplex method.

$$\text{Maximize } z = -15x_1 + 5x_2 + 4x_3 + 2x_4 + 3x_5,$$

subject to

$$\begin{aligned} -x_1 + 2x_2 \phantom{{}+x_3} + 3x_4 \phantom{{}+x_5} &\leqslant 3, \\ -x_1 \phantom{{}+2x_2} + x_3 - x_4 \phantom{{}+x_5} &\leqslant 4, \\ -x_1 - x_2 - x_3 - x_4 + x_5 &\leqslant 1, \\ x_1, x_2, x_3, x_4, x_5 &\geqslant 0. \end{aligned}$$

Solution

Add slack variables x_6, x_7, x_8.

$$\mathbf{A}^R = \begin{pmatrix} 1 & 15 & -5 & -4 & -2 & -3 & 0 & 0 & 0 \\ 0 & -1 & 2 & 0 & 3 & 0 & 1 & 0 & 0 \\ 0 & -1 & 0 & 1 & -1 & 0 & 0 & 1 & 0 \\ 0 & -1 & -1 & -1 & -1 & 1 & 0 & 0 & 1 \end{pmatrix}.$$

Tableau 1 (Example 3.6)

Basic Variables	$\mathbf{d}_1$	$\mathbf{d}_2$	$\mathbf{d}_3$	$\mathbf{x}_B{}^R$	x_2
z	0	0	0	0	−5
x_6	1	0	0	3	2*
x_7	0	1	0	4	0
x_8	0	0	1	1	−1

In Tableau 1, the column vectors $\mathbf{d}_1$, $\mathbf{d}_2$, $\mathbf{d}_3$ are the last three columns of the fourth order matrix $(\mathbf{B}^R)^{-1} = \mathbf{I}$. Also, $\mathbf{x}_B{}^R = [z, x_6, x_7, x_8] = [0, 3, 4, 1]$. Now

$$z_j - c_j = -c_j = a_{0j}$$

for all non-basic variables x_j (and, incidentally, for all basic variables), using both of the equations (3.81); the element $d_{00} = 1$ does not appear in the tableau. Thus the values of $z_j - c_j$ appear in the first row of $\mathbf{A}^R$; this will normally be the case for the initial tableau, when every basic variable has a zero price and hence $z_j = \mathbf{c}_B{}'\boldsymbol{\beta}_j = 0$ for all j. Equation (3.82) gives $k = 2$. From equation (3.83) we find $\boldsymbol{\beta}_2 = \mathbf{a}_2$, since $\mathbf{B}^{-1} = \mathbf{I}$, so that the last column of Tableau 1 is simply the third column ($j = 2$) of $\mathbf{A}^R$. Having completed Tableau 1, we find its pivot; then every column of Tableau 2, except the last, is obtained from Tableau 1 by the usual simplex transformation.

Tableau 2 (Example 3.6)

Basic Variables	$\mathbf{d}_1$	$\mathbf{d}_2$	$\mathbf{d}_3$	$\mathbf{x}_B{}^R$	x_3
z	5/2	0	0	15/2	−4
x_2	1/2	0	0	3/2	0
x_7	0	1	0	4	1*
x_8	1/2	0	1	5/2	−1

Next, from equation (3.81), we evaluate (in a convenient matrix form)

$$z_j - c_j = (d_{00}, d_{01}, d_{02}, d_{03}) \begin{pmatrix} a_{01} & a_{03} & a_{04} & a_{05} & a_{06} \\ a_{11} & a_{13} & a_{14} & a_{15} & a_{16} \\ a_{21} & a_{23} & a_{24} & a_{25} & a_{26} \\ a_{31} & a_{33} & a_{34} & a_{35} & a_{36} \end{pmatrix}$$

$$= (1, 5/2, 0, 0) \begin{pmatrix} 15 & -4 & -2 & -3 & 0 \\ -1 & 0 & 3 & 0 & 1 \\ -1 & 1 & -1 & 0 & 0 \\ -1 & -1 & -1 & 1 & 0 \end{pmatrix}$$

$$= (25/2, -4, 11/2, -3, 5/2), \quad j = 1, 3, 4, 5, 6.$$

Hence $k = 3$, and the last column of Tableau 2 is completed by inserting $z_3 - c_3 = -4$ and evaluating

$$\beta_3 = \mathbf{B}^{-1}\mathbf{a}_3 = \begin{pmatrix} 1/2 & 0 & 0 \\ 0 & 1 & 0 \\ 1/2 & 0 & 1 \end{pmatrix} \begin{pmatrix} 0 \\ 1 \\ -1 \end{pmatrix} = \begin{pmatrix} 0 \\ 1 \\ -1 \end{pmatrix}.$$

It is now a routine matter to obtain the remaining tableaux.

Tableau 3 (Example 3.6)

Basic Variables	$\mathbf{d}_1$	$\mathbf{d}_2$	$\mathbf{d}_3$	$\mathbf{x}_B{}^R$	x_5
z	5/2	4	0	47/2	−3
x_2	1/2	0	0	3/2	0
x_3	0	1	0	4	0
x_8	1/2	1	1	13/2	1*

From Tableau 3 and $\mathbf{A}^R$,

$$z_j - c_j = (1, 5/2, 4, 0) \begin{pmatrix} 15 & -2 & -3 & 0 & 0 \\ -1 & 3 & 0 & 1 & 0 \\ -1 & -1 & 0 & 0 & 1 \\ -1 & -1 & 1 & 0 & 0 \end{pmatrix}$$

$$= (17/2, 3/2, -3, 5/2, 4), \quad j = 1, 4, 5, 6, 7,$$

from which $k = 5$. Also

$$\beta_5 = \mathbf{B}^{-1}\mathbf{a}_5 = \begin{pmatrix} 1/2 & 0 & 0 \\ 0 & 1 & 0 \\ 1/2 & 1 & 1 \end{pmatrix} \begin{pmatrix} 0 \\ 0 \\ 1 \end{pmatrix} = \begin{pmatrix} 0 \\ 0 \\ 1 \end{pmatrix}.$$

Tableau 4 (Example 3.6)

Basic Variables	$\mathbf{d}_1$	$\mathbf{d}_2$	$\mathbf{d}_3$	$\mathbf{x}_B{}^R$	x_4
z	4	7	3	43	0
x_2	1/2	0	0	3/2	3/2*
x_3	0	1	0	4	−1
x_5	1/2	1	1	13/2	−1/2

From Tableau 4 and $\mathbf{A}^R$,

$$z_j - c_j = (1, 4, 7, 3) \begin{pmatrix} 15 & -2 & 0 & 0 & 0 \\ -1 & 3 & 1 & 0 & 0 \\ -1 & -1 & 0 & 1 & 0 \\ -1 & -1 & 0 & 0 & 1 \end{pmatrix}$$

$$= (1, 0, 4, 7, 3), \quad j = 1, 4, 6, 7, 8.$$

Hence Tableau 4 is optimal, with

$$(x_1^*, x_2^*, x_3^*, x_4^*, x_5^*) = (0, 3/2, 4, 0, 13/2);\ z^* = 43.$$

Since $z_4 - c_4 = 0$, alternative optima exist, and so we construct Tableau 5. To complete Tableau 4, we require

$$\mathbf{B}^{-1}\mathbf{a}_4 = \begin{pmatrix} 1/2 & 0 & 0 \\ 0 & 1 & 0 \\ 1/2 & 1 & 1 \end{pmatrix}\begin{pmatrix} 3 \\ -1 \\ -1 \end{pmatrix} = \begin{pmatrix} 3/2 \\ -1 \\ -1/2 \end{pmatrix}.$$

Tableau 5 (Example 3.6)

Basic Variables	$\mathbf{d}_1$	$\mathbf{d}_2$	$\mathbf{d}_3$	$\mathbf{x}_B{}^R$	
z	4	7	3	43	
x_4	1/3	0	0	1	
x_3	1/3	1	0	5	
x_5	2/3	1	1	7	

From Tableau 5 the alternative optimal basic solution is

$$(x_1^*, x_2^*, x_3^*, x_4^*, x_5^*) = (0, 0, 5, 1, 7);\ z^* = 43.$$

The dual problem is

$$\text{Minimize } w = 3y_1 + 4y_2 + y_3,$$

subject to

$$\begin{aligned} -y_1 - y_2 - y_3 &\geqslant -15, \\ 2y_1 \quad\ - y_3 &\geqslant 5, \\ y_2 - y_3 &\geqslant 4, \\ 3y_1 - y_2 - y_3 &\geqslant 2, \\ y_3 &\geqslant 3, \\ y_1, y_2, (y_3) &\geqslant 0. \end{aligned}$$

(The non-negativity restriction on y_3 is redundant.)

From the first row of Tableau 4 (or 5), we find that the solution of the dual problem is

$$(y_1^*, y_2^*, y_3^*) = (4, 7, 3);\ w^* = 43. \tag{3.84}$$

The optimal values of the basic dual surplus variables may also be required; they can now be obtained easily from the dual constraints or, more interestingly, from the values of $z_j - c_j$ for the non-basic primal main variables, using equation (3.81) and the complementary slackness principle, as follows. In Tableau 4, x_1 and

x_4 are the non-basic primal main variables, and by the complementary slackness principle (Section 3.3)

$$(x_1^*, x_4^*) \sim (y_4^*, y_7^*),$$

which leads to

$$\left.\begin{aligned} y_4^* &= z_1^* - c_1 = 1, \\ y_7^* &= z_4^* - c_4 = 0. \end{aligned}\right\} \tag{3.85}$$

A degenerate optimal solution for the dual problem is, of course, a necessary consequence of alternative optima in the primal (see the proof of Theorem 3.7).

Similarly, for Tableau 5,

$$(x_1^*, x_2^*) \sim (y_4^*, y_5^*),$$

and therefore

$$\left.\begin{aligned} y_4^* &= z_1^* - c_1 = 1, \\ y_5^* &= z_2^* - c_2 = 0. \end{aligned}\right\} \tag{3.86}$$

As expected, the two optimal basic solutions of the dual problem, given by (3.84) with (3.85), and (3.84) with (3.86), are numerically identical, and both are degenerate.

Artificial Variables

When artificial variables are present in the initial basic feasible solution, the revised simplex method is used in conjunction with the two-phase method, described in Section 2.7. It will be remembered that in phase 1 the objective function for a minimizing or maximizing problem is the sum, or negative sum, respectively, of the artificial variables. In phase 2 the given objective function is optimized. With regard to the possible situations that may arise at the end of phase 1, which were discussed in detail in Section 2.7, it is still necessary to ensure that in case 3 (page 41) the degenerate artificial basic variables remain degenerate throughout phase 2. The method described previously can still be used, though the following alternative method was used by Dantzig and Orchard-Hays [11].

Assume that an artificial variable is added to each constraint, and denote the artificial variables by $x_{a1}, \ldots, x_{am}$. Only trivial modifications are necessary when there are fewer artificial variables than constraints, as will be seen in Example 3.8. For the maximizing problem (3.61), the objective function in phase 1 is

$$z_a = -x_{a1} - \ldots - x_{am}. \tag{3.87}$$

The constraint equations in (3.61) become

$$\begin{pmatrix} 1 & \mathbf{0}' & \mathbf{e}' \\ \mathbf{0} & \mathbf{A} & \mathbf{I}_m \end{pmatrix} \begin{pmatrix} z_a \\ \mathbf{x} \\ \mathbf{x}_a \end{pmatrix} = \begin{pmatrix} 0 \\ \mathbf{b} \end{pmatrix}, \tag{3.88}$$

where $\mathbf{e}'$ is the m-component row vector $(1, 1, \ldots, 1)$, $\mathbf{I}_m$ is the unit matrix of order

m, and $\mathbf{x}_a$ is the vector of artificial variables. Now assume that at the end of phase 1 there are one or more artificial basic variables, and that all of them are degenerate. To ensure that they stay degenerate throughout phase 2, we add to the usual non-negativity restrictions on the artificial variables the constraint

$$x_{a1} + \ldots + x_{am} = 0. \tag{3.89}$$

The objective function in phase 2 is

$$z = c_1 x_1 + \ldots + c_n x_n, \tag{3.90}$$

and the constraints, apart from (3.89), are

$$\begin{pmatrix} 1 & -\mathbf{c}' & \mathbf{0}' \\ \mathbf{0} & \mathbf{A} & \mathbf{I}_m \end{pmatrix} \begin{pmatrix} z \\ \mathbf{x} \\ \mathbf{x}_a \end{pmatrix} = \begin{pmatrix} 0 \\ \mathbf{b} \end{pmatrix}. \tag{3.91}$$

Equations (3.88) and (3.91) can be combined to give

$$\begin{pmatrix} 1 & 0 & -\mathbf{c}' & \mathbf{0}' \\ 0 & 1 & \mathbf{0}' & \mathbf{e}' \\ \mathbf{0} & \mathbf{0} & \mathbf{A} & \mathbf{I}_m \end{pmatrix} \begin{pmatrix} z \\ z_a \\ \mathbf{x} \\ \mathbf{x}_a \end{pmatrix} = \begin{pmatrix} 0 \\ 0 \\ \mathbf{b} \end{pmatrix}. \tag{3.92}$$

The superscript S will be used to designate the extended matrices and vectors that are used when artificial variables are present in a problem being solved by the revised simplex method. This replaces the superscript R which is used when no artificial variable is present. Thus equation (3.92) is written

$$\mathbf{A}^S \mathbf{x}^S = \mathbf{b}^S.$$

The constraints (3.92) are used in both phase 1 and phase 2. In phase 1, z_a is maximized, and z is an extra variable which remains basic, though its value at this stage is irrelevant. In phase 2, z is maximized and z_a remains zero: that is, z_a is either basic and degenerate, or non-basic. Hence the constraint representing the objective function in phase 1, equation (3.87), is used to take care of any degenerate artificial basic variables in phase 2, since equations (3.87) and (3.89) are then identical. In phase 2, z_a has the same status as the other artificial basic variables (all of which must be degenerate); in particular, once z_a has become non-basic it may subsequently be ignored. There are no non-negativity restrictions on z_a and z when they appear as basic variables. The notation $(z_j - c_j)_a$ will be used to indicate phase 1 values of $z_j - c_j$ (the suffix a indicating that artificial variables are present). Note that the first two columns of the matrix on the left-hand side of equation (3.92) will always be the unit vectors $\mathbf{e}_1$ and $\mathbf{e}_2$, respectively.

The rules for the application of the revised simplex method when artificial variables are present are explained by means of Examples 3.7, 3.8 and 3.9.

Example 3.7

Solve the following problem by the revised simplex method, and discuss the solution of the dual problem.

$$\text{Minimize } z = 2x_1 + 7x_2,$$

subject to

$$\begin{aligned} 5x_1 + x_2 &\geqslant 10, \\ x_1 + 4x_2 &\geqslant 4, \\ x_1, x_2 &\geqslant 0. \end{aligned}$$

Solution

Subtract surplus variables x_3, x_4 and add artificial variables x_5, x_6:

$$\begin{aligned} 5x_1 + x_2 - x_3 + x_5 &= 10, \\ x_1 + 4x_2 - x_4 + x_6 &= 4. \end{aligned}$$

Change the problem into a maximizing problem:

$$\text{Maximize } \bar{z} = -2x_1 - 7x_2,$$

where $\bar{z} = -z$. Corresponding to equation (3.87), we have

$$z_a = -x_5 - x_6,$$

and the full set of constraint equations (3.92) becomes

$$\begin{array}{cccccccc} \bar{z} & z_a & x_1 & x_2 & x_3 & x_4 & x_5 & x_6 \end{array}$$
$$\begin{pmatrix} 1 & 0 & 2 & 7 & 0 & 0 & 0 & 0 \\ 0 & 1 & 0 & 0 & 0 & 0 & 1 & 1 \\ 0 & 0 & 5 & 1 & -1 & 0 & 1 & 0 \\ 0 & 0 & 1 & 4 & 0 & -1 & 0 & 1 \end{pmatrix} \begin{pmatrix} \bar{z} \\ z_a \\ x_1 \\ x_2 \\ x_3 \\ x_4 \\ x_5 \\ x_6 \end{pmatrix} = \begin{pmatrix} 0 \\ 0 \\ 10 \\ 4 \end{pmatrix},$$

which can be identified with

$$\mathbf{A}^S \mathbf{x}^S = \mathbf{b}^S.$$

(It is useful, for reference, to label the columns of $\mathbf{A}^S$, as shown.)

The initial basic variables are $\bar{z}$, z_a, x_5 and x_6 ($\bar{z}$ and z_a *must* be basic throughout phase 1), giving the initial basis matrix

$$\mathbf{B}^S = \begin{pmatrix} 1 & 0 & 0 & 0 \\ 0 & 1 & 1 & 1 \\ 0 & 0 & 1 & 0 \\ 0 & 0 & 0 & 1 \end{pmatrix},$$

whose inverse is easily found to be

$$(\mathbf{B}^S)^{-1} = \begin{pmatrix} 1 & 0 & 0 & 0 \\ 0 & 1 & -1 & -1 \\ 0 & 0 & 1 & 0 \\ 0 & 0 & 0 & 1 \end{pmatrix}.$$

Hence

$$\mathbf{x}_B{}^S = (\mathbf{B}^S)^{-1}\mathbf{b}^S = \begin{pmatrix} 1 & 0 & 0 & 0 \\ 0 & 1 & -1 & -1 \\ 0 & 0 & 1 & 0 \\ 0 & 0 & 0 & 1 \end{pmatrix} \begin{pmatrix} 0 \\ 0 \\ 10 \\ 4 \end{pmatrix} = \begin{pmatrix} 0 \\ -14 \\ 10 \\ 4 \end{pmatrix}.$$

It is now possible to begin the construction of Tableau 1.

The first two columns $\mathbf{e}_1$ and $\mathbf{e}_2$ of $(\mathbf{B}^S)^{-1}$ are omitted from every tableau, and $\mathbf{d}_1, \ldots, \mathbf{d}_m$ are now the last m columns of $(\mathbf{B}^S)^{-1}$.

Tableau 1 (Example 3.7)

Basic Variables	$\mathbf{d}_1$	$\mathbf{d}_2$	$\mathbf{x}_B{}^S$	x_1
$\bar{z}$	0	0	0	2
z_a	−1	−1	−14	−6
x_5	1	0	10	5*
x_6	0	1	4	1

The values of $(z_j - c_j)_a$ are found by taking the scalar product of the *second* row of $(\mathbf{B}^S)^{-1}$ (i.e. the row corresponding to the constraint on z_a, the quantity being maximized) with $\mathbf{a}_j{}^S$, for all j for which x_j is non-basic. The first two terms in each scalar product may be omitted when artificial variables are present, since they make no contribution to $(z_j - c_j)_a$: the first element of the second row of $(\mathbf{B}^S)^{-1}$ is always zero, and the second element in any column vector $\mathbf{a}_j{}^S$ is zero when x_j is non-artificial. (Artificial variables, as usual, are ignored once they have become non-basic.) Thus, from Tableau 1 and $\mathbf{A}^S$,

$$(z_j - c_j)_a = (-1, -1)\begin{pmatrix} 5 & 1 & -1 & 0 \\ 1 & 4 & 0 & -1 \end{pmatrix}$$

$$= (-6, \ -5, \ 1, \ 1), \qquad j = 1, 2, 3, 4.$$

Hence $k = 1$, and the last column of Tableau 1 is

$$\boldsymbol{\beta}_1{}^S = (\mathbf{B}^S)^{-1}\,\mathbf{a}_1{}^S = \begin{pmatrix} 1 & 0 & 0 & 0 \\ 0 & 1 & -1 & -1 \\ 0 & 0 & 1 & 0 \\ 0 & 0 & 0 & 1 \end{pmatrix} \begin{pmatrix} 2 \\ 0 \\ 5 \\ 1 \end{pmatrix} = \begin{pmatrix} 2 \\ -6 \\ 5 \\ 1 \end{pmatrix}.$$

Note that the second component of $\boldsymbol{\beta}_1{}^S$ has already been evaluated as $(z_1 - c_1)_a$. This slight repetition of computation is adequately compensated for: the matrix $(\mathbf{B}^S)^{-1}$ and the vector $\mathbf{a}_1{}^S$ are very easy to write down.

Tableau 2 (Example 3.7)

Basic Variables	$\mathbf{d}_1$	$\mathbf{d}_2$	$\mathbf{x}_B{}^S$	x_2
$\bar{z}$	$-2/5$	0	-4	33/5
z_a	1/5	-1	-2	$-19/5$
x_1	1/5	0	2	1/5
x_6	$-1/5$	1	2	19/5*

From Tableau 2 and $\mathbf{A}^S$,

$$(z_j - c_j)_a = (1/5, -1) \begin{pmatrix} 1 & -1 & 0 \\ 4 & 0 & -1 \end{pmatrix}$$

$$= (-19/5,\ -1/5,\ 1), \quad j = 2, 3, 4.$$

(The artificial variable x_5 is ignored, since it has become non-basic.) Hence $k = 2$, and the last column of Tableau 2 is

$$\boldsymbol{\beta}_2{}^S = (\mathbf{B}^S)^{-1}\,\mathbf{a}_2{}^S = \begin{pmatrix} 1 & 0 & -2/5 & 0 \\ 0 & 1 & 1/5 & -1 \\ 0 & 0 & 1/5 & 0 \\ 0 & 0 & -1/5 & 1 \end{pmatrix} \begin{pmatrix} 7 \\ 0 \\ 1 \\ 4 \end{pmatrix} = \begin{pmatrix} 33/5 \\ -19/5 \\ 1/5 \\ 19/5 \end{pmatrix}.$$

Tableau 3 (Example 3.7)

Basic Variables	$\mathbf{d}_1$	$\mathbf{d}_2$	$\mathbf{x}_B{}^S$	
$\bar{z}$	$-1/19$	$-33/19$	$-142/19$	
z_a	0	0	0	
x_1	4/19	$-1/19$	36/19	
x_2	$-1/19$	5/19	10/19	

In Tableau 3 we notice that $z_a = 0$. Thus Tableau 3 gives a basic feasible solution of the original problem, and phase 1 has ended.

In phase 2, since no basic artificial variable is present, the second row of Tableau 3 can be deleted together with the second row and column of $\mathbf{A}^S$. Then $\mathbf{B}^S$ becomes $\mathbf{B}^R$, and $\mathbf{A}^S$ becomes $\mathbf{A}^R$. We evaluate $z_j - c_j$ for the values of j corresponding to non-basic x_j by taking the scalar product of the *first* row of $(\mathbf{B}^R)^{-1}$ with $\mathbf{a}_j^R$. We must now use the complete first row of $(\mathbf{B}^R)^{-1}$ in the scalar product, including the initial 1 which does not appear in the tableau. Similarly, we use the complete $\mathbf{a}_j^R$ column, including the first entry. Hence, from Tableau 3 and $\mathbf{A}^R$,

$$z_j - c_j = (1, \ -1/19, \ -33/19) \begin{pmatrix} 0 & 0 \\ -1 & 0 \\ 0 & -1 \end{pmatrix}$$

$$= (1/19, \ 33/19), j = 3, 4.$$

This shows that Tableau 3 is optimal, with

$$(x_1{}^*, x_2{}^*) = (36/19, \ 10/19); \quad z^* = -\bar{z}^* = 142/19,$$

and there is no need to proceed with phase 2.

The original minimizing problem has been solved by maximizing $\bar{z} = -z$. The dual of this maximizing problem is

$$\left.\begin{aligned} &\text{Minimize } \bar{w} = -10y_1 - 4y_2, \\ &\text{subject to} \\ &5y_1 + y_2 \leqslant 2, \\ &y_1 + 4y_2 \leqslant 7, \\ &y_1, y_2 \geqslant 0. \end{aligned}\right\} \qquad (3.93)$$

Before considering the dual of the original minimizing problem, it is useful to discuss the optimal solution of problem (3.93).

It should be noted that the negative elements in the first row of Tableau 3 are not the values of the main variables of problem (3.93), a result which apparently disagrees with equation (3.66). The reason is that a problem with constraints of $\geqslant$ type has been solved as a *maximizing* problem, so that the standard theory of duality, based on problems (3.1) and (3.2), does not apply. In this situation the correct values of the main variables for problem (3.93) may always obtained by mere changes of sign. For if the $\geqslant$ constraints in a maximizing problem are put into the correct $\leqslant$ form, then any basis matrix $\mathbf{B}$ becomes $-\mathbf{B}$. In particular, the optimal $\mathbf{c}_B{}'\mathbf{B}^{-1}$ becomes $-\mathbf{c}'_B\mathbf{B}^{-1}$. Hence, for problem (3.93),

$$(y_1{}^*, y_2{}^*) = (1/19, \ 33/19).$$

(More generally, when only *some* of the initial inequality constraints are not in the correct direction, the corresponding values of the main dual variables are obtained by changes of sign in the corresponding elements of the first row of the optimal primal tableau. This follows from the fact that a change of sign throughout the ith row of a matrix produces a change of sign throughout the ith column of its inverse; hence the ith component of $\mathbf{c}'_B\mathbf{B}^{-1}$ changes sign.)

Alternatively we can use the complementary slackness principle (Section 3.3) to show that the optimal values of the main variables of problem (3.93) are obtained by changes of sign in the first row of Tableau 3. The optimal values of the basic variables in the dual problem (3.93) are the optimal values of $z_j - c_j$ for non-basic variables x_j in the corresponding primal problem. The latter have already been found to be

$$z_j - c_j = (1/19,\ 33/19),\ j = 3,\ 4;$$

but

$$(x_3{}^*,\ x_4{}^*) \sim (y_1{}^*,\ y_2{}^*).$$

Therefore

$$(y_1{}^*,\ y_2{}^*) = (1/19,\ 33/19), \tag{3.94}$$

as before, and using Theorem 3.4 (or otherwise) we obtain

$$\bar{w}^* = \bar{z}^* = -142/19. \tag{3.95}$$

Finally, the dual of the original *minimizing* problem is

$$\text{Maximize } w = 10y_1 + 4y_2,$$

subject to

$$\begin{aligned} 5y_1 + y_2 &\leqslant 2, \\ y_1 + 4y_2 &\leqslant 7, \\ y_1,\ y_2 &\geqslant 0. \end{aligned}$$

This maximizing problem is numerically identical to the minimizing problem (3.93), apart from the sign of the objective function. Hence, from equations (3.94) and (3.95) or, equivalently, by changes of sign in the first row of Tableau 3,

$$(y_1{}^*,\ y_2{}^*) = (1/19,\ 33/19); \quad w^* = 142/19.$$

Example 3.8

Solve by the revised simplex method:

$$\text{Minimize } z = 3x_1 + x_2 + 2x_3,$$

subject to

$$\begin{aligned} x_1 + 3x_2 + 5x_3 &\geqslant 10, \\ 2x_1 - x_2 - 9x_3 &\geqslant 1, \\ 4x_1 + 5x_2 + x_3 &\leqslant 7, \\ x_1,\ x_2,\ x_3 &\geqslant 0. \end{aligned}$$

Solution

Introduce surplus, slack and artificial variables, and change to a maximizing problem:

$$\text{Maximize } \bar{z} = -3x_1 - x_2 - 2x_3,$$

subject to

$$\begin{aligned} x_1 + 3x_2 + 5x_3 - x_4 + x_7 &= 10, \\ 2x_1 - x_2 - 9x_3 - x_5 + x_8 &= 1, \\ 4x_1 + 5x_2 + x_3 + x_6 &= 7, \\ x_j \geq 0, \quad j = 1, \ldots, 8. \end{aligned}$$

$$\mathbf{A}^S = \begin{pmatrix} \bar{z} & z_a & x_1 & x_2 & x_3 & x_4 & x_5 & x_6 & x_7 & x_8 \\ 1 & 0 & 3 & 1 & 2 & 0 & 0 & 0 & 0 & 0 \\ 0 & 1 & 0 & 0 & 0 & 0 & 0 & 0 & 1 & 1 \\ 0 & 0 & 1 & 3 & 5 & -1 & 0 & 0 & 1 & 0 \\ 0 & 0 & 2 & -1 & -9 & 0 & -1 & 0 & 0 & 1 \\ 0 & 0 & 4 & 5 & 1 & 0 & 0 & 1 & 0 & 0 \end{pmatrix}.$$

Phase 1

$$\mathbf{B}^S = \begin{pmatrix} 1 & 0 & 0 & 0 & 0 \\ 0 & 1 & 1 & 1 & 0 \\ 0 & 0 & 1 & 0 & 0 \\ 0 & 0 & 0 & 1 & 0 \\ 0 & 0 & 0 & 0 & 1 \end{pmatrix}, \quad (\mathbf{B}^S)^{-1} = \begin{pmatrix} 1 & 0 & 0 & 0 & 0 \\ 0 & 1 & -1 & -1 & 0 \\ 0 & 0 & 1 & 0 & 0 \\ 0 & 0 & 0 & 1 & 0 \\ 0 & 0 & 0 & 0 & 1 \end{pmatrix},$$

$$\therefore \quad \mathbf{x}_B{}^S = \begin{pmatrix} 1 & 0 & 0 & 0 & 0 \\ 0 & 1 & -1 & -1 & 0 \\ 0 & 0 & 1 & 0 & 0 \\ 0 & 0 & 0 & 1 & 0 \\ 0 & 0 & 0 & 0 & 1 \end{pmatrix} \begin{pmatrix} 0 \\ 0 \\ 10 \\ 1 \\ 7 \end{pmatrix} = \begin{pmatrix} 0 \\ -11 \\ 10 \\ 1 \\ 7 \end{pmatrix}.$$

Tableau 1 (Example 3.8)

Basic Variables	$\mathbf{d}_1$	$\mathbf{d}_2$	$\mathbf{d}_3$	$\mathbf{x}_B{}^S$	x_1
$\bar{z}$	0	0	0	0	3
z_a	−1	−1	0	−11	−3
x_7	1	0	0	10	1
x_8	0	1	0	1	2*
x_6	0	0	1	7	4

From Tableau 1 and $\mathbf{A}^S$,

$$(z_j - c_j)_a = (-1, -1, 0)\begin{pmatrix} 1 & 3 & 5 & -1 & 0 \\ 2 & -1 & -9 & 0 & -1 \\ 4 & 5 & 1 & 0 & 0 \end{pmatrix}$$

$$= (-3, -2, 4, 1, 1), \quad j = 1, 2, 3, 4, 5.$$

Hence $k = 1$, and

$$\boldsymbol{\beta}_1{}^S = \begin{pmatrix} 1 & 0 & 0 & 0 & 0 \\ 0 & 1 & -1 & -1 & 0 \\ 0 & 0 & 1 & 0 & 0 \\ 0 & 0 & 0 & 1 & 0 \\ 0 & 0 & 0 & 0 & 1 \end{pmatrix}\begin{pmatrix} 3 \\ 0 \\ 1 \\ 2 \\ 4 \end{pmatrix} = \begin{pmatrix} 3 \\ -3 \\ 1 \\ 2 \\ 4 \end{pmatrix}.$$

Tableau 2 (Example 3.8)

Basic Variables	$\mathbf{d}_1$	$\mathbf{d}_2$	$\mathbf{d}_3$	$\mathbf{x}_B{}^S$	x_3
$\bar{z}$	0	$-3/2$	0	$-3/2$	$31/2$
z_a	-1	$1/2$	0	$-19/2$	$-19/2$
x_7	1	$-1/2$	0	$19/2$	$19/2$
x_1	0	$1/2$	0	$1/2$	$-9/2$
x_6	0	-2	1	5	**19***

From Tableau 2 and $\mathbf{A}^S$,

$$(z_j - c_j)_a = (-1, 1/2, 0)\begin{pmatrix} 3 & 5 & -1 & 0 \\ -1 & -9 & 0 & -1 \\ 5 & 1 & 0 & 0 \end{pmatrix}$$

$$= (-7/2, -19/2, 1, -1/2), \quad j = 2, 3, 4, 5.$$

Hence $k = 3$, and

$$\boldsymbol{\beta}_3{}^S = \begin{pmatrix} 1 & 0 & 0 & -3/2 & 0 \\ 0 & 1 & -1 & 1/2 & 0 \\ 0 & 0 & 1 & -1/2 & 0 \\ 0 & 0 & 0 & 1/2 & 0 \\ 0 & 0 & 0 & -2 & 1 \end{pmatrix}\begin{pmatrix} 2 \\ 0 \\ 5 \\ -9 \\ 1 \end{pmatrix} = \begin{pmatrix} 31/2 \\ -19/2 \\ 19/2 \\ -9/2 \\ 19 \end{pmatrix}.$$

Tableau 3 (Example 3.8)

Basic Variables	$\mathbf{d}_1$	$\mathbf{d}_2$	$\mathbf{d}_3$	$\mathbf{x}_B{}^S$	x_4
$\bar{z}$	0	5/38	−31/38	−106/19	0
z_a	−1	−1/2	1/2	−7	1
x_7	1	1/2	−1/2	7	−1*
x_1	0	1/38	9/38	32/19	0
x_3	0	−2/19	1/19	5/19	0

From Tableau 3 and $\mathbf{A}^S$,

$$(z_j - c_j)_a = (-1,\ -1/2,\ 1/2)\begin{pmatrix} 3 & -1 & 0 & 0 \\ -1 & 0 & -1 & 0 \\ 5 & 0 & 0 & 1 \end{pmatrix}$$

$$= (0, 1, 1/2, 1/2), \quad j = 2, 4, 5, 6,$$

showing that Tableau 3 is optimal. But the artificial variable x_7 is still basic and non-degenerate; hence the original problem has no feasible solution. Investigating further, as explained in Section 2.8.2, page 45, we find

$$\beta_4{}^S = \begin{pmatrix} 1 & 0 & 0 & 5/38 & -31/38 \\ 0 & 1, & -1 & -1/2 & 1/2 \\ 0 & 0 & 1 & 1/2 & -1/2 \\ 0 & 0 & 0 & 1/38 & 9/38 \\ 0 & 0 & 0 & -2/19 & 1/19 \end{pmatrix}\begin{pmatrix} 0 \\ 0 \\ -1 \\ 0 \\ 0 \end{pmatrix} = \begin{pmatrix} 0 \\ 1 \\ -1 \\ 0 \\ 0 \end{pmatrix}$$

Taking $\beta_4{}^S$ to be the last column of Tableau 3, it is possible to make x_7 non-basic, using a simplex transformation with a negative pivot. This leads to Tableau 4.

Tableau 4 (Example 3.8)

Basic Variables	$\mathbf{d}_1$	$\mathbf{d}_2$	$\mathbf{d}_3$	$\mathbf{x}_B{}^S$	
$\bar{z}$	0	5/38	−31/38	−106/19	
z_a	0	0	0	0	
x_4	−1	−1/2	1/2	−7	
x_1	0	1/38	9/38	32/19	
x_3	0	−2/19	1/19	5/19	

Tableau 4 gives a non-feasible solution in which the value of the surplus variable x_4 is strictly negative. It can be shown that *every* solution of the original equality constraints (including surplus and slack variables, but excluding artificial variables) contains at least one surplus or slack variable with a strictly negative value, cf. Example 2.6. Hence the original inequality constraints are inconsistent.

Example 3.9

In Example 3.8, change the direction of the inequality in the third constraint. Solve the new problem and its dual problem.

Solution

Proceeding as in Example 3.8, with only minor changes, we obtain

$$\mathbf{A}^S = \begin{pmatrix} \bar{z} & z_a & x_1 & x_2 & x_3 & x_4 & x_5 & x_6 & x_7 & x_8 & x_9 \\ 1 & 0 & 3 & 1 & 2 & 0 & 0 & 0 & 0 & 0 & 0 \\ 0 & 1 & 0 & 0 & 0 & 0 & 0 & 0 & 1 & 1 & 1 \\ 0 & 0 & 1 & 3 & 5 & -1 & 0 & 0 & 1 & 0 & 0 \\ 0 & 0 & 2 & -1 & -9 & 0 & -1 & 0 & 0 & 1 & 0 \\ 0 & 0 & 4 & 5 & 1 & 0 & 0 & -1 & 0 & 0 & 1 \end{pmatrix}.$$

Phase 1

$$\mathbf{B}^S = \begin{pmatrix} 1 & 0 & 0 & 0 & 0 \\ 0 & 1 & 1 & 1 & 1 \\ 0 & 0 & 1 & 0 & 0 \\ 0 & 0 & 0 & 1 & 0 \\ 0 & 0 & 0 & 0 & 1 \end{pmatrix}, \quad (\mathbf{B}^S)^{-1} = \begin{pmatrix} 1 & 0 & 0 & 0 & 0 \\ 0 & 1 & -1 & -1 & -1 \\ 0 & 0 & 1 & 0 & 0 \\ 0 & 0 & 0 & 1 & 0 \\ 0 & 0 & 0 & 0 & 1 \end{pmatrix}.$$

$$\therefore \; \mathbf{x}_B{}^S = \begin{pmatrix} 1 & 0 & 0 & 0 & 0 \\ 0 & 1 & -1 & -1 & -1 \\ 0 & 0 & 1 & 0 & 0 \\ 0 & 0 & 0 & 1 & 0 \\ 0 & 0 & 0 & 0 & 1 \end{pmatrix} \begin{pmatrix} 0 \\ 0 \\ 10 \\ 1 \\ 7 \end{pmatrix} = \begin{pmatrix} 0 \\ -18 \\ 10 \\ 1 \\ 7 \end{pmatrix}.$$

Tableau 1 (Example 3.9)

Basic Variables	$\mathbf{d}_1$	$\mathbf{d}_2$	$\mathbf{d}_3$	$\mathbf{x}_B{}^S$	x_1
$\bar{z}$	0	0	0	0	3
z_a	−1	−1	−1	−18	−7
x_7	1	0	0	10	1
x_8	0	1	0	1	2*
x_9	0	0	1	7	4

From Tableau 1 and $\mathbf{A}^S$,

$$(z_j - c_j)_a = (-1, -1, -1) \begin{pmatrix} 1 & 3 & 5 & -1 & 0 & 0 \\ 2 & -1 & -9 & 0 & -1 & 0 \\ 4 & 5 & 1 & 0 & 0 & -1 \end{pmatrix}$$

$$= (-7, -7, 3, 1, 1, 1), \quad j = 1, 2, 3, 4, 5, 6.$$

Hence $k = 1$ or 2. We choose $k = 1$. Then

$$\boldsymbol{\beta}_1{}^S = \begin{pmatrix} 1 & 0 & 0 & 0 & 0 \\ 0 & 1 & -1 & -1 & -1 \\ 0 & 0 & 1 & 0 & 0 \\ 0 & 0 & 0 & 1 & 0 \\ 0 & 0 & 0 & 0 & 1 \end{pmatrix} \begin{pmatrix} 3 \\ 0 \\ 1 \\ 2 \\ 4 \end{pmatrix} = \begin{pmatrix} 3 \\ -7 \\ 1 \\ 2 \\ 4 \end{pmatrix}.$$

Tableau 2 (Example 3.9)

Basic Variables	$\mathbf{d}_1$	$\mathbf{d}_2$	$\mathbf{d}_3$	$\mathbf{x}_B{}^S$	x_3
$\bar{z}$	0	$-3/2$	0	$-3/2$	$31/2$
z_a	-1	$5/2$	-1	$-29/2$	$-57/2$
x_7	1	$-1/2$	0	$19/2$	$19/2$
x_1	0	$1/2$	0	$1/2$	$-9/2$
x_9	0	-2	1	5	19*

From Tableau 2 and $\mathbf{A}^S$,

$$(z_j - c_j)_a = (-1,\ 5/2,\ -1) \begin{pmatrix} 3 & 5 & -1 & 0 & 0 \\ -1 & -9 & 0 & -1 & 0 \\ 5 & 1 & 0 & 0 & -1 \end{pmatrix}$$

$$= (-21/2,\ -57/2,\ 1,\ -5/2,\ 1), \quad j = 2, 3, 4, 5, 6.$$

Hence $k = 3$, and

$$\boldsymbol{\beta}_3{}^S = \begin{pmatrix} 1 & 0 & 0 & -3/2 & 0 \\ 0 & 1 & -1 & 5/2 & -1 \\ 0 & 0 & 1 & -1/2 & 0 \\ 0 & 0 & 0 & 1/2 & 0 \\ 0 & 0 & 0 & -2 & 1 \end{pmatrix} \begin{pmatrix} 2 \\ 0 \\ 5 \\ -9 \\ 1 \end{pmatrix} = \begin{pmatrix} 31/2 \\ -57/2 \\ 19/2 \\ -9/2 \\ 19 \end{pmatrix}.$$

Tableau 3 (Example 3.9)

Basic Variables	$\mathbf{d}_1$	$\mathbf{d}_2$	$\mathbf{d}_3$	$\mathbf{x}_B{}^S$	$\mathbf{x}_6$
$\bar{z}$	0	$5/38$	$-31/38$	$-106/19$	$31/38$
z_a	-1	$-1/2$	$1/2$	-7	$-1/2$
x_7	1	$1/2$	$-1/2$	7	1/2*
x_1	0	$1/38$	$9/38$	$32/19$	$-9/38$
x_3	0	$-2/19$	$1/19$	$5/19$	$-1/19$

From Tableau 3 and $\mathbf{A}^S$,

$$(z_j - c_j)_a = (-1, \ -1/2, \ 1/2) \begin{pmatrix} 3 & -1 & 0 & 0 \\ -1 & 0 & -1 & 0 \\ 5 & 0 & 0 & -1 \end{pmatrix}$$

$$= (0, \ 1, \ 1/2, \ -1/2) \quad j = 2, 4, 5, 6.$$

Hence $k = 6$, and

$$\boldsymbol{\beta}_6{}^S = \begin{pmatrix} 1 & 0 & 0 & 5/38 & -31/38 \\ 0 & 1 & -1 & -1/2 & 1/2 \\ 0 & 0 & 1 & 1/2 & -1/2 \\ 0 & 0 & 0 & 1/38 & 9/38 \\ 0 & 0 & 0 & -2/19 & 1/19 \end{pmatrix} \begin{pmatrix} 0 \\ 0 \\ 0 \\ 0 \\ -1 \end{pmatrix} = \begin{pmatrix} 31/38 \\ -1/2 \\ 1/2 \\ -9/38 \\ -1/19 \end{pmatrix}.$$

Tableau 4 (Example 3.9)

Basic Variables	$\mathbf{d}_1$	$\mathbf{d}_2$	$\mathbf{d}_3$	$\mathbf{x}_B{}^S$	x_2
$\bar{z}$	$-31/19$	$-13/19$	0	-17	$-61/19$
z_a	0	0	0	0	
x_6	2	1	-1	14	0
x_1	9/19	5/19	0	5	22/19
x_3	2/19	$-1/19$	0	1	7/19*

In Tableau 4, $z_a = 0$, indicating that phase 1 has ended.

Phase 2

Since there is no basic artificial variable, we delete the second row of Tableau 4 and the second row and column of $\mathbf{A}^S$. Proceeding according to the rules for the case when no artificial variable is present (pp. 111–112), we obtain from Tableau 4 and $\mathbf{A}^R$

$$z_j - c_j = (1, \ -31/19, \ -13/19, \ 0) \begin{pmatrix} 1 & 0 & 0 \\ 3 & -1 & 0 \\ -1 & 0 & -1 \\ 5 & 0 & 0 \end{pmatrix}$$

$$= (-61/19, \ 31/19, \ 13/19), \quad j = 2, 4, 5.$$

Hence $k = 2$, and

$$\boldsymbol{\beta}_2 = \begin{pmatrix} 2 & 1 & -1 \\ 9/19 & 5/19 & 0 \\ 2/19 & -1/19 & 0 \end{pmatrix} \begin{pmatrix} 3 \\ -1 \\ 5 \end{pmatrix} = \begin{pmatrix} 0 \\ 22/19 \\ 7/19 \end{pmatrix}.$$

Tableau 5 (Example 3.9)

Basic Variables	$\mathbf{d}_1$	$\mathbf{d}_2$	$\mathbf{d}_3$	$\mathbf{x}_B{}^R$	
$\bar{z}$	$-5/7$	$-8/7$	0	$-58/7$	
x_6	2	1	-1	14	
x_1	$1/7$	$3/7$	0	$13/7$	
x_2	$2/7$	$-1/7$	0	$19/7$	

From Tableau 5 and $\mathbf{A}^R$,

$$z_j - c_j = (1,\ -5/7,\ -8/7,\ 0)\begin{pmatrix} 2 & 0 & 0 \\ 5 & -1 & 0 \\ -9 & 0 & -1 \\ 1 & 0 & 0 \end{pmatrix}$$

$$= (61/7,\ 5/7,\ 8/7), \quad j = 3, 4, 5,$$

showing that Tableau 5 is optimal, with

$$(x_1{}^*, x_2{}^*, x_3{}^*) = (13/7, 19/7, 0); \quad z^* = -\bar{z}^* = 58/7.$$

The dual of the original minimizing problem is

$$\text{Maximize } w = 10y_1 + y_2 + 7y_3,$$

subject to

$$\begin{aligned} y_1 + 2y_2 + 4y_3 &\leqslant 3, \\ 3y_1 - \ y_2 + 5y_3 &\leqslant 1, \\ 5y_1 - 9y_2 + \ y_3 &\leqslant 2, \\ y_1, y_2, y_3 &\geqslant 0. \end{aligned}$$

By changing the signs in the first row of Tableau 5, as explained in connection with Example 3.7, we obtain the optimal solution of the dual problem:

$$(y_1{}^*, y_2{}^*, y_3{}^*) = (5/7, 8/7, 0); \ w^* = 58/7.$$

*3.8 Sensitivity Analysis

When a linear programming problem has been solved, it is often necessary to investigate the effect on the optimal solution of changes in the initial data. For example, it may be important to know whether the solution remains optimal if uncertainties in the initial data are taken into account. In particular, we shall consider the effects of changes in the coefficients a_{ij}, b_i and c_j, and also the effect of introducing a new variable. A linear programming problem may also be varied by adding a new constraint: techniques for obtaining the new optimal solution in this case were considered in Section 3.5. In deriving the results of this section, we shall deal only with maximizing problems; the corresponding results for minimizing problems may be obtained by making the necessary trivial alterations, as shown in Example 3.10. It will be assumed that an optimal simplex tableau (standard or revised) is available in each case.

(a) *Change in* a_{ij}. There are two cases to consider: the corresponding variable x_j may be basic or non-basic in the original optimal solution.

If x_j is non-basic, then a change in a_{ij} (to a_{ij}^{v}, say) may be introduced by associating the new activity vector $\mathbf{a}_j^{\text{v}}$ with a new variable x_j^{v} and discarding the old variable x_j. The price associated with x_j^{v} is $c_j^{\text{v}} = c_j$. It is necessary to modify the old optimal tableau by discarding the x_j column and introducing an x_j^{v} column containing the components of $\boldsymbol{\beta}_j^{\text{v}}$, where

$$\boldsymbol{\beta}_j^{\text{v}} = \mathbf{B}^{-1}\mathbf{a}_j^{\text{v}}, \tag{3.96}$$

from equation (2.24). The elements of $\mathbf{B}^{-1}$ are immediately available if the revised simplex method has been used, and are sometimes available if the standard simplex method has been used—see page 65; otherwise $\mathbf{B}^{-1}$ is found by inverting $\mathbf{B}$. The optimality condition $z_j - c_j \geqslant 0$ (for a maximizing problem) is replaced by

$$z_j^{\text{v}} - c_j^{\text{v}} = \mathbf{c}_B'\boldsymbol{\beta}_j^{\text{v}} - c_j^{\text{v}} \geqslant 0.$$

If the modified tableau is not optimal, then the usual simplex calculations are carried out until optimality is again reached.

If x_j is basic, then a change in a_{ij} may still be accomplished by adding a new variable x_j^{v}, with price $c_j^{\text{v}} = c_j$. As before, the new column vector $\boldsymbol{\beta}_j^{\text{v}}$ is evaluated using equation (3.96). In this case, however, the old variable x_j is retained and its price is set equal to $-M$, a number sufficiently negative (for a maximizing problem) to ensure that x_j does not appear in the optimal solution. New values of

$$z_j - c_j = \mathbf{c}_B'\boldsymbol{\beta}_j - c_j, \quad j = 1, \ldots, N,$$

together with $z_j^{\text{v}} - c_j^{\text{v}}$, are then calculated. The simplex calculations proceed normally with the augmented tableau and the new objective function.

(b) *Change in* b_i. Suppose that b_i is increased by an amount Δb_i. We can say immediately that the new solution is optimal provided that it contains the same basic variables as the old optimal solution and is feasible, since the optimality conditions ($z_j - c_j \geqslant 0$, $j = 1, \ldots, N$, for a maximizing problem) are independent of $\mathbf{b}$. The old optimal basic solution is

$$\mathbf{x}_B = \mathbf{B}^{-1}\mathbf{b}, \tag{3.97}$$

and so the change in $\mathbf{x}_B$ is

$$\Delta\mathbf{x}_B = \mathbf{B}^{-1}\Delta\mathbf{b}. \tag{3.98}$$

Hence the condition that the new solution is feasible, and therefore optimal, is

$$\mathbf{x}_B + \mathbf{B}^{-1}\Delta\mathbf{b} \geqslant \mathbf{0}. \tag{3.99}$$

Since $z = \mathbf{c}_B'\mathbf{x}_B$, and $\mathbf{c}_B$ remains unchanged, the increase in the value of the objective function is

$$\Delta z = \mathbf{c}_B'\Delta\mathbf{x}_B = \mathbf{c}_B'\mathbf{B}^{-1}\Delta\mathbf{b}, \tag{3.100}$$

using equation (3.98). Equation (3.100) shows that there are several ways of computing Δz. If the revised simplex method has been used, then the components of the vector $\mathbf{c}_B'\mathbf{B}^{-1}$ appear in the first row of the tableau; they also appear in the last row of the standard simplex tableau, since (for a maximizing problem)

$$[\mathbf{c}_B'\mathbf{B}^{-1}]_i = y_i = z_{n+i} = z_{n+i} - c_{n+i}, \tag{3.101}$$

from equations (3.26), where y_i is the main dual variable corresponding to the ith primal constraint, i.e. $y_i \sim x_{n+i}$.

When the inequality (3.99) is not satisfied, the new optimal solution may be obtained with the help of the dual simplex method, as follows. In the old optimal simplex tableau (standard or revised), replace the old values $\mathbf{x}_B$ of the basic variables by the new values

$$\mathbf{x}_B^{\text{v}} = \mathbf{x}_B + \mathbf{B}^{-1}\Delta\mathbf{b}.$$

The modified tableau represents an optimal, but non-feasible, solution to which the dual simplex method may be applied. Alternatively, the whole problem may be reworked from the beginning.

(c) *Change in* c_j. The optimality conditions for a maximizing problem are

$$\left.\begin{aligned} z_j - c_j &\geqslant 0, \\ \text{i.e.} \quad \mathbf{c}_B'\boldsymbol{\beta}_j - c_j &\geqslant 0. \end{aligned}\right\} \quad j = 1, \ldots, N. \tag{3.102}$$

Suppose that c_j is increased by an amount Δc_j. Then, from (3.102), the optimality conditions are still satisfied if

$$z_j - c_j + \Delta\mathbf{c}_B'\boldsymbol{\beta}_j - \Delta c_j \geqslant 0, \quad j = 1, \ldots, N. \tag{3.103}$$

When (3.103) holds, the old basic variables remain basic and retain their old values. The vector $\boldsymbol{\beta}_j$ is available from the optimal simplex tableau (the standard simplex tableau is more convenient than the revised simplex tableau for this analysis). The increase Δz in the objective function is given by

$$\Delta z = \Delta\mathbf{c}_B'\mathbf{x}_B. \tag{3.104}$$

In particular, if $\Delta\mathbf{c}_B = \mathbf{0}$, i.e. if there are no changes in the prices of the *basic* variables, then (3.103) reduces to

$$z_j - c_j - \Delta c_j \geqslant 0, \quad j = 1, \ldots, N,$$

and equation (3.104) shows that there is no change in the optimal value of the objective function.

If (3.103) is not satisfied, then the new $z_j - c_j$ values [left-hand side of (3.103)] are entered in the tableau, and the simplex calculations proceed normally until the tableau again becomes optimal.

(d) *Introduction of a New Variable.* Suppose that after an optimal solution has been reached it becomes necessary to consider the effect of a variable x_{N+1} ($\geqslant 0$) which has not previously featured in the problem. Let x_{N+1} have an activity vector $\mathbf{a}_{N+1}$ and a price c_{N+1}, and at first consider x_{N+1} to be an additional non-basic variable. The original optimal solution (of a maximizing problem) will remain optimal if

$$z_{N+1} - c_{N+1} \geqslant 0,$$

i.e. if

$$\mathbf{c}_B{}'\mathbf{B}^{-1}\mathbf{a}_{N+1} - c_{N+1} \geqslant 0, \tag{3.105}$$

since

$$z_{N+1} = \mathbf{c}_B{}'\boldsymbol{\beta}_{N+1} = \mathbf{c}_B{}'\mathbf{B}^{-1}\mathbf{a}_{N+1},$$

using (2.24) and (2.36). The components of $\mathbf{c}_B{}'\mathbf{B}^{-1}$ (in 3.105) are readily available from the optimal tableau, as explained after equation (3.100). When condition (3.105) holds, the original optimal solution is unchanged by the introduction of x_{N+1}.

If condition (3.105) is not satisfied, then a column for x_{N+1} is attached to the optimal standard simplex tableau, the entries being the components of the column vector

$$\boldsymbol{\beta}_{N+1} = \mathbf{B}^{-1}\mathbf{a}_{N+1}$$

together with the value of

$$z_{N+1} - c_{N+1} = \mathbf{c}_B{}'\boldsymbol{\beta}_{N+1} - c_{N+1}.$$

The usual simplex iterations are carried out until the solution again becomes optimal. The same quantities may be found, and the calculation completed, if the revised simplex method is used.

(e) *Parametric Programming.* Instead of considering the effects of discrete changes in the coefficients a_{ij}, b_i, and c_j, as in (a), (b), and (c) above, it is often useful to allow these quantities to vary continuously. For example, we can replace a_{ij}, b_i, and c_j, respectively, by

$$a_{ij}^+ = a_{ij} + \theta,$$
$$b_i^+ = b_i + \phi,$$
$$c_j^+ = c_j + \psi,$$

where θ, ϕ, and ψ are scalar parameters. As a further generalization, we can replace $\mathbf{A}$, $\mathbf{b}$, and $\mathbf{c}$, respectively, by

$$\mathbf{A}^+ = \mathbf{A} + \theta\mathbf{K},$$
$$\mathbf{b}^+ = \mathbf{b} + \phi\mathbf{r},$$
$$\mathbf{c}^+ = \mathbf{c} + \psi\mathbf{s},$$

where θ, ϕ, and ψ are scalar parameters, $\mathbf{K}$ is a specified, though arbitrary, matrix, and $\mathbf{r}$ and $\mathbf{s}$ are specified, though arbitrary, vectors.

The solution of problems in which some or all of the coefficients a_{ij}, etc. are expressed in parametric form is known as *parametric programming*. Where more than one parameter is allowed to vary, a general analysis soon becomes unwieldy owing to the multiplicity of cases that arise, although no new principle is involved. We therefore confine the discussion to problems with a single parameter; the theory is then precisely as given in (a), (b), and (c) above. In general, the three stages in the solution of such problems are:

(i) Solve the given problem with the appropriate parameter (θ, ϕ, or ψ) taking the value zero, or some other suitable value.

(ii) Find the critical value (or values) of the parameter at which the solution (i) first becomes non-optimal.

(iii) Find the new optimal solutions for those values of the parameter for which the solution (i) is no longer optimal.

Example 3.10

Consider again the problem of Example 3.5:

$$\text{Minimize } z = 2x_1 + 3x_2 + 4x_3 + 5x_4,$$

subject to

$$\begin{aligned} x_1 - x_2 + x_3 - x_4 &\geqslant 10, \\ x_1 - 2x_2 + 3x_3 - 4x_4 &\geqslant 6, \\ 3x_1 - 4x_2 + 5x_3 - 6x_4 &\geqslant 15, \\ x_1, x_2, x_3, x_4 &\geqslant 0. \end{aligned}$$

Find the effects on the optimal solution of

(a) an increase of 3 in a_{21} and a decrease of 2 in a_{31},

(b) a decrease of 20 in b_1,

(c) an increase of 5 in c_1,

(d) the introduction of a new variable x_8 into the problem, with $a_8 = [1, 1, 1]$ and $c_8 = 1$,

(e) an arbitrary change in c_1.

Solution

The optimal tableau for the problem is Tableau 1, in which x_5, x_6 and x_7 are surplus variables for the three constraints, taken in order.

(a) Since a_{21} and a_{31} are coefficients of the basic variable x_1, we introduce a new variable $x_1{}^{\text{v}}$, and retain the old variable x_1. From equation (3.96),

Tableau 1 (Example 3.10)

	$\mathbf{c}'$		2	3	4	5	0	0	0
$\mathbf{c}_B$	Basic Variables		x_1	x_2	x_3	x_4	x_5	x_6	x_7
0	x_7	15	0	1	−2	3	−3	0	1
0	x_6	4	0	1	−2	3	−1	1	0
2	x_1	10	1	−1	1	−1	−1	0	0
	$z_j - c_j$	20	0	−5	−2	−7	−2	0	0

$$\boldsymbol{\beta}_1{}^{\mathrm{v}} = \mathbf{B}^{-1}\mathbf{a}_1{}^{\mathrm{v}} = \begin{pmatrix} 0 & 0 & 1 \\ 0 & -1 & 1 \\ -1 & 0 & 3 \end{pmatrix}^{-1} \begin{pmatrix} 1 \\ 4 \\ 1 \end{pmatrix}$$

$$= \begin{pmatrix} 3 & 0 & -1 \\ 1 & -1 & 0 \\ 1 & 0 & 0 \end{pmatrix} \begin{pmatrix} 1 \\ 4 \\ 1 \end{pmatrix} = \begin{pmatrix} 2 \\ -3 \\ 1 \end{pmatrix}.$$

Hence we obtain Tableau 2, which is completed by calculating new values of $z_j - c_j$, $j = 1, \ldots, 7$, together with $z_1{}^{\mathrm{v}} - c_1{}^{\mathrm{v}}$.

Tableau 2 (Example 3.10)

	$\mathbf{c}'$		M	3	4	5	0	0	0	2
$\mathbf{c}_B$	Basic Variables		x_1	x_2	x_3	x_4	x_5	x_6	x_7	$x_1{}^{\mathrm{v}}$
0	x_7	15	0	1	−2	3	−3	0	1	2
0	x_6	4	0	1	−2	3	−1	1	0	−3
M	x_1	10	1	−1	1*	−1	−1	0	0	1
	$z_j - c_j$	$10M$	0	$-3-M$	$-4+M$	$-5-M$	$-M$	0	0	$-2+M$

The price of x_1 is $+M$, since we are dealing with a minimizing problem. The remainder of the calculation follows the standard simplex method for the solution of a minimizing problem. Proceeding from Tableau 2, it is convenient to make x_1 non-basic, giving Tableau 3.

The x_1 column could have been omitted from Tableau 3, and will be omitted henceforth, since x_1 will never become basic.

Tableau 4 is optimal. Reverting to the original notation, the new optimal solution is

$$(x_1{}^*, x_2{}^*, x_3{}^*, x_4{}^*) = (35/4, 0, 5/4, 0);\ z^* = 45/2.$$

Tableau 3 (Example 3.10)

	$\mathbf{c}'$		M	3	4	5	0	0	0	2
$\mathbf{c}_B$	Basic Variables		x_1	x_2	x_3	x_4	x_5	x_6	x_7	x_1^v
0	x_7	35	2	−1	0	1	−5	0	1	4*
0	x_6	24	2	−1	0	1	−3	1	0	−1
4	x_3	10	1	−1	1	−1	−1	0	0	1
	$z_j - c_j$	40	$4-M$	−7	0	−9	−4	0	0	2

Tableau 4 (Example 3.10)

	$\mathbf{c}'$		3	4	5	0	0	0	2
$\mathbf{c}_B$	Basic Variables		x_2	x_3	x_4	x_5	x_6	x_7	x_1^v
2	x_1^v	35/4	−1/4	0	1/4	−5/4	0	1/4	1
0	x_6	131/4	−5/4	0	5/4	−17/4	1	1/4	0
4	x_3	5/4	−3/4	1	−5/4	1/4	0	−1/4	0
	$z_j - c_j$	45/2	−13/2	0	−19/2	−3/2	0	−1/2	0

(b) $\Delta b_1 = -20$, and from part (*a*) of the solution,

$$\mathbf{B}^{-1} = \begin{pmatrix} 3 & 0 & -1 \\ 1 & -1 & 0 \\ 1 & 0 & 0 \end{pmatrix}.$$

The left-hand side of (3.99) is

$$\begin{pmatrix} 15 \\ 4 \\ 10 \end{pmatrix} + \begin{pmatrix} 3 & 0 & -1 \\ 1 & -1 & 0 \\ 1 & 0 & 0 \end{pmatrix} \begin{pmatrix} -20 \\ 0 \\ 0 \end{pmatrix} = \begin{pmatrix} -45 \\ -16 \\ -10 \end{pmatrix}.$$

Hence condition (3.99) is not satisfied.

Tableau 1 is modified (by changing the values of the x_{Bi} and of z) to become Tableau 5, to which the dual simplex method is applied.

Omitting an intermediate tableau, we find that Tableau 6 is the required new optimal tableau.

This part of Example 3.10 can equally well be solved as a completely new linear programming problem, leading again to Tableau 6. The first constraint becomes

$$-x_1 + x_2 - x_3 + x_4 \leqslant 10;$$

the variable x_5 in Tableau 6 can be interpreted as the slack variable for this

Tableau 5 (Example 3.10)

	$\mathbf{c}'$		2	3	4	5	0	0	0
$\mathbf{c}_B$	Basic Variables		x_1	x_2	x_3	x_4	x_5	x_6	x_7
0	x_7	-45	0	1	-2	3	-3*	0	1
0	x_6	-16	0	1	-2	3	-1	1	0
2	x_1	-10	1	-1	1	-1	-1	0	0
	$z_j - c_j$	-20	0	-5	-2	-7	-2	0	0

Tableau 6 (Example 3.10)

	$\mathbf{c}'$		2	3	4	5	0	0	0
$\mathbf{c}_B$	Basic Variables		x_1	x_2	x_3	x_4	x_5	x_6	x_7
0	x_5	29/2	0	0	0	0	1	1/2	$-1/2$
4	x_3	3/4	0	$-1/2$	1	$-3/2$	0	$-3/4$	1/4
2	x_1	15/4	1	$-1/2$	0	1/2	0	5/4	$-3/4$
	$z_j - c_j$	21/2	0	-6	0	-10	0	$-1/2$	$-1/2$

constraint. In the above calculation, x_5 was the *surplus* variable for the constraint in its $\geqslant$ form with negative b_1:

$$x_1 - x_2 + x_3 - x_4 \geqslant -10.$$

(c) $\Delta c_1 = 5$. From Tableau 1, we find

$$z_j - c_j + \Delta \mathbf{c}_B' \boldsymbol{\beta}_j - \Delta c_j = (0,\ -10,\ 3,\ -12,\ -7,\ 0,\ 0), \quad j = 1, \ldots, 7,$$

so that the inequalities (3.103), reversed in direction for a *minimizing* problem, are not satisfied, i.e. Tableau 1 is no longer optimal; it is therefore modified to become Tableau 7.

Tableau 7 (Example 3.10)

	$\mathbf{c}'$		7	3	4	5	0	0	0
$\mathbf{c}_B$	Basic Variables		x_1	x_2	x_3	x_4	x_5	x_6	x_7
0	x_7	15	0	1	-2	3	-3	0	1
0	x_6	4	0	1	-2	3	-1	1	0
7	x_1	10	1	-1	1*	-1	-1	0	0
	$z_j - c_j$	70	0	-10	3	-12	-7	0	0

In one simplex iteration we obtain Tableau 8, which is optimal.

Tableau 8 (Example 3.10)

	$\mathbf{c}'$		7	3	4	5	0	0	0
$\mathbf{c}_B$	Basic Variables		x_1	x_2	x_3	x_4	x_5	x_6	x_7
0	x_7	35	2	−1	0	1	−5	0	1
0	x_6	24	2	−1	0	1	−3	1	0
4	x_3	10	1	−1	1	−1	−1	0	0
	$z_j - c_j$	40	−3	−7	0	−9	−4	0	0

(d) The left-hand side of (3.105) is

$$z_8 - c_8 = \mathbf{c}_B{}'\mathbf{B}^{-1}\mathbf{a}_8 - c_8 = (0, 0, 2)\begin{pmatrix} 3 & 0 & -1 \\ 1 & -1 & 0 \\ 1 & 0 & 0 \end{pmatrix}\begin{pmatrix} 1 \\ 1 \\ 1 \end{pmatrix} - 1$$

$$= (0, 0, 2)\,[2, 0, 1] - 1$$

$$= 1.$$

Hence the optimality condition for a *minimizing* problem, corresponding to (3.105), is not satisfied. An extra column is added to Tableau 1, giving Tableau 9.

Tableau 9 (Example 3.10)

	$\mathbf{c}'$		2	3	4	5	0	0	0	1
$\mathbf{c}_B$	Basic Variables		x_1	x_2	x_3	x_4	x_5	x_6	x_7	x_8
0	x_7	15	0	1	−2	3	−3	0	1	2*
0	x_6	4	0	1	−2	3	−1	1	0	0
2	x_1	10	1	−1	1	−1	−1	0	0	1
	$z_j - c_j$	20	0	−5	−2	−7	−2	0	0	1

In Tableau 9,

$$\boldsymbol{\beta}_8 = \mathbf{B}^{-1}\mathbf{a}_8 = [2, 0, 1]$$

and

$$z_8 - c_8 = 1$$

have already been found in evaluating the left-hand side of (3.105). In one simplex iteration we obtain Tableau 10, which is optimal.

Tableau 10 (Example 3.10)

	$\mathbf{c}'$		2	3	4	5	0	0	0	1
$\mathbf{c}_B$	Basic Variables		x_1	x_2	x_3	x_4	x_5	x_6	x_7	x_8
1	x_8	15/2	0	1/2	-1	3/2	$-3/2$	0	1/2	1
0	x_6	4	0	1	-2	3	-1	1	0	0
2	x_1	5/2	1	$-3/2$	2	$-5/2$	1/2	0	$-1/2$	0
	z_j-c_j	25/2	0	$-11/2$	-1	$-17/2$	$-1/2$	0	$-1/2$	0

(e) This is a parametric programming problem. Let

$$c_1^+ = 2+\psi,$$

where ψ is a variable parameter. From (3.103), reversed in direction, the optimality conditions for the case $\psi = 0$ are still satisfied if

$$z_j^+ - c_j^+ = z_j - c_j + [0,0,\psi]'\boldsymbol{\beta}_j - [\psi,0,0,0,0,0,0] \leqslant 0, \quad j = 1,\ldots,7,$$

i.e. if

$$[0,-5-\psi,-2+\psi,-7-\psi,-2-\psi,0,0] \leqslant 0.$$

Thus, for the original solution to remain optimal, we must have

$$-2 \leqslant \psi \leqslant 2.$$

If $\psi > 2$, then $z_3^+ - c_3^+ > 0$ and Tableau 1 becomes non-optimal. Proceeding by the simplex method, the variable x_3 becomes basic, and after constructing part of the new tableau we find that the new solution,

$$\mathbf{x}^* = [0,0,10,0]; \quad z^* = 40,$$

remains optimal for all values of ψ greater than 2. It is also clear from the new optimal tableau that there are alternative optima when $\psi = 2$.

If $\psi < -2$, then $z_5^+ - c_5^+ > 0$, and inspection of Tableau 1 shows that there is an unbounded solution with an unbounded value of z. When $\psi = -2$, then $z_5^+ - c_5^+ = 0$, and there is an unbounded solution with a finite value (zero) of z. It is obvious from geometrical considerations that when $\mathbf{c}$ is represented parametrically the borderline cases will yield alternative optima (including unbounded solutions with a finite value of z).

Exercises

1. Write down the dual of the following linear programming problem:

$$\text{Maximize } z = 7x_1 - 8x_2 + 9x_3 + 10x_4,$$

subject to

$$
\begin{aligned}
7x_1 + 2x_2 - 3x_3 - x_4 &\geqslant 5, \\
6x_1 - x_2 + x_4 &= 7, \\
8x_1 - 2x_2 + 5x_3 &\leqslant -5, \\
x_1, x_2, x_3, x_4 &\geqslant 0.
\end{aligned}
$$

2. Obtain the dual of the linear programming problem with bounded variables:

$$\text{Maximize } z = \mathbf{c}'\mathbf{x},$$

subject to

$$\mathbf{A}\mathbf{x} = \mathbf{b} \quad \text{and} \quad \mathbf{x}_l \leqslant \mathbf{x} \leqslant \mathbf{x}_u.$$

3. Prove that a necessary and sufficient condition for both the primal and dual problems to have optimal solutions is that both have feasible solutions.
Hint. Necessary—use the optimality conditions in conjunction with the relationships between the optimal primal and dual tableaux. Sufficient—by the theory of the simplex method, a feasible solution implies either an optimal solution or an unbounded solution, etc.

In the following four problems, use the complementary slackness principle to verify that the given solutions are optimal.

4. $$\text{Maximize } z = x_1 + 2x_2 + x_3,$$

subject to

$$
\begin{aligned}
x_1 &\leqslant 3, \\
x_2 &\leqslant 4, \\
x_1 + x_2 + x_3 &\leqslant 5, \\
x_1, x_2, x_3 &\geqslant 0. \\
\mathbf{x} &= [1, 4, 0].
\end{aligned}
$$

5. $$\text{Maximize } z = 5x_1 + 3x_2 + 2x_3 + 12x_4 - 5x_5,$$

subject to

$$
\begin{aligned}
x_1 + 2x_2 + x_3 + 3x_4 + 4x_5 &= 5, \\
2x_1 - 3x_2 + x_3 + 4x_4 - 5x_5 &= -3, \\
x_1, x_2, x_3, x_4, x_5 &\geqslant 0. \\
\mathbf{x} &= [9/7, 13/7, 0, 0, 0].
\end{aligned}
$$

6. $$\text{Maximize } z = 18x_1 + 12x_2 + 24x_3,$$

subject to

$$
\begin{aligned}
2x_1 + x_2 + 4x_3 &\leqslant 20, \\
3x_1 + 3x_2 + 3x_3 &\leqslant 25, \\
x_1, x_2, x_3 &\geqslant 0. \\
\mathbf{x} &= [20/3, 0, 5/3].
\end{aligned}
$$

7. Minimize $w = y_1 + y_2 + y_3$,

subject to

$$
\begin{aligned}
2y_1 + y_2 + y_3 &\geqslant 2,\\
6y_1 + y_2 &\geqslant 3,\\
y_1, y_2, y_3 &\geqslant 0.\\
\mathbf{y} &= [2/3, 2/3, 0].
\end{aligned}
$$

Solve the duals of the following three linear programming problems, and in each case construct the optimal primal tableau from the optimal dual tableau.

8. Maximize $z = -9x_1 - x_2 + x_3 - 3x_4$,

subject to

$$
\begin{aligned}
-3x_1 + 4x_3 - x_4 &\leqslant 3,\\
2x_1 + 5x_2 + x_3 + x_4 &\geqslant 1,\\
x_1 + x_2 - x_4 &\leqslant 2,\\
x_1, x_2, x_3, x_4 &\geqslant 0.
\end{aligned}
$$

9. Minimize $z = -x_1 + 10x_2 + 4x_3$,

subject to

$$
\begin{aligned}
x_1 + x_2 - x_3 &\geqslant 0,\\
-2x_1 + x_2 + 3x_3 &\geqslant 6,\\
3x_1 - x_2 + 6x_3 &\geqslant 10,\\
x_1, x_2, x_3 &\geqslant 0.
\end{aligned}
$$

10. Minimize $z = 2x_1 + 5x_2 - 3x_3$,

subject to

$$
\begin{aligned}
x_1 - 2x_2 + 3x_3 &\geqslant 4,\\
3x_1 + 7x_2 + x_3 &\geqslant 11,\\
-x_1 + x_2 + 3x_3 &\leqslant 2,\\
x_1, x_2, x_3 &\geqslant 0.
\end{aligned}
$$

11. Repeat Exercise 8 with the variable x_4 unrestricted in sign.

12. Solve, by any method, the dual of the following linear programming problem.

Minimize $w = -7y_1 - 2y_2 + 5y_3 + 4y_4$,

subject to

$$
\begin{aligned}
y_1 + y_2 + y_3 &\geqslant 1,\\
-2y_1 - 3y_2 + 4y_3 + y_4 &\geqslant 7,\\
-y_1 + 3y_3 + y_4 &\geqslant 9,\\
y_1 \text{ unrestricted in sign; } y_2, y_3, y_4 &\geqslant 0.
\end{aligned}
$$

13. Solve the dual of the following linear programming problem.

$$\text{Minimize } w = -y_1 + 7y_2 - 10y_3 + 3y_4,$$

subject to

$$\begin{aligned} -y_1 + y_2 - y_3 &\geqslant 3, \\ -y_1 + y_2 - 2y_3 + y_4 &\geqslant 2, \\ y_1, y_2, y_3, y_4 &\geqslant 0. \end{aligned}$$

14. Find the optimal value of the objective function for the following problem.

$$\text{Maximize } z = -3x_1 - x_2 + 6x_3,$$

subject to

$$\begin{aligned} 2x_1 - 13x_2 + 6x_3 &\leqslant 4, \\ x_1 + 2x_2 - x_3 &\geqslant -2, \\ 3x_1 + 9x_2 - 4x_3 &\leqslant -1, \\ x_1, x_2 \geqslant 0, \quad & x_3 \text{ unrestricted in sign.} \end{aligned}$$

Use the dual simplex method to solve Exercises 15, 16, and 17.

15. $$\text{Minimize } z = 3x_1 + 4x_2 + x_3,$$

subject to

$$\begin{aligned} x_1 + x_2 + x_3 &\leqslant 15, \\ 2x_1 - x_3 &\geqslant 5, \\ x_2 - x_3 &\geqslant 4, \\ 3x_1 - x_2 - x_3 &\geqslant 2, \\ x_1, x_2 \geqslant 0, \quad x_3 &\geqslant 3. \end{aligned}$$

16. $$\text{Minimize } z = 3x_1 + 2x_2 + x_3,$$

subject to

$$\begin{aligned} 6x_1 + x_2 - 5x_3 &\geqslant 5, \\ x_1 + x_2 + x_3 &\geqslant 6, \\ 2x_1 - 3x_2 + 4x_3 &\geqslant -2, \\ x_1, x_2, x_3 &\geqslant 0. \end{aligned}$$

17. $$\text{Maximize } z = -7x_1 - x_2 - 3x_3 - x_4,$$

subject to

$$\begin{aligned} 2x_1 - 3x_2 - x_3 + x_4 &\geqslant 8, \\ 6x_1 + x_2 + 2x_3 - 2x_4 &\geqslant 12, \\ -x_1 + x_2 + x_3 + x_4 &\geqslant 10, \\ x_1, x_2, x_3, x_4 &\geqslant 0. \end{aligned}$$

18. The additional constraints

$$\begin{aligned} x_1+5x_2+x_3+7x_4 &\leqslant 50, \\ 3x_1+2x_2-x_3-x_4 &\leqslant 20, \end{aligned}$$

are added to those of Exercise 17. Solve the new problem, starting with the optimal tableau for Exercise 17.

19. $$\text{Minimize } z = x_1+x_2+x_3,$$

subject to

$$\begin{aligned} x_1-3x_2+5x_3 &\geqslant 6, \\ 3x_1+2x_2-x_3 &\geqslant 0, \\ 2x_1-3x_2+4x_3 &\geqslant 12, \\ -2x_1+x_2-x_3 &\geqslant 4, \\ x_1,x_2,x_3 &\geqslant 0. \end{aligned}$$

20. Solve the following linear programming problem by (i) Charnes' M-method, (ii) the dual simplex method.

$$\text{Maximize } z = 2x_1+3x_2-4x_3,$$

subject to

$$\begin{aligned} x_1+x_2-x_3 &\geqslant 4, \\ -2x_1+3x_2+x_3 &\geqslant 3, \\ 3x_1-4x_2-x_3 &\geqslant 1, \\ -3x_1+9x_2 &\geqslant 10, \\ x_1,x_2,x_3 &\geqslant 0. \end{aligned}$$

21. Consider the problem of finding a balanced diet which must contain at least c_j units of nutrient j, $j = 1, \ldots, n$. The diet can be chosen from any number of foods i, $i = 1, \ldots, m$. The number of units of nutrient j in one unit of food i is p_{ji}. The cost of one unit of food i is b_i. It is required to produce the balanced diet at minimum cost.

Set up this problem as a linear programming problem. Write down the dual problem, and interpret the meaning of the dual variables, constraints, and objective function. Explain briefly why the objective functions for the primal and dual problems take equal values in an optimal solution.

22. Explain how to modify the row-sum check of Exercise 3, Chapter 2, so that it may be used with the revised simplex method.

Solve the following two problems and their dual problems by the revised simplex method.

23. Maximize $z = x_1 + x_2$,

subject to

$$8x_1 + 5x_2 \leqslant 20,$$
$$3x_1 + 4x_2 \leqslant 15,$$
$$x_1, x_2 \geqslant 0.$$

24. Minimize $z = 10x_1 - x_2 + 4x_3$,

subject to

$$x_1 + x_2 - x_3 \geqslant 3,$$
$$x_1 - 2x_2 + 3x_3 \geqslant 6,$$
$$-x_1 + 3x_2 + 6x_3 \geqslant 10,$$
$$x_1, x_2, x_3 \geqslant 0.$$

25. Starting with the optimal primal tableau for Exercise 8, find the effects on the optimal solution of

(a) a decrease of 3 in a_{23},
(b) an increase of 2 in b_2,
(c) an increase of 5 in c_2,
(d) the introduction of a new variable x_8 ($\geqslant 0$) into the problem, with $\mathbf{a}_8 = [8, 7, 6]$ and $c_8 = 10$.

26. Obtain $\mathbf{x}^*$ and z^* for the following problem.

Maximize $z = 7x_1 + 11x_2 + 4x_3 + x_4$,

subject to

$$2x_1 + 3x_2 + x_3 + 2x_4 \leqslant 5,$$
$$3x_1 + 5x_2 + 2x_3 + x_4 \leqslant 8,$$
$$x_1, x_2, x_3, x_4 \geqslant 0.$$

If $\mathbf{b}$ is changed from $[5, 8]$ to $[2, 5]$, find the new values of $\mathbf{x}^*$ and z^*.

27. Repeat Exercise 26 for the following problem.

Maximize $z = -10x_1 + 7x_2 + 4x_3$,

subject to

$$-7x_1 + 5x_2 + 3x_3 \leqslant 15,$$
$$-6x_1 + 6x_2 + 2x_3 \leqslant 6,$$
$$x_1, x_2, x_3 \geqslant 0,$$

where the change in $\mathbf{b}$ is from $[15, 6]$ to $[1, 2]$.

28. In Example 2.3, p. 37, suppose that the requirements vector $\mathbf{b}$ is changed from $[5, 9, 1, 6]$ to (a) $[6, 10, 2, 7]$, (b) $[6, 20, 2, 5]$. In each case, find the new optimal solution starting from the old optimal tableau, p. 40.

29. Starting with an optimal tableau for Example 3.6, p. 112 (e.g. Tableau 4, p. 114), find the effects of

(a) an increase of 4 in a_{21},
(b) a decrease of 8 in a_{21},
(c) a decrease of 2 in b_1,
(d) a decrease of 4 in b_1,
(e) an increase of 3 in c_4,
(f) the introduction of a new variable x_9 ($\geqslant 0$) into the problem, with $\mathbf{a}_9 = [2, 3, 7]$ and $c_9 = 3$,
(g) same as (f), except that $\mathbf{a}_9 = [0, -3, 6]$,
(h) same as (f), except that $\mathbf{a}_9 = [1, -1, 1]$.

30. In Example 1.1, p. 2 (also Example 2.2, p. 33), suppose that a_{12} is replaced by $a_{12} + \theta$, where $\theta > 0$. Determine the new optimal solutions, and deduce that they remain valid when $-7/4 < \theta \leqslant 0$.

31. In Example 3.6, p. 112, suppose that the requirements vector $\mathbf{b}$ is replaced by

$$\mathbf{b}^+ = \mathbf{b} + \phi\mathbf{r},$$

where ϕ is a scalar parameter and $\mathbf{r} = [1, 2, 4]$. Determine the new optimal solutions for all values of ϕ, including alternative optima.

32. The rules described in Section 3.7 for the application of the revised simplex method refer only to the maximizing problem. Making any necessary alterations to these rules, solve the problem of Exercise 24 directly as a minimizing problem.

4

Applications

4.1 The Transportation Problem

One of the earliest applications of linear programming was to the problem of making the most economic use of transport. The standard form of the problem, which became known as the *transportation problem*, was first given by Hitchcock [22] in 1941, following an earlier paper by Kantorovich [23] in 1939 which dealt with the machine assignment and other problems. An outstanding contribution to the early development of the transportation problem was made by Koopmans [26] with a paper on the optimum use of shipping. The transportation problem has many applications in economics and physics. We shall formulate the problem in terms of the classic example of factories and warehouses; more generally, we shall speak of origins and destinations between which goods have to be transported at minimum cost.

Consider, then, the problem of transporting goods from m factories to n warehouses. Measuring the quantities of goods in any convenient units, assume that

(i) a quantity $a_i > 0$ is available at factory i,

(ii) a quantity $b_j > 0$ is required at warehouse j,

(iii) $$\sum_{i=1}^{m} a_i = \sum_{j=1}^{n} b_j, \tag{4.1}$$

(iv) the cost of transportation of one unit of goods from factory i to warehouse j is c_{ij}.

It is required to find the transportation pattern that minimizes the total cost.

Assumption (iii) means that all the goods produced in the factories are required at the warehouses. This assumption involves no loss in generality, since an out-of-balance system can always be brought into balance by including either a fictitious factory or a fictitious warehouse (or both). Transportation costs associated with a fictitious factory or warehouse depend on the nature of the problem; for example, there may be penalties for under-production, or storage costs due to overproduction.

Let x_{ij} be the quantity transported from factory i to warehouse j. The transportation problem is then the linear programming problem of minimizing the function

$$z = \sum_{i=1}^{m} \sum_{j=1}^{n} c_{ij}x_{ij}, \tag{4.2}$$

subject to the equality constraints

$$\sum_{j=1}^{n} x_{ij} = a_i, \quad a_i > 0, \quad i = 1, \ldots, m, \tag{4.3}$$

$$\sum_{i=1}^{m} x_{ij} = b_j, \quad b_j > 0, \quad j = 1, \ldots, n, \tag{4.4}$$

and the non-negativity restrictions

$$x_{ij} \geqslant 0, \quad i = 1, \ldots, m, \quad j = 1, \ldots, n. \tag{4.5}$$

The constraints (4.3) and (4.4) imply equation (4.1), as required, since

$$\sum_{i=1}^{m} a_i = \sum_{i=1}^{m} \sum_{j=1}^{n} x_{ij} = \sum_{j=1}^{n} \sum_{i=1}^{m} x_{ij} = \sum_{j=1}^{n} b_j. \tag{4.6}$$

The transportation problem can, of course, be solved by the standard simplex method or one of its variants, as described in previous chapters. However, writing the constraints in the standard form

$$\mathbf{Ax} = \mathbf{b}, \tag{4.7}$$

we find that the matrix **A** has certain special properties which allow a more efficient algorithm to be developed. Our first aim, therefore, is to express the constraints (4.3), (4.4) in the form (4.7), and examine the matrix **A**. Let

$$\begin{aligned} \mathbf{x} &= [x_{11}, \ldots, x_{1n}, x_{21}, \ldots, x_{2n}, \; x_{31}, \ldots, x_{mn}], \\ \mathbf{b} &= [a_1, \ldots, a_m, b_1, \ldots, b_n]. \end{aligned}$$

It is useful to write out the constraints (4.3) and (4.4) in full, as in equations (4.8).

$$\begin{array}{llllllllll}
x_{11} + x_{12} + \ldots + x_{1n} & & & & & & & & & = a_1, \\
& & & x_{21} + x_{22} + \ldots + x_{2n} & & & & & & = a_2, \\
& & & & \cdot & & & & & \cdot \\
& & & & & \cdot & & & & \cdot \\
& & & & & & \cdot & & & \cdot \\
& & & & & & & x_{m1} + x_{m2} + \ldots + x_{mn} & & = a_m, \\
x_{11} & & & + x_{21} & & & \ldots + x_{m1} & & & = b_1, \\
& x_{12} & & & + x_{22} & & & \ldots + x_{m2} & & = b_2, \\
\cdot & & & & & & & & & \cdot \\
& \cdot & & & & & & & & \cdot \\
& & \cdot & & & & & & & \cdot \\
& x_{1n} & & & + x_{2n} & & & & \ldots + x_{mn} & = b_n.
\end{array} \tag{4.8}$$

Equations (4.8) show that every element in **A** is either 0 or 1. In partitioned form,

$$\mathbf{A} = \begin{pmatrix} \mathbf{e}' & \mathbf{0}' & \mathbf{0}' \ldots \mathbf{0}' \\ \mathbf{0}' & \mathbf{e}' & \mathbf{0}' \ldots \mathbf{0}' \\ \cdot & \cdot & \cdot \quad \cdot \\ \cdot & & \cdot \\ \cdot & & \cdot \quad \cdot \\ \mathbf{0}' & \mathbf{0}' & \ldots \mathbf{e}' \\ \mathbf{I}_n & \mathbf{I}_n & \ldots \mathbf{I}_n \end{pmatrix},$$

where $\mathbf{e}'$ is the row vector (1, 1, . . . , 1) with n components, and $\mathbf{I}_n$ is the unit matrix of order n. The matrix **A** is of order $(m+n) \times mn$.

The constraints (4.8) are not independent, since summing the first m constraints gives the same result as summing the last n constraints. Performing the equivalent operations on the rows of **A**, we deduce that the rank of **A** is less than $(m+n)$. In fact, the rank of **A** is exactly $(m+n-1)$, since a non-singular triangular matrix—with every element in its leading diagonal equal to unity—can be formed by deleting the last row of **A** and then selecting columns $n, 2n, \ldots, mn, 1, 2, \ldots, n-1$. In other words, one of the $(m+n)$ constraints is redundant, and its removal leaves $(m+n-1)$ independent constraints. A basic solution of equations (4.7) therefore contains at most $(m+n-1)$ non-zero x_{ij}. Because of the linear relationship between the rows of **A**, involving *every* row of **A**, it follows from the lemma on page 22 that *any* constraint may be regarded as redundant. However, it is convenient to retain all the constraints during the solution of the problem.

4.2 Solution of the Transportation Problem

We begin by proving that equation (4.1) is a sufficient condition for the constraints (4.3) and (4.4) to have a basic feasible solution. Suppose that equation (4.1) is satisfied; then a feasible solution can be constructed as follows, using the notation O_i for the ith factory (origin) and D_j for the jth warehouse (destination):

1. Transport $\min\{a_1, b_1\}$ from O_1 to D_1.

2a. If $a_1 > b_1$, transport $\min\{a_1 - b_1, b_2\}$ from O_1 to D_2.

2b. If $a_1 < b_1$, transport $\min\{a_2, b_1 - a_1\}$ from O_2 to D_1, etc.

At each step one of the origin constraints (4.3), or one of the destination constraints (4.4), is satisfied. At the last step two constraints are satisfied because of equation (4.1). Hence a feasible solution with not more than $(m+n-1)$ non-zero x_{ij} is obtained. This solution is basic, since the rank of **A** in equation (4.7) is $(m+n-1)$.

The above method of constructing a basic feasible solution suggests the *transportation tableau* as shown.

Transportation Tableau

	D_1	D_2		D_j		D_n	
O_1	c_{11} x_{11}	c_{12} x_{12}	...	c_{1j} x_{1j}	...	c_{1n} x_{1n}	u_1 a_1
O_2	c_{21} x_{21}	c_{22} x_{22}	...	c_{2j} x_{2j}	...	c_{2n} x_{2n}	u_2 a_2
	...	...	...	...	...	...	...
O_i	c_{i1} x_{i1}	c_{i2} x_{i2}	...	c_{ij} x_{ij}	...	c_{in} x_{in}	u_i a_i
	...	...	...	...	...	...	...
O_m	c_{m1} x_{m1}	c_{m2} x_{m2}	...	c_{mj} x_{mj}	...	c_{mn} x_{mn}	u_m a_m
	v_1 b_1	v_2 b_2	...	v_j b_j	...	v_n b_n	Σ

The first m rows represent the origin constraints (4.3), the first n columns represent the destination constraints (4.4), and the element in the bottom right-hand corner may be used to check equation (4.1) or may be omitted. The significance of the u_i and v_j in the marginal cells will appear later in this section—equation (4.11) *et seq.*

An initial basic feasible solution should be as close to the optimal solution as possible, in order to avoid an excessive number of subsequent iterations. Hence, although the method of taking the constraints in numerical order (as described in the opening paragraph of this section) will certainly provide an initial basic feasible solution, it is usually advantageous to choose the lowest-priced variable to be the first basic variable whose value is entered in the tableau. The tableau is then completed by entering values of basic variables whose prices are as low as possible, subject to the constraints. As the value of each basic variable is entered, either a row constraint or a column constraint is satisfied. Any row or column whose constraint is satisfied must be checked off, and no further entry made in it. If a row and column constraint are satisfied simultaneously, then either the row or the column is checked off, but not both—the one that is not checked off is completed by entering one or more zeros, following exactly the same rules as for any other entries. In this case the solution is degenerate, since fewer than $(m+n-1)$ of the basic variables take non-zero values. Thus for every entry that is made in the tableau, except the final one, either a row or a column is checked off. The final entry in the tableau causes the last remaining row and column constraints to be satisfied simultaneously.

Example 4.1

Find an initial basic feasible solution of the transportation problem given by the following tableau.

Tableau 0 (Example 4.1)

	D_1	D_2	D_3	D_4	D_5	
O_1	3	1	1	2	6	20
O_2	4	5	3	2	1	30
O_3	1	4	2	5	4	40
	10	15	25	5	35	90

Solution

A possible solution is

Tableau 1 (Example 4.1)

	√	√	√	√	√	
√	3	1 15	1 5	2	6	20
√	4	5	3	2 5	1 25	30
√	1 10	4	2 20	5	4 10	40
	10	15	25	5	35	90

The values of the variables were inserted in Tableau 1 in the following order:

$x_{12} = 15$, col. 2 checked off

$x_{13} = 5$, row 1 checked off

$x_{33} = 20$, col. 3 checked off

$x_{31} = 10$, col. 1 checked off

$x_{35} = 10$, row 3 checked off

$x_{25} = 25$, col. 5 checked off

$x_{24} = 5$, row 2 and col. 4 checked off

The variables with non-zero values give a basic feasible solution of the given problem. Empty cells in the tableau correspond to non-basic variables. It is advisable to check that there are exactly $(m+n-1)$ basic entries in the tableau; in the present example, $m = 3$, $n = 5$. The value of the objective function is

$$z = 1(15)+1(5)+2(5)+1(25)+1(10)+2(20)+4(10) = 145.$$

Having obtained an initial basic feasible solution, the next step is to test it for optimality, and improve the objective function, if necessary. The method we are about to describe for the solution of the transportation problem is known as the '*uv*-method'. Consider first the dual of the given transportation problem.

Let $U_i, i = 1, \ldots, m$; $V_j, j = 1, \ldots, n$, be the dual variables corresponding to the primal constraints (4.3), (4.4), respectively. Then, as is easily seen from equations (4.8) and Section 3.1, the dual constraints are

$$U_i + V_j \leqslant c_{ij}, \quad i = 1, \ldots, m, \quad j = 1, \ldots, n, \tag{4.9}$$

where all the U_i and V_j are unrestricted in sign, because all the primal constraints are equations. We are interested in finding the values of $z_{ij} - c_{ij}$ for the current primal solution. The required formula, (4.14), is intimately related to the result of the following theorem.

■ Theorem 4.1

For *optimal* solutions of the transportation problem (4.2)–(4.5) and its dual, with the dual constraints given by (4.9),

$$z_{ij} - c_{ij} = U_i + V_j - c_{ij}, \quad i = 1, \ldots, m, \quad j = 1, \ldots, n. \tag{4.10}$$

Proof

The *primal* problem is now the minimizing problem, and contains only equality constraints. Thus every primal variable is a main variable, while every main dual variable is unrestricted in sign. Making the necessary changes in notation in

Tables 3.2 and 3.3, we find that the value of $z_{ij} - c_{ij} (\leqslant 0)$ is equal to minus the value of the slack dual variable that is complementary to the main primal variable x_{ij}. But from (4.9) and the complementary slackness principle, the value of this slack dual variable is $-(U_i + V_j - c_{ij})$. This proves equations (4.10).

We now multiply the ith constraint of (4.3) by u_i, and the jth constraint of (4.4) by v_j, where the multipliers u_i and v_j are unrestricted in sign. Adding the results for all i and j, and then subtracting equation (4.2), we obtain

$$\sum_{i=1}^{m} \sum_{j=1}^{n} (u_i + v_j - c_{ij}) x_{ij} = z_1 - z, \tag{4.11}$$

where

$$z_1 = \sum_{i=1}^{m} a_i u_i + \sum_{j=1}^{n} b_j v_j.$$

We choose the u_i and v_j in equation (4.11) such that

$$u_i + v_j = c_{ij}, \quad x_{ij} \text{ basic.} \tag{4.12}$$

Equations (4.12) are $(m+n-1)$ equations for the $(m+n)$ unknowns u_i, $i = 1, \ldots, m$, and $v_j, j = 1, \ldots, n$. The solution is not unique, and so one of the unknowns is given an arbitrary value; it is then a simple matter to solve equations (4.12) sequentially, because of the following theorem and its consequences.

■ **Theorem 4.2**

Every basis matrix for the transportation problem is triangular.

Proof

Each row and column of an $m \times n$ transportation tableau represents a constraint, and there are $(m+n-1)$ basic variables. Since $a_i > 0$ and $b_j > 0$ for all i and j, each row and column of the tableau contains at least one basic entry. We have to prove that (i) at least one row or column of the tableau contains only one basic entry; (ii) if this row or column is deleted, the resulting tableau has the same property.

Suppose that every row and column of the tableau contains two or more basic entries. Assume $n > m$. Then, counting the basic entries column by column, we must have

$$2n \leqslant m + n - 1,$$

i.e.

$$n \leqslant m - 1,$$

which contradicts $n > m$. A similar contradiction arises if we assume $n < m$. Hence (i) is proved. If the row or column containing only one basic entry is deleted, then the above argument may be repeated with m or n reduced by unity. This proves (ii).

The matrix of coefficients on the left-hand side of equations (4.12) is the transpose of the primal basis matrix, since it may be obtained by transposing the matrix of coefficients of basic x_{ij} on the left-hand side of equations (4.8). Since the transpose of a triangular matrix is itself triangular, it follows that equations (4.12) are triangular, and may therefore be solved sequentially as stated above.

The optimality conditions for the transportation problem are

$$z_{ij}-c_{ij} \leqslant 0, \quad i=1,\ldots,m, \quad j=1,\ldots,n. \tag{4.13}$$

Consider equation (4.11). If $u_i+v_j-c_{ij} \leqslant 0$ for all i and j, then the greatest value of z_1-z for any feasible solution $\mathbf{x}$ is zero, i.e.

$$\min z = z_1.$$

In particular, for the basic feasible solution for which equations (4.12) are satisfied,

$$z = z_1,$$

and therefore this basic feasible solution is optimal. Hence, provided that equations (4.12) are satisfied, the optimality conditions for the transportation problem are

$$u_i+v_j-c_{ij} \leqslant 0, \quad i=1,\ldots,m, \qquad j=1,\ldots,n.$$

Since these conditions must be identical with the optimality conditions (4.13), it follows that

$$z_{ij}-c_{ij} = k_{ij}(u_i+v_j-c_{ij}), \quad k_{ij}>0, \quad x_{ij} \text{ non-basic.}$$

But z_{ij}, by definition, and u_i+v_j are independent of the price c_{ij} of the *non-basic* variable x_{ij}. Therefore $k_{ij}=1$ for all i and j for which x_{ij} is non-basic, and

$$z_{ij}-c_{ij} = u_i+v_j-c_{ij}, \quad i=1,\ldots,m, \quad j=1,\ldots,n, \tag{4.14}$$

each side vanishing when x_{ij} is basic.

It is important to notice that the u_i and v_j in equations (4.14) are inadmissible as dual variables, except when the solution is optimal. [The change in notation between equations (4.10) and (4.14) emphasizes this point.] For the u_i and v_j satisfy *all* the dual constraints (4.9) only when *all* the primal optimality conditions

$$z_{ij}-c_{ij} \leqslant 0, \quad i=1,\ldots,m, \quad j=1,\ldots,n,$$

are satisfied.

Knowing the u_i and v_j from equations (4.12), the $z_{ij}-c_{ij}$ for *non-basic* x_{ij} (the unoccupied cells) are determined from equations (4.14), and the variable to become basic at the next iteration is x_{kl}, where, following the usual simplex rule for a minimizing problem,

$$z_{kl}-c_{kl} = \max_{\text{all } i,j} \{z_{ij}-c_{ij}: z_{ij}-c_{ij}>0\}.$$

When $z_{ij}-c_{ij} \leqslant 0$ for all i and j, the optimal solution has been reached.

The evaluation of the u_i, v_j and $z_{ij}-c_{ij}$, and the determination of new values for the basic variables, are carried out entirely in the transportation tableau. Example 4.2 illustrates the procedure in detail.

Example 4.2

Tableau 0 shows the output of three factories, the requirements of five warehouses, and the transportation costs between the factories and warehouses. Find the transportation schedule (or schedules) that minimize the total cost.

Tableau 0 (Example 4.2)

Factories ↓ / Warehouses →	1	2	3	4	5	Output
1	1	2	2	2	4	60
2	2	4	2	3	3	45
3	3	4	4	5	3	40
Requirements	15	30	25	50	25	145

Solution

Tableau 1 (Example 4.2)

	√	√	√	√	√	
√	1 15	2 30	2 15	2 1	4	0 60
√	2	4	2 10	3 35	3	0 45
√	3	4	4	5 15	3 25	2 40
	1 15	2 30	2 25	3 50	1 25	145

The initial basic feasible solution is found as in Example 4.1. As soon as they are known, the values of the u_i and v_j are written in the top left-hand corners of the marginal cells, as indicated on page 148. One of the u_i or v_j is arbitrary, and is conveniently taken to be zero. Usually it is chosen such that its row or column contains the greatest number of basic entries. The evaluation of the u_i and v_j therefore proceeds as follows.

Choose $u_1 = 0$ arbitrarily. Use equations (4.12) on the occupied cells, to give in turn

$$\begin{aligned} v_1 &= c_{11} - u_1 = 1 - 0 = 1, \\ v_2 &= c_{12} - u_1 = 2 - 0 = 2, \\ v_3 &= c_{13} - u_1 = 2 - 0 = 2. \end{aligned}$$

It is now clear that v_1, v_2 and v_3 are merely copied from c_{11}, c_{12} and c_{13}, respectively, showing the convenience of the choice of $u_1 = 0$. Next,

$$\begin{aligned} u_2 &= c_{23} - v_3 = 2 - 2 = 0, \\ v_4 &= c_{24} = 3, \text{ since } u_2 = 0, \\ u_3 &= c_{34} - v_4 = 5 - 3 = 2, \\ v_5 &= c_{35} - u_3 = 3 - 2 = 1. \end{aligned}$$

The order in which the u_i and v_j are determined is immaterial.

Equations (4.14) are now used to determine the $z_{ij} - c_{ij}$ for the non-basic variables (unoccupied cells). The values of the $z_{ij} - c_{ij}$ are written in the top right-hand corners of the empty cells; however, it is only necessary to record the greatest *positive* value of $z_{ij} - c_{ij}$ so far found, since we are trying to find the greatest positive $z_{ij} - c_{ij}$ in the tableau. (Zero values of $z_{ij} - c_{ij}$ are required only when searching for alternative optima in an optimal tableau.) Following this procedure, we find

$$\begin{aligned} z_{14} - c_{14} &= 0 + 3 - 2 = 1, & z_{25} - c_{25} &= 0 + 1 - 3 = -2, \\ z_{15} - c_{15} &= 0 + 1 - 4 = -3, & z_{31} - c_{31} &= 2 + 1 - 3 = 0, \\ z_{21} - c_{21} &= 0 + 1 - 2 = -1, & z_{32} - c_{32} &= 2 + 2 - 4 = 0. \\ z_{22} - c_{22} &= 0 + 2 - 4 = -2, & z_{33} - c_{33} &= 2 + 2 - 4 = 0. \end{aligned}$$

Tableau 1 is not optimal, since $z_{14} - c_{14} = 1 > 0$. Following the usual simplex rules, this means that the variable x_{14} must become basic. Suppose that x_{14} is increased from zero to θ. The numerical procedures for adjusting the values of the other variables are normally carried out in the old tableau; for the sake of clarity we redraw Tableau 1 and call it Tableau 1a.

The row and column requirements must still be satisfied in Tableau 1a. This leads to the following unique set of adjustments:

To balance row 1, take $x_{13} = 15 - \theta$.
To balance col. 3, take $x_{23} = 10 + \theta$.
To balance row 2, take $x_{24} = 35 - \theta$.

Then column 4 is also balanced. That the θ-adjustments (half positive, half negative) can always be made uniquely follows from the triangular property of

Tableau 1a (Example 4.2)

1 15	2 30	2 $15-\theta$	2 1 θ	4	0 60
2	4	2 $10+\theta$	3 $35-\theta$	3	0 45
3	4	4	5 15	3 25	2 40
1 15	2 30	2 25	3 50	1 25	145

the primal basis matrix (Theorem 4.2). For if a non-basic variable is given the value θ, it is always possible to solve the set of triangular constraint equations sequentially and uniquely for the new values of the basic variables, since a basis matrix is non-singular by definition; but the process of searching through the triangular equations for an equation containing only one undetermined basic variable is equivalent to the process of making θ-adjustments in the tableau.

Returning to Tableau 1a, the greatest possible value of θ is 15, since every x_{ij} must be non-negative. We take θ to be exactly 15; then the variable x_{13} becomes non-basic, and we can enter the new values of the basic variables in Tableau 2, thus completing the first iteration. (The θ's in Tableau 2 have not yet been entered.)

Tableau 2 (Example 4.2)

1 $15-\theta$	2 30	2	2 $15+\theta$	4	0 60
2	4	2 25	3 20	3	1 45
3 1 θ	4 1	4	5 $15-\theta$	3 25	3 40
1 15	2 30	1 25	2 50	0 25	145

In Tableau 2, after calculating new values of the u_i and v_j, starting with $u_1 = 0$, we find

$$z_{31} - c_{31} = z_{32} - c_{32} = 1,$$

and choose x_{31} as the variable to become basic, since it has the lower price. Carrying out the θ-adjustments, we obtain $\theta = 15$, and *two* variables, x_{11} and x_{34}, take the value zero. Since only one variable can become non-basic, the other must remain basic with the value zero: the new basic solution is degenerate. We choose x_{11} arbitrarily to be the degenerate variable, thus obtaining Tableau 3.

Tableau 3 (Example 4.2)

1 $0-\theta$	2 30	2	2 $30+\theta$	4	0 60
2 0 θ	4	2 25	3 $20-\theta$	3	1 45
3 15	4 0	4	5	3 25	2 40
1 15	2 30	1 25	2 50	1 25	145

In Tableau 3, $z_{ij} - c_{ij} \leqslant 0$ for all i and j; hence the solution is optimal. But since

$$z_{21} - c_{21} = z_{32} - c_{32} = 0,$$

there are alternative optima. These are obtained, following the usual simplex rules, by bringing into the basic set, in turn, the variables for which $z_{ij} - c_{ij} = 0$, and repeating this procedure systematically with all the new tableaux until every alternative optimal basic solution has been found. It is useful to note that, during the calculations for alternative optima, the values of all the $z_{ij} - c_{ij}$ remain unchanged; this means that there is no need to recalculate the values of the u_i and v_j in subsequent tableaux. First we make x_{21} basic, which leads to $\theta = 0$, and x_{11} becomes non-basic, giving Tableau 4.

The solution given by Tableau 4 is numerically the same as that given by Tableau 3. Next, making x_{32} basic in Tableau 3, we obtain Tableau 5.
No further alternative optimum can be derived from Tableau 3, and so we turn to Tableau 4. In Tableau 4, we have

$$z_{11} - c_{11} = z_{32} - c_{32} = 0.$$

Tableau 4 (Example 4.2)

1 0	2 $30-\theta$	2	2 $30+\theta$	4	0 60
2 $0+\theta$	4	2 25	3 $20-\theta$	3	1 45
3 $15-\theta$	4 0 θ	4	5	3 25	2 40
1 15	2 30	1 25	2 50	1 25	145

Tableau 5 (Example 4.2)

1 15	2 15	2	2 30	4	0 60
2 0	4	2 25	3 20	3	1 45
3 0	4 15	4	5	3 25	2 40
1 15	2 30	1 25	2 50	1 25	145

Making x_{11} basic would merely reproduce Tableau 3, but making x_{32} basic leads to Tableau 6.

In Tableau 5 we have

$$z_{21}-c_{21} = z_{31}-c_{31} = 0.$$

Making x_{21} basic would reproduce Tableau 6, and making x_{31} basic would reproduce Tableau 3.

In Tableau 6 we have

$$z_{11}-c_{11} = z_{31}-c_{31} = 0.$$

Making x_{11} basic would reproduce Tableau 5, and making x_{31} basic would reproduce Tableau 3 or 4, as is easily seen by performing the θ-adjustments.

We conclude that there is no other alternative optimum. Hence the optimal transportation schedules are given by Tableaux 3, 4, 5 and 6 (ignoring the θ's),

Tableau 6 (Example 4.2)

1 0	2 15	2	2 45	4	0 60
2 15	4	2 25	3 5	3	1 45
3 0	4 15	4	5	3 25	2 40
1 15	2 30	1 25	2 50	1 25	145

Tableaux 3 and 4 being numerically identical. The total cost of transportation is 350 units.

The *uv*-method is, of course, a simplified version of the standard simplex method of Chapter 2, and has the remarkable feature that the only calculations required are additions and subtractions. This makes possible the solution of quite large problems by hand, although the pattern of θ-adjustments becomes harder to find as the size of the tableau increases. Extremely large transportation problems have been solved on computers: problems with 200 constraints and over 1 000 variables were already being solved in 1956, using a program written by Orchard-Hays [32] for an IBM 704. At about the same time, Munkres [30] published an algorithm for the systematic solution of large-scale transportation problems. Early successes with these large-scale problems helped to popularize linear programming.

4.3 The Assignment Problem

Suppose that each of n men is to be assigned to one of n jobs, and that it is possible to determine a number r_{ij} which measures the efficiency rating (or productivity, or other desirable characteristic) of the ith man on the jth job. The assignment problem is the problem of assigning the men to the jobs in such a way that the sum of the ratings

$$z = \sum_{i=1}^{n} \sum_{j=1}^{n} r_{ij}$$

is a maximum. Let $\mathbf{R}$ be the $n \times n$ *rating matrix* $\{r_{ij}\}$. Then the problem is to find n

elements of **R**, one and only one in each row and column, such that the sum of these elements is a maximum.

Theorem 4:3

Every assignment problem is equivalent to some transportation problem, and conversely.

Proof

Let $x_{ij} = 1$ if the ith man is assigned to the jth job,
$= 0$ otherwise.
Also, let $c_{ij} = -r_{ij}$. The assignment problem is then the problem of minimizing the function

$$
\left.\begin{aligned}
z &= \sum_{i=1}^{n} \sum_{j=1}^{n} c_{ij} x_{ij}, \\
&\text{subject to the equality constraints} \\
&\sum_{j=1}^{n} x_{ij} = 1, \quad i = 1, \ldots, n, \\
&\sum_{i=1}^{n} x_{ij} = 1, \quad j = 1, \ldots, n, \\
&\text{and the conditions} \\
&x_{ij} = 1 \text{ or } 0, \quad \text{all } i, j.
\end{aligned}\right\} \tag{4.15}
$$

Problem (4.15) is in the form of the transportation problem defined by (4.2)–(4.5), except that the non-negativity restrictions $x_{ij} \geqslant 0$ in the transportation problem are replaced by $x_{ij} = 1$ or 0. Therefore, in order to prove the first part of the theorem we have to show that if, in problem (4.15), the conditions

$$x_{ij} = 1 \text{ or } 0, \quad \text{all } i, j,$$

are replaced by

$$x_{ij} \geqslant 0, \quad \text{all } i, j,$$

then the optimal solution is unchanged.

Consider any transportation problem with row and column sums a_i, b_j, respectively, where i and j run through suitable values. It is clear from the way in which the transportation tableau is constructed (Section 4.2) that the values of the basic variables are given by

$$[x_{ij}]_{\text{basic}} = \pm \sum_{\substack{\text{some}\\ r}} a_r \mp \sum_{\substack{\text{some}\\ s}} b_s, \tag{4.16}$$

where the upper signs apply to some basic variables and the lower signs to the others. In particular, if the row and column sums are integers, then so are the values of the basic variables. Hence for problem (4.15), since every row and column sum is unity, the only possible value for any x_{ij} is 1 or 0, and the first part of the theorem is proved.

To prove the converse, consider a transportation problem with row sums a_i, $i = 1, \ldots, m$, and column sums $b_j, j = 1, \ldots, n$. There is no loss in generality in assuming that the a_i and b_j are integers, since irrational numbers can be approximated to any desired accuracy by rational numbers, and constraints containing rational fractions can be multiplied throughout by a suitable factor. The given transportation constraints can be changed into equivalent assignment-type constraints by replacing each row constraint

$$\sum_{j=1}^{n} x_{ij} = a_i$$

by the a_i constraints

$$\sum_{j=1}^{n} x_{ij}' = 1, \quad \sum_{j=1}^{n} x_{ij}'' = 1, \ldots, \quad \sum_{j=1}^{n} x_{ij}^{(a_i)} = 1,$$

where the new variables $x_{ij}', \ldots, x_{ij}^{(a_i)}$ satisfy

$$x_{ij}' + \ldots + x_{ij}^{(a_i)} = x_{ij},$$

and their prices are given by

$$c_{ij}' = \ldots = c_{ij}^{(a_i)} = c_{ij},$$

and then applying exactly the same procedure to the column constraints. Also, it has already been proved that the conditions $x_{ij} \geqslant 0$ and $x_{ij} = 1$ or 0 are equivalent when the row and column sums are each unity. Hence any transportation problem can be formulated as an assignment problem.

Theorem 4.3 shows that every assignment problem can be solved by turning it into an equivalent transportation problem. In the next section, however, we shall find a more efficient method of solving the assignment problem. Meanwhile, it is interesting to investigate further the consequences of equations (4.16).

Suppose that we try to generalize the assignment problem by allowing x_{ij} to represent the *fraction* of his time that the ith man spends on the jth job. Then the condition that the jth job will be completed is

$$\sum_{i=1}^{n} x_{ij} = 1, \quad j = 1, \ldots, n. \tag{4.17}$$

and the condition that the ith man is fully employed is

$$\sum_{j=1}^{n} x_{ij} = 1, \quad i = 1, \ldots, n. \tag{4.18}$$

The quantity to be maximized is now the weighted sum of the ratings:

$$z = \sum_{i=1}^{n} \sum_{j=1}^{n} x_{ij} r_{ij}. \tag{4.19}$$

Equations (4.17)–(4.19) represent a transportation problem with $a_i = b_j = 1$ for all i, j. Also, $0 \leqslant x_{ij} \leqslant 1$ for all i, j. But equation (4.16) shows that every basic variable x_{ij} must take an integral value. Hence $[x_{ij}]_{\text{basic}} = 1$ or 0, and any optimal basic solution assigns one man full-time to one job.

This result has a remarkable application to the marriage problem—how to achieve maximum overall happiness for n men and n women if the ith man rates the jth woman $r_{ij}{}^M$, and the ith woman rates the jth man $r_{ij}{}^W$. Define

$$r_{ij} = \tfrac{1}{2}(r_{ij}{}^M + r_{ji}{}^W),$$

and let x_{ij} denote the fraction of his time that the ith man spends with the jth woman. Then any basic variable x_{ij} takes the value 1 or 0, i.e. monogamy maximizes overall happiness. Unfortunately, the same argument applies when the sign of every r_{ij} is reversed, so it is also true that monogamy minimizes overall happiness. The pairings for these two extreme solutions will, of course, be different! It should be pointed out that this result depends on the assumption of a linear happiness function—an assumption which may be very far from the truth. If the happiness of the couples is assumed to vary with time, then the problem is nonlinear and has a different solution.

4.4 Solution of the Assignment Problem

The 'Hungarian method' [27], [28] for the solution of the assignment problem is based on the work of two Hungarian mathematicians, D. König and J. Egerváry, and particularly on a theorem due to König.† A proof of this theorem using graph theory has been given by Kuhn [28]. König's theorem is now stated without proof. Three preliminary definitions are required.

Definition 1. A *line* is a row or column of a matrix.

Definition 2. A set of elements in a matrix is *independent* if no two of the elements lie in the same line.

Definition 3. If the letter c is written on the right of a row or at the foot of a column, then the corresponding row or column (line) is said to be *covered.* An element in a covered line is said to be covered, and may be covered twice.

† A method of solving the assignment problem which does not depend on König's theorem has been devised by C. Mack. 'The Bradford method for the assignment problem', in *The New Journal of Statistics and Operational Research*, **1**, part I, 17–29, published by C. Mack, University of Bradford, 1969.

■ **Theorem 4.4** König's theorem

Let **A** be a square matrix. Then the maximum number of independent zeros of **A** is equal to the minimum number of lines required to cover all the zeros of **A**.

As an example of König's theorem, consider the following matrix.

$$\mathbf{A} = \begin{array}{c} \left(\begin{array}{ccccc} 8 & 0* & 0 & 2 & 0 \\ 2 & 0 & 5 & 0* & 6 \\ 1 & 1 & 0* & 1 & 4 \\ 3 & 2 & 0 & 2 & 1 \\ 0* & 0 & 4 & 7 & 0 \end{array}\right) \begin{array}{c} \mathrm{c} \\ \mathrm{c} \\ \\ \\ \mathrm{c} \end{array} \\ \begin{array}{ccccc} & & \mathrm{c} & & \end{array} \end{array}$$

The maximum number of independent zeros of **A** is 4; one such set is marked by asterisks. The minimum number of lines required to cover all the zeros of **A** is also 4, by König's theorem.

We shall now describe the Hungarian method for the solution of the assignment problem. Given an $n \times n$ rating matrix **R**, the problem is to find n independent elements of **R** whose sum is a maximum. Let

$$r = \max_{ij} \{r_{ij}\},$$

and define a new matrix

$$\mathbf{S} = \{s_{ij}: s_{ij} = r - r_{ij}\}, \tag{4.20}$$

i.e. the elements of **S** are formed from the elements of **R** by subtracting each element of **R** from its largest element. The problem is then to find n independent elements of the $n \times n$ matrix **S** whose sum is a minimum. It is obvious, but nevertheless important, that the problem is unaltered by subtracting an arbitrary number u_i from each element of the ith row of **S**, or an arbitrary number v_j from each element of the jth column of **S**. Hence the matrix **S** is manipulated in the following way, the object being to reduce it to a standard form to which König's theorem may be applied.

Step 1. Subtract the smallest element in each row of **S** from every element in that row, giving $\mathbf{S}_1$.

Step 2. Subtract the smallest element in each column of $\mathbf{S}_1$ from every element in that column, giving **A**. Then **A** contains at least one zero in every row and column, and is said to be in *standard form.*

Step 3. Find k_m, the maximum number of independent zeros of **A**. By König's theorem, k_m is also the minimum number of lines required to cover all the zeros of **A**.

If $k_m = n$, then there are n independent zeros in **A**, and the elements in corresponding positions in **R** provide a solution of the given assignment problem.

Step 4. If $k_m < n$, let **N** denote the matrix of non-covered elements of **A**, and let $h(> 0)$ be the smallest element in **N**. Add h to each twice-covered element of **A**, and subtract h from each non-covered element of **A**.

This step leaves every element of **A** non-negative, but *decreases* the sum of all the elements in **A** by

$$nh(n - k_m),$$

for it effectively adds h to each of the n elements in the covered lines of **A** (increasing the sum of the elements by nhk_m), and then subtracts h from every element of the resulting matrix (decreasing the sum of the elements by n^2h). Suppose that **A** becomes **A*** as a result of this step. Repeat Step 3 using **A*** instead of **A**. If $k_m = n$, then the problem is solved. If $k_m < n$, derive **A**** from **A*** just as **A*** was derived from **A**. Continue in this way until $k_m = n$. The process must terminate in a finite number of steps, because of the reduction at each step of the sum of the elements in the matrices **A**, **A***, ...

Example 4.3

The percentage efficiency ratings of 4 men for 4 jobs are given by the matrix

$$\mathbf{R} = \begin{array}{c} \text{Jobs} \\ \begin{array}{cccc} 1 & 2 & 3 & 4 \end{array} \\ \begin{pmatrix} 15 & 30 & 72 & 18 \\ 58 & 82 & 90 & 65 \\ 45 & 35 & 95 & 45 \\ 80 & 45 & 35 & 57 \end{pmatrix} \end{array} \begin{array}{c} 1 \\ 2 \\ 3 \\ 4 \end{array} \text{ Men}$$

How should the men be assigned to the jobs so that overall efficiency is maximized?

Solution

Subtract each element of **R** from the largest element (95) to give

$$\mathbf{S} = \begin{pmatrix} 80 & 65 & 23 & 77 \\ 37 & 13 & 5 & 30 \\ 50 & 60 & 0 & 50 \\ 15 & 50 & 60 & 38 \end{pmatrix}.$$

Step 1

$$\mathbf{S}_1 = \begin{pmatrix} 57 & 42 & 0 & 54 \\ 32 & 8 & 0 & 25 \\ 50 & 60 & 0 & 50 \\ 0 & 35 & 45 & 23 \end{pmatrix}.$$

Step 2.

$$\mathbf{A} = \begin{pmatrix} 57 & 34 & 0^* & 31 \\ 32 & 0^* & 0 & 2 \\ 50 & 52 & 0 & 27 \\ 0 & 27 & 45 & 0^* \end{pmatrix} \begin{matrix} \\ c \\ \\ c \end{matrix} .$$
$$\qquad\qquad c$$

Step 3. The maximum number of independent zeros in **A** is $k_m = 3$. One such maximal set is indicated by asterisks. All the zeros (whether 0's or 0*'s) can be covered by the three lines marked c.

Step 4. Since $k_m < 4$, we form the matrix of non-covered elements of **A**:

$$\mathbf{N} = \begin{pmatrix} 57 & 34 & 31 \\ 50 & 52 & 27 \end{pmatrix},$$

whence $h = 27$. Then

$$\mathbf{A}^* = \begin{pmatrix} 30 & 7 & 0^* & 4 \\ 32 & 0^* & 27 & 2 \\ 23 & 25 & 0 & 0^* \\ 0^* & 27 & 72 & 0 \end{pmatrix},$$

which contains a set of 4 independent zeros, as shown. Hence the problem is solved by referring back to the corresponding positions in **R**, giving $(r_{13}, r_{22}, r_{34}, r_{41})$ as the optimal assignment.

When the order of the matrix **A** is small, as in Example 4.3, the maximum number k_m of independent zeros in **A**, **A***, . . . is found (Step 3) by inspection. For larger problems a systematic method for finding these zeros is required. Several such methods have been proposed [13], [21], [27], [28], [30]; the one described here is based on Kuhn's own modification [28] of his original Hungarian method [27].

The initial data are the matrix **A** (in standard form), and a subset of the independent zeros of **A**, marked by asterisks; thus no two asterisks are in the same row or column. Suppose that there are k zeros in this initial subset. If $k = n$, then the problem is solved. If $k < n$, then a single application of the routine (given below) for the determination of k_m must end in one of two mutually exclusive situations, which we shall call Alternative 1 and Alternative 2. These two situations, and the procedures to be followed when they arise, are:

Alternative 1. A new set of $(k + 1)$ zeros marked by asterisks, with no two asterisks in the same row or column. The routine (for the determination of k_m) is repeated until either $k = n$ and the problem is solved, or Alternative 2 is reached.

Alternative 2. A set of $k(<n)$ lines which contain all the zeros of **A**. In this case, $k = k_m$. The matrix **A** is replaced by **A*** as described in Step 4 above, and the routine is repeated.

These procedures must eventually lead to $k = n$ and the solution of the problem.

Routine for the Determination of k_m

Search each column of **A** in turn for a 0*, continuing until a column that does not contain a 0* is found. (If every column contains a 0*, then $k = n$ and the problem is solved.) The column which has been found to contain no 0* is called *pivotal*, and is searched for all its 0's.

The rows in which these 0's appear are searched in turn for 0*'s , until a row containing no 0* is found. The 0 in this row and in the pivotal column is marked with an asterisk—Alternative 1.

If each 0 in the pivotal column has a 0* in its row, then these row numbers are listed in any order: $i_1, i_2, \ldots, i_t$. Further terms are added to this sequence of row numbers in the following way. Consider the 0* in row i_1, and all the 0's in its column; add to the sequence, in any order, the row numbers of these 0's, except those row numbers that already appear in the sequence (in order to avoid duplication). Now consider the 0*'s in rows $i_2, \ldots, i_t$, in turn, and add further terms to the sequence in the same way. Continue this procedure with the terms of the sequence that come *after* i_t. There are two possibilities: either a row i_s is reached which does not contain a 0*, or every row whose number comes after i_t in the sequence contains a 0*.

In the former case, a *transfer* (of an asterisk) is carried out as follows. The row number i_s was added to the sequence because row i_s contained a 0 in the column of a 0* belonging to row i_r. (We shall say that i_s was *generated in the sequence* by i_r.) This asterisk in row i_r is transferred to the 0 in row i_s (and therefore stays in the same column). Following this transfer, there is no 0* in row i_r, and i_r precedes i_s in the sequence. If i_r does not belong to the initial sequence of row numbers $i_1, \ldots, i_t$, then further transfers are carried out until an asterisk is removed from one of these initial rows. Then the 0 in this row and in the pivotal column can be marked by an asterisk—Alternative 1.

In the latter case, suppose that v rows are represented in the sequence; each of these v rows contains a 0*. The v columns containing these 0*'s, together with the pivotal column, contain 0's (with or without asterisks) only in the v rows represented in the sequence. Thus these v rows contain all the 0's and 0*'s that appear in $(v+1)$ columns. It follows that these v rows and the remaining $(n-v-1)$ columns are $(n-1)$ lines which contain all the zeros of **A**—Alternative 2.

Example 4.4

Find the maximum number of independent zeros of the matrix

$$\mathbf{A} = \begin{pmatrix} 0 & 3 & 0 & 0 & 4 & 6 \\ 4 & 8 & 0 & 7 & 0 & 1 \\ 3 & 0 & 9 & 0 & 0 & 5 \\ 0 & 1 & 0 & 0 & 2 & 0 \\ 6 & 7 & 8 & 0 & 1 & 8 \\ 0 & 2 & 6 & 9 & 4 & 0 \end{pmatrix}.$$

Solution

Since the question asks only for the value of k_m, the maximum number of independent zeros of **A**, we apply the routine for the determination of k_m until either $k = n$, or Alternative 2 appears. In the former case $k_m = n$; in the latter $k_m < n$. Note that in this type of problem the result is unchanged if every non-zero element of **A** is replaced, for example, by unity.

In order to illustrate the routine as fully as possible suppose that, initially, only two independent zeros of **A** are marked by asterisks:

$$\mathbf{A} = \begin{pmatrix} 0^* & 3 & 0 & 0 & 4 & 6 \\ 4 & 8 & 0 & 7 & 0 & 1 \\ 3 & 0^* & 9 & 0 & 0 & 5 \\ 0 & 1 & 0 & 0 & 2 & 0 \\ 6 & 7 & 8 & 0 & 1 & 8 \\ 0 & 2 & 6 & 9 & 4 & 0 \end{pmatrix}.$$

Column 3 is pivotal, and contains 0's in rows 1, 2 and 4. Row 2 contains no 0*; hence the 0 in row 2 in the pivotal column 3 is marked with an asterisk. Then column 4 is pivotal, and contains 0's in rows 1, 3, 4 and 5. Row 4 contains no 0*; hence the 0 in row 4 and in the pivotal column 4 is marked with an asterisk. At this stage,

$$\mathbf{A} = \begin{pmatrix} 0^* & 3 & 0 & 0 & 4 & 6 \\ 4 & 8 & 0^* & 7 & 0 & 1 \\ 3 & 0^* & 9 & 0 & 0 & 5 \\ 0 & 1 & 0 & 0^* & 2 & 0 \\ 6 & 7 & 8 & 0 & 1 & 8 \\ 0 & 2 & 6 & 9 & 4 & 0 \end{pmatrix}.$$

Column 5 is pivotal and contains 0's only in rows 2 and 3, each of which contains contains a 0*. These row numbers form the initial sequence 2, 3. The 0* in row 2 has 0's in its column in rows 1 and 4; hence the row number sequence becomes 2, 3; 1, 4. (The semicolon indicates the end of the initial sequence.) The 0* in row 3 has no 0's in its column, so there is no contribution from this row to the sequence. The 0* in row 1 has 0's in its column in rows 4 and 6; hence the sequence becomes

2, 3; 1, 4, 6. The 0* in row 4 has 0's in its column in rows 1, 3, 4, 5; hence the sequence becomes 2, 3; 1, 4, 6, 5. Row 6 contains no 0*, and a transfer is carried out. Since 6 was generated in the sequence by 1, the asterisk in row 1 is transferred to row 6, column 1. Then

$$\mathbf{A} = \begin{pmatrix} 0 & 3 & 0 & 0 & 4 & 6 \\ 4 & 8 & 0^* & 7 & 0 & 1 \\ 3 & 0^* & 9 & 0 & 0 & 5 \\ 0 & 1 & 0 & 0^* & 2 & 0 \\ 6 & 7 & 8 & 0 & 1 & 8 \\ 0^* & 2 & 6 & 9 & 4 & 0 \end{pmatrix}.$$

Now row 1 contains no 0*, and another transfer is carried out (since 1 does not belong to the initial sequence 2, 3). Since 1 was generated in the sequence by 2, the asterisk in row 2 is transferred to row 1, column 3, giving

$$\mathbf{A} = \begin{pmatrix} 0 & 3 & 0^* & 0 & 4 & 6 \\ 4 & 8 & 0 & 7 & 0 & 1 \\ 3 & 0^* & 9 & 0 & 0 & 5 \\ 0 & 1 & 0 & 0^* & 2 & 0 \\ 6 & 7 & 8 & 0 & 1 & 8 \\ 0^* & 2 & 6 & 9 & 4 & 0 \end{pmatrix}.$$

Now row 2, which is represented in the initial sequence 2, 3, contains no 0*. Hence the 0 in row 2 and in the pivotal column 5 is marked with an asterisk. At this stage,

$$\mathbf{A} = \begin{pmatrix} 0 & 3 & 0^* & 0 & 4 & 6 \\ 4 & 8 & 0 & 7 & 0^* & 1 \\ 3 & 0^* & 9 & 0 & 0 & 5 \\ 0 & 1 & 0 & 0^* & 2 & 0 \\ 6 & 7 & 8 & 0 & 1 & 8 \\ 0^* & 2 & 6 & 9 & 4 & 0 \end{pmatrix}$$

Column 6 is pivotal, and contains 0's in rows 4 and 6, each of which contains a 0*. These row numbers form the initial sequence 4, 6. Proceeding as before, this sequence is extended to 4, 6; 1, 3, 5, 2. Row 5 contains no 0*, and 5 was generated in the sequence by 4; hence the asterisk in row 4 is transferred to row 5, column 4. Then row 4 contains no 0*; hence the 0 in row 4 and in the pivotal column 6 is marked with an asterisk. This gives, finally,

$$\mathbf{A} = \begin{pmatrix} 0 & 3 & 0^* & 0 & 4 & 6 \\ 4 & 8 & 0 & 7 & 0^* & 1 \\ 3 & 0^* & 9 & 0 & 0 & 5 \\ 0 & 1 & 0 & 0 & 2 & 0^* \\ 6 & 7 & 8 & 0^* & 1 & 8 \\ 0^* & 2 & 6 & 9 & 4 & 0 \end{pmatrix},$$

so that **A** has 6 independent zeros.

Example 4.5

Find the optimal assignment of 5 men to 5 jobs, given the rating matrix

$$\mathbf{R} = \begin{pmatrix} 8 & 2 & 7 & 5 & 1 \\ 2 & 2 & 2 & 2 & 2 \\ 9 & 1 & 9 & 1 & 9 \\ 7 & 9 & 9 & 8 & 4 \\ 9 & 8 & 5 & 5 & 3 \end{pmatrix}.$$

Solution

Forming, in turn $\mathbf{S}$, $\mathbf{S}_1$, and $\mathbf{A}$, from equation (4.20), Step 1, and Step 2, respectively, we find

$$\mathbf{A} = \begin{pmatrix} 0 & 6 & 1 & 3 & 7 \\ 0 & 0 & 0 & 0 & 0 \\ 0 & 8 & 0 & 8 & 0 \\ 2 & 0 & 0 & 1 & 5 \\ 0 & 1 & 4 & 4 & 6 \end{pmatrix}.$$

Initially, three obviously independent zeros are marked with asterisks:

$$\mathbf{A} = \begin{pmatrix} 0^* & 6 & 1 & 3 & 7 \\ 0 & 0^* & 0 & 0 & 0 \\ 0 & 8 & 0^* & 8 & 0 \\ 2 & 0 & 0 & 1 & 5 \\ 0 & 1 & 4 & 4 & 6 \end{pmatrix}.$$

Column 4 is pivotal, and contains a 0 only in row 2, which contains a 0*; thus the initial row number sequence consists of the single term 2. The 0* in row 2 has a 0 in its column in row 4; hence the sequence becomes 2; 4. Row 4 contains no 0*, and 4 was generated in the sequence by 2; hence the asterisk in row 2 is transferred to row 4, column 2, and the 0 in row 2 and in the pivotal column 4 is marked with an asterisk. This gives

$$\mathbf{A} = \begin{pmatrix} 0^* & 6 & 1 & 3 & 7 \\ 0 & 0 & 0 & 0^* & 0 \\ 0 & 8 & 0^* & 8 & 0 \\ 2 & 0^* & 0 & 1 & 5 \\ 0 & 1 & 4 & 4 & 6 \end{pmatrix}.$$

Column 5 is pivotal and contains 0's only in rows 2 and 3, each of which contains a 0*. These row numbers form the initial sequence 2, 3. The 0* in row 3 has 0's in its column in rows 2 and 4; hence the sequence becomes 2, 3; 4, and cannot be extended further. But rows 2, 3 and 4 each contain a 0*; hence all the zeros of **A** can be covered by 4 lines, as shown.

$$\mathbf{A} = \begin{pmatrix} 0^* & 6 & 1 & 3 & 7 \\ 0 & 0 & 0 & 0^* & 0 \\ 0 & 8 & 0^* & 8 & 0 \\ 2 & 0^* & 0 & 1 & 5 \\ 0 & 1 & 4 & 4 & 6 \end{pmatrix} \begin{matrix} \\ c \\ c \\ c \\ \\ \end{matrix}.$$
$$\begin{matrix} c & & & & \end{matrix}$$

Note that columns 2, 3, 4 and 5 contain zeros only in rows 2, 3 and 4. As explained in the last paragraph of the 'Routine for the Determination of k_m' (page 165), the lines that are covered are the rows represented in the sequence, and the columns whose numbers are not in the sequence—except that the pivotal column is not covered.

Following Alternative 2, with $h = 1$, we form

$$\mathbf{A}^* = \begin{pmatrix} 0^* & 5 & 0 & 2 & 6 \\ 1 & 0 & 0 & 0^* & 0 \\ 1 & 8 & 0^* & 8 & 0 \\ 3 & 0^* & 0 & 1 & 5 \\ 0 & 0 & 3 & 3 & 5 \end{pmatrix},$$

where the positions of the asterisks have been copied from the previous **A**.

Column 5 is pivotal, and contains 0's only in rows 2 and 3, each of which contains a 0*. The initial row number sequence is therefore 2, 3, and in the usual way is extended to 2, 3; 1, 4, 5. Row 5 contains no 0*, and 5 was generated in the sequence by 1. Hence the asterisk in row 1 is transferred to row 5, column 1, giving

$$\mathbf{A}^* = \begin{pmatrix} 0 & 5 & 0 & 2 & 6 \\ 1 & 0 & 0 & 0^* & 0 \\ 1 & 8 & 0^* & 8 & 0 \\ 3 & 0^* & 0 & 1 & 5 \\ 0^* & 0 & 3 & 3 & 5 \end{pmatrix}.$$

Now row 1 contains no 0*, and 1 was generated in the sequence by 3; hence the asterisk in row 3 is transferred to row 1, column 3. Then row 3 contains no 0*; hence the 0 in row 3 and in the pivotal column 5 is marked with an asterisk. This gives, finally,

$$\mathbf{A}^* = \begin{pmatrix} 0 & 5 & 0^* & 2 & 6 \\ 1 & 0 & 0 & 0^* & 0 \\ 1 & 8 & 0 & 8 & 0^* \\ 3 & 0^* & 0 & 1 & 5 \\ 0^* & 0 & 3 & 3 & 5 \end{pmatrix}.$$

The positions of the 0* in **A*** give the optimal assignment in **R**.

4.5 The Theory of Games

It has already been mentioned in Section 3.1 that there is a close relationship between linear programming and the theory of games. This relationship was first pointed out in 1947 by John von Neumann, who had been developing the theory of games since 1928. The earliest textbook on the theory of games, by von Neumann and Morgenstern [34], dates from 1944. An entertaining and instructive introduction to the subject is given by Williams [36].

In this and the following sections we shall consider only a special class of games, known as *matrix games* or, alternatively, as *two-person zero-sum games*. In such a game there are two players, A and B, who may be persons, organizations, countries, etc. The players have diametrically opposed interests: whatever A wins, B must lose, and vice versa. A *pure strategy* for a given player is a complete advance specification of the exact choices to be made by that player throughout the game, taking into account every possible move that his opponent may make. It is assumed that after each play of the game there is a pay-off to the winner from the loser; also, it is convenient to think of a negative pay-off to the loser from the winner, so that the sum of the pay-offs is zero—hence the expression *zero-sum game*. The object of each player is to find an *optimal strategy*, i.e. either a pure strategy or some combination of pure strategies, that will maximize the pay-off to that player. It is useful to discuss a specific example.

Example 4.6

Two punters, A and B, go to a race meeting where there are five races with six horses in each race. They decide to stake all their money on a single horse! Unfortunately, given the following table of odds, they cannot agree on which horse to back. They decide finally that A (who likes long odds) should choose the race, and that B (who likes short odds) should choose, inependently, the number of the horse. Find optimal strategies for A and B.

		Horse (B's choice).					
		B_1	B_2	B_3	B_4	B_5	B_6
	A_1	11–4	9–2	5–1	8–1	2–1	9–1
	A_2	10–1	12–1	16–1	4–1	5–2	13–8
Race	A_3	8–1	5–1	14–1	9–1	4–1	10–1
(A's choice)	A_4	11–2	13–2	20–1	50–1	11–10	14–1
	A_5	6–4	9–4	7–1	3–1	100–30	8–11

Solution

The odds are first converted to pure numbers to form the pay-off matrix, as shown below.

$$\begin{array}{c} \\ A_1 \\ A_2 \\ A_3 \\ A_4 \\ A_5 \end{array}\begin{array}{c} \begin{array}{cccccc} B_1 & B_2 & B_3 & B_4 & B_5 & B_6 \end{array} \\ \begin{pmatrix} 2{\cdot}75 & 4{\cdot}5 & 5 & 8 & 2 & 9 \\ 10 & 12 & 16 & 4 & 2{\cdot}5 & 1{\cdot}62 \\ 8 & 5 & 14 & 9 & 4 & 10 \\ 5{\cdot}5 & 6{\cdot}5 & 20 & 50 & 1{\cdot}1 & 14 \\ 1{\cdot}5 & 2{\cdot}25 & 7 & 3 & 3{\cdot}33 & 0{\cdot}73 \end{pmatrix} \end{array}$$

A chooses a row and B chooses a column of this matrix. Thus A has five pure strategies, which we call $A_1, \ldots, A_5$, and B has six: $B_1, \ldots, B_6$.

In any matrix game, the (i, j)th element of the pay-off matrix represents the advantage to A of the pair of pure strategies (A_i, B_j). A is called the *maximizing player*, and B the *minimizing player*. The basic rules of the theory of games are as follows:

(i) Both players are intelligent, and will play as well as they possibly can.

(ii) Hence A chooses the strategy that *maximizes the smallest amount* he can gain from any strategy (B will ensure that 'the smallest amount' is all that A *will* gain).

(iii) Similarly, B chooses the strategy that *minimizes the greatest amount* he can lose from any strategy.

The fundamental theorem of zero-sum, two-person games, in which each player has only a finite number of pure strategies from which to choose his optimal strategy, states that a solution of such a game always exists. In other words, it is always possible to find optimal strategies for A and B which satisfy rules (i), (ii) and (iii). This theorem is proved in Section 4.7.

Returning to the example, A and B have conflicting interests—A likes long odds and B likes short odds. Hence, although A is tempted by certain horses in the fourth race, a superior strategy is to choose the third race, since the 4 in row 3 is the maximum of the row minima. A is then assured of odds of at least 4–1, regardless of B's choice of horse. Conversely, B fancies the odds-on favourite (no. 6) in the last race, but a superior strategy is to choose the no. 5 horses, since the 4 in column 5 is the minimum of the column maxima. B is then assured of odds of not more than 4–1, regardless of A's choice of race.

Neither A nor B regrets his choice when he finds out what the other has chosen. For example, if A had known beforehand that B's choice was the no. 5 horses, he would still have chosen the third race. This result occurs because an entry appears in the pay-off matrix which is the smallest in its row and the largest in its column. The maximum of the row minima is called the *maximin*; the minimum of the column maxima is called the *minimax*. In the present example, the maximin is equal to the minimax, since

$$\max\{2, 1{\cdot}62, 4, 1{\cdot}1, 0{\cdot}73\} = \min\{10, 12, 20, 50, 4, 14\} = 4,$$

and the entry 4 is called (appropriately enough for this problem) a *saddle-point*. Its value, denoted in general by V, is called the *value of the game*, and the pair of pure strategies leading to it (A_3, B_5), is called a *solution* of the game. These pure strategies are the required optimal strategies. If the value of a game is zero, the game is said to be *fair*. In general, if the pay-off matrix is $\{a_{ij}\}$, with a saddle-point at a_{rk}, then the optimal strategies are A_r for A, and B_k for B, given by the rth row and the kth column of the matrix, respectively.

4.6 Mixed Strategies

Not all games have saddle-points. In order to solve a game that has no saddle-point, von Neumann introduced the notion of a *mixed strategy*, which will now be explained.

Given any pay-off matrix $\{a_{ij}\}$, it is easy to prove that the maximin (a_{rv}) is less than or equal to the minimax (a_{uk}), i.e.

$$a_{rv} = \max_i \min_j a_{ij} \leqslant \min_j \max_i a_{ij} = a_{uk}.$$

For a_{rk} is the element in the row of the maximin and in the column of the minimax, and therefore

$$a_{rv} \leqslant a_{rk} \leqslant a_{uk}.$$

Now if A chooses strategy r, and *discloses his choice* to B, then B will choose strategy v, and the pay-off to A will be a_{rv}, the maximin. This will be unsatisfactory from A's point of view, since a_{rv} is the smallest element in row r. A will regret his choice for, if he knew in advance that B was going to choose strategy v, then A would choose strategy $w(\neq r)$, with a pay-off $a_{wv} > a_{rv}$. Similarly, if B has first choice of strategy, and discloses his choice to A, then B will regret his choice. Again, an example will help the discussion.

Example 4.7

A holds three cards in his hand, viz. K, Q, J. He places a card face downwards on the table, and B guesses which card it is. If B guesses correctly, he scores 3 points for the K, 2 for the Q, or 1 for the J; if B guesses wrongly, then A scores these points. Find optimal strategies for A and B.

Solution

The pay-off matrix is

$$\begin{array}{cc} & \begin{array}{ccc} & B & \\ B_{\mathrm{K}} & B_{\mathrm{Q}} & B_{\mathrm{J}} \end{array} \\ A \quad \begin{array}{c} A_{\mathrm{K}} \\ A_{\mathrm{Q}} \\ A_{\mathrm{J}} \end{array} & \begin{pmatrix} -3 & 3 & 3 \\ 2 & -2 & 2 \\ 1 & 1 & -1 \end{pmatrix}. \end{array}$$

The maximin (-1) is not equal to the minimax (2), and so there is no saddle-point. In this situation we have just seen that neither player wishes to disclose his strategy—his opponent could take advantage of this information. A sure way of not disclosing one's strategy is to be ignorant of it oneself! This can be achieved by leaving the choice of strategy to chance; the only problem is to assign suitable probabilities to the pure strategies. A probability distribution defined over the set of pure strategies is called a *mixed strategy*. By the pay-off for a mixed strategy, we mean the expected pay-off in the usual probabilistic sense.

Suppose that A chooses the pure strategies A_K, A_Q, A_J with probabilities u_1, u_2, u_3, respectively, where

$$u_1 + u_2 + u_3 = 1. \tag{4.21}$$

His expected pay-offs are

$$\begin{aligned} -3u_1 + 2u_2 + u_3 &\text{ against } B_K, \\ 3u_1 - 2u_2 + u_3 &\text{ against } B_Q, \\ 3u_1 + 2u_2 - u_3 &\text{ against } B_J. \end{aligned}$$

Now A has no information concerning B's intended strategy (pure or mixed) beyond the fact that B will choose a strategy that minimizes A's pay-off, whatever strategy A chooses. Hence, in order to avoid any subsequent regret at having chosen the wrong strategy, A must make his three expected pay-offs equal, i.e. he must choose u_1, u_2, u_3 such that

$$-3u_1 + 2u_2 + u_3 = 3u_1 - 2u_2 + u_3 = 3u_1 + 2u_2 - u_3. \tag{4.22}$$

Solving equations (4.21) and (4.22), we find

$$u_1 = 2/11, \quad u_2 = 3/11, \quad u_3 = 6/11, \tag{4.23}$$

so that A should use the pure strategies A_K, A_Q, A_J in the proportions 2 : 3 : 6. The pure strategy to be used by A at any single play of the game can be chosen, for example, by means of a table of random numbers from 1–99: choose a random number n, play K if $1 \leqslant n \leqslant 18$, Q if $19 \leqslant n \leqslant 45$, J if $46 \leqslant n \leqslant 99$.

Since there is no saddle-point, B's problem is precisely the same as A's: he must equalize his expected negative pay-offs, or losses, against A's three pure strategies. Suppose B chooses the pure strategies B_K, B_Q, B_J with probabilities v_1, v_2, v_3, respectively, where

$$v_1 + v_2 + v_3 = 1. \tag{4.24}$$

His expected losses are

$$\begin{aligned} -3v_1 + 3v_2 + 3v_3 &\text{ against } A_K, \\ 2v_1 - 2v_2 + 2v_3 &\text{ against } A_Q, \\ v_1 + v_2 - v_3 &\text{ against } A_J. \end{aligned}$$

Hence

$$-3v_1+3v_2+3v_3 = 2v_1-2v_2+2v_3 = v_1+v_2-v_3, \tag{4.25}$$

which, together with equation (4.24), yield

$$v_1 = 9/22, \quad v_2 = 4/11, \quad v_3 = 5/22, \tag{4.26}$$

so that B should use the pure strategies B_K, B_Q, B_J in the proportions 9:8:5. Using the table of random numbers from 1–99, B could choose a random number n, guess K if $1 \leqslant n \leqslant 36$, Q if $37 \leqslant n \leqslant 68$, J if $69 \leqslant n \leqslant 88$, and choose another random number if $89 \leqslant n \leqslant 99$.

The expected pay-off to A against strategy B_K is, from (4.23),

$$\tfrac{2}{11}(-3)+\tfrac{3}{11}(2)+\tfrac{6}{11}(1) = \tfrac{6}{11},$$

and the same expected pay-off is obtained against B_Q or B_J, as may easily be verified. Similarly, the expected loss to B against any pure strategy of A, and therefore against any combination of A's pure strategies, is

$$\tfrac{9}{22}(-3)+\tfrac{4}{11}(3)+\tfrac{5}{22}(3) = \tfrac{6}{11},$$

which is, of course, exactly the same as A's expected gain. The game is biased in A's favour; to make it fair, A should give B six points for every eleven plays of the game.

Neither player has any regrets, for the expected pay-off to A is 6/11, regardless of B's strategy, as long as A keeps to his optimal mixed strategy. Similarly, B's expected loss is 6/11, regardless of A's strategy, as long as B keeps to his optimal mixed strategy.

The pair of optimal mixed strategies, which may be represented by the vectors

$$\mathbf{u}^* = [2/11,\ 3/11,\ 6/11], \quad \mathbf{v}^* = [9/22,\ 4/11,\ 5/22],$$

is again called a *solution* of the game. Also, the expected pay-off to A is called the *value of the game*, and is denoted by V. The optimal mixed strategies $\mathbf{u}^*$, $\mathbf{v}^*$ may be regarded as defining a generalized saddle-point for the game.

N.B. In the examples of this chapter, we shall find it convenient to use the notation $u_1, u_2, \ldots$ and $v_1, v_2, \ldots$ to represent strategies both for the given game and for sub-games of the given game. To avoid confusion, the vector notation $\mathbf{u}^*$, $\mathbf{v}^*$ will always refer to optimal strategies for the *given* game.

The following miscellaneous points are worth noting.

(a) A game may contain chance events beyond the control of either player, e.g. the effect of weather on crop yields. The *expected* pay-offs are entered in the pay-off matrix; otherwise the theory is unchanged. Such chance events are quite independent of the random choices associated with a mixed strategy.

(b) A game is said to be of *perfect information* when no simultaneous moves are made, and every previous move is known to both players. Chess is such a game. It can be proved that every game of perfect information, when expressed as a matrix game, has a saddle-point.

(c) A game may have more than one solution, but it can have only one value. For there may be more than one saddle-point, but its value (the maximin) is unique; if there is no saddle-point, there may be more than one generalized saddle-point, but the expected pay-off to A (or loss to B) is uniquely determined by any of the optimal mixed strategies. For example, the game with pay-off matrix

$$A \quad \overset{B}{\begin{pmatrix} 3^* & 7 & 3^* & 4 \\ 3^* & 6 & 3^* & 6 \\ 2 & 8 & 1 & 1 \\ 1 & 3 & 2 & 4 \end{pmatrix}}$$

has four saddle-points. A's optimal strategy is any combination of strategies A_1, A_2; B's optimal strategy is any combination of B_1, B_3. Example 4.11, Section 4.8 is an example of a game which has alternative optimal mixed strategies (for one of the players).

(d) The play of a game is unaltered if each element in the pay-off matrix is multiplied by a positive constant, or if a constant is added to each element. It is therefore possible to avoid fractions and negative numbers in a pay-off matrix with rational elements. The original pay-off matrix must, of course, be used to determine the value of the game.

Example 4.8

Given the pay-off matrix

$$A \quad \overset{B}{\begin{pmatrix} -7/10 & -1/3 \\ 3/4 & -2/5 \end{pmatrix}},$$

show that the optimal mixed strategies are

$$\mathbf{u}^* = [69/91, 22/91], \quad \mathbf{v}^* = [4/91, 87/91]$$

for A and B, respectively, and that the value of the game is $-159/455$.

4.7 Linear Programming and the Theory of Games

■ **Theorem 4.5.** The Fundamental Theorem of Two-Person, Zero-Sum, Finite Games

Every two-person, zero-sum, finite game has a solution.

Proof

The method of proof is first to reduce the game to a pair of dual linear programming problems, one for the maximizing player A, and one for the minimizing player B, and then to show that both these problems have optimal solutions.

Let the pay-off matrix be of order $m \times n$. Suppose that A uses the mixed strategy defined by

$$\mathbf{u} \geqslant \mathbf{0}, \qquad \sum_{i=1}^{m} u_i = 1.$$

Similarly, suppose that B uses the mixed strategy defined by

$$\mathbf{v} \geqslant \mathbf{0}, \qquad \sum_{j=1}^{n} v_j = 1.$$

The expected pay-off to A is

$$E(\mathbf{u}, \mathbf{v}) = \sum_{i=1}^{m} \sum_{j=1}^{n} a_{ij} u_i v_j, \tag{4.27}$$

where $\{a_{ij}\}$ is the pay-off matrix.

Now A expects to win at least

$$\min_{\mathbf{v}} E(\mathbf{u}, \mathbf{v}),$$

the operation $\min_{\mathbf{v}}$ being due to B's choice of strategy. But A, the maximizing player, can choose $\mathbf{u}$ such that he expects to win at least

$$M_A{}^* = \max_{\mathbf{u}} \min_{\mathbf{v}} E(\mathbf{u}, \mathbf{v}). \tag{4.28}$$

Similarly, B can choose $\mathbf{v}$ such that he expects to lose not more than

$$M_B{}^* = \min_{\mathbf{v}} \max_{\mathbf{u}} E(\mathbf{u}, \mathbf{v}). \tag{4.29}$$

$M_A{}^*$ and $M_B{}^*$ may be regarded as the generalized maximin and minimax, respectively. If $\mathbf{u}^*$, $\mathbf{v}^*$ exist such that

$$M_A{}^* = M_B{}^* = E(\mathbf{u}^*, \mathbf{v}^*),$$

then the optimal mixed strategies $\mathbf{u}^*$, $\mathbf{v}^*$ represent a generalized saddle-point for the game. The rest of the proof consists in showing that $\mathbf{u}^*$, $\mathbf{v}^*$ do always exist.

If B uses the pure strategy B_j, then, from equation (4.27), the expected pay-off to A is $\Sigma_{i=1}^{m} a_{ij} u_i$. A's problem is to find a mixed strategy $\mathbf{u}$ such that his pay-off is not less than some amount M_A, which should be as large as possible, given that B might use any pure strategy. That is, A requires

$$\sum_{i=1}^{m} a_{ij} u_i \geqslant M_A, \quad j = 1, \ldots, n,$$

or, in matrix form,

$$\mathbf{A}'\mathbf{u} \geqslant M_A\mathbf{e}, \quad \mathbf{u} \geqslant \mathbf{0}, \quad \mathbf{e}'\mathbf{u} = 1, \tag{4.30}$$

where **e** is the column vector $[1, 1, \ldots, 1]$ with m components. Because of (d), page 175, we can add a positive quantity to each element of the pay-off matrix so that the value of the game is positive, i.e. we can assume $M_A > 0$. Define

$$y_i = \frac{u_i}{M_A}, \quad i = 1, \ldots, m.$$

Then (4.30) can be written

$$\mathbf{A}'\mathbf{y} \geqslant \mathbf{e}, \quad \mathbf{y} \geqslant \mathbf{0}, \quad \mathbf{e}'\mathbf{y} = \frac{1}{M_A} = w, \text{ say.} \tag{4.31}$$

The problem of maximizing M_A is the problem of minimizing w in (4.31), subject to the constraints and non-negativity restrictions on **y**. This is A's linear programming problem.

Similarly, B's problem is to find a mixed strategy **v**, with M_B as small as possible, such that

$$\sum_{j=1}^{n} a_{ij}v_j \leqslant M_B, \quad i = 1, \ldots, m,$$

or, in matrix form,

$$\mathbf{A}\mathbf{v} \leqslant M_B\mathbf{e}, \quad \mathbf{v} \geqslant \mathbf{0}, \quad \mathbf{e}'\mathbf{v} = 1. \tag{4.32}$$

Define

$$x_j = \frac{v_j}{M_B}, \qquad j = 1, \ldots, n,$$

assuming that $M_B > 0$. Then (4.32) can be written

$$\mathbf{A}\mathbf{x} \leqslant \mathbf{e}, \quad \mathbf{x} \geqslant \mathbf{0}, \quad \mathbf{e}'\mathbf{x} = \frac{1}{M_B} = z, \text{ say.} \tag{4.33}$$

The problem of minimizing M_B is the problem of maximizing z in (4.33), subject to the constraints and non-negativity restrictions on **x**. This is B's problem, and is seen to be the dual of A's problem.

It is now a simple matter to show that there exist optimal solutions $\mathbf{x}^*$, $\mathbf{y}^*$ of problems (4.33) and (4.31), respectively. Certainly, feasible solutions **x**, **y** always exist for these problems since each player can use a pure strategy. For the purposes of discussion, assume that (4.33) is the primal. Since the primal has a feasible solution, it must have either an unbounded solution with an unbounded value of z, or an optimal solution—see page 29. But, from Theorem 3.5, if the primal has an unbounded solution with an unbounded value of z, then the dual has no feasible solution, a contradiction. Hence the primal must have an optimal solution—and by Theorem 3.4, so must the dual. It also follows from Theorem 3.4 that

$$\max z = \min w,$$

i.e. $\mathbf{x}^*$, $\mathbf{y}^*$ exist, and therefore $\mathbf{u}^*$, $\mathbf{v}^*$ exist, such that

$$M_B^* = \min M_B = \max M_A = M_A^*, \tag{4.34}$$

which completes the proof of the theorem.

Example 4.9

Solve the matrix game

$$\begin{array}{cc} & \text{B} \\ A & \begin{pmatrix} 3 & 2 & 1 \\ 2 & 6 & 5 \end{pmatrix}. \end{array}$$

Reduce the game to a pair of dual linear programming problems, and verify that the solution of the game corresponds to the optimal solutions of the linear programming problems.

Solution

There is no saddle-point. The game reduces to

$$\begin{pmatrix} 3 & 1 \\ 2 & 5 \end{pmatrix},$$

since strategy B_2 is always rejected by B—it gives him greater losses than strategy B_3, whatever strategy A may choose. (The reduction of games by 'dominance' considerations is discussed in more detail in Example 4.10, Section 4.8.) The solution of the reduced game is

$$(u_1, u_2) = (3/5, 2/5), \quad (v_1, v_2) = (4/5, 1/5).$$

Hence the solution of the original 2×3 game is

$$\mathbf{u}^* = [3/5, 2/5], \quad \mathbf{v}^* = [4/5, 0, 1/5]; \quad V = 13/5.$$

From equation (4.31) the minimizing linear programming problem is

$$\left.\begin{aligned} &\text{Minimize } w = y_1 + y_2, \\ \text{subject to} \quad & \\ &3y_1 + 2y_2 \geqslant 1, \\ &2y_1 + 6y_2 \geqslant 1, \\ &y_1 + 5y_2 \geqslant 1, \\ &y_1, y_2 \geqslant 0. \end{aligned}\right\} \tag{4.35}$$

From equation (4.33) the maximizing linear programming problem is

$$\left.\begin{aligned} &\text{Maximize } z = x_1 + x_2 + x_3, \\ \text{subject to}\quad & \\ &3x_1 + 2x_2 + x_3 \leqslant 1, \\ &2x_1 + 6x_2 + 5x_3 \leqslant 1, \\ &x_1, x_2, x_3 \geqslant 0. \end{aligned}\right\} \tag{4.36}$$

To verify that the solution of the game corresponds to the optimal solutions of problem (4.35) and (4.36), we have

$$\left.\begin{aligned} y_i &= \frac{u_i}{M_A} = \frac{u_i}{13/5} = \frac{5u_i}{13}, \quad i = 1, 2, \\ \text{and}\quad & \\ x_j &= \frac{v_j}{M_B} = \frac{v_j}{13/5} = \frac{5v_j}{13}, \quad j = 1, 2, 3, \end{aligned}\right\} \tag{4.37}$$

since, from equation (4.34), $M_A = M_B (= V)$ for the optimal solutions of problems (4.31) and (4.33). From equations (4.37), and using $\mathbf{u}^*$ and $\mathbf{v}^*$ from the solution of the game, we find

$$(y_1, y_2) = (3/13, 2/13), \; (x_1, x_2, x_3) = (4/13, 0, 1/13). \tag{4.38}$$

It is easy to verify that these values of the variables satisfy the constraints in (4.35) and (4.36), and also that they give

$$w = z = 5/13.$$

It follows from Theorem 3.3 that the y_i and x_j in (4.38) are optimal solutions of problems (4.35) and (4.36) respectively.

The general method for solving matrix games provided by Theorem 4.5 is often inefficient from a computational viewpoint. Some alternative techniques for the solution of large matrix games are discussed in the next section, but whatever method is employed it is useful to remember that optimal strategies for the players A and B are also optimal solutions of a pair of dual linear programming problems. In particular, for an $m \times n$ matrix game, with $m < n$, B has n pure strategies from which to choose his optimal strategy. His linear programming problem (4.33) has m constraints—hence at most m variables in the optimal solution of (4.33) are basic. In the absence of alternative optima, this means that B's optimal strategy is either a pure strategy or a mixed strategy formed from not more than m pure strategies. It follows that every $m \times n$ matrix game has a solution in common with an $m \times m$ matrix game.

During the proof of Theorem 4.5, a general matrix game was converted into a pair of dual linear programming problems; this is equivalent to converting the game into a single linear programming problem (either a maximizing or a minimizing problem). It is interesting, though not very useful, to note that the reverse procedure is always possible: any linear programming problem may be converted into a matrix game. Details of the required transformations are given by Hadley [20].

4.8 Large Matrix Games

In this section we shall discuss the solution of some large matrix games, using numerical examples to illustrate the methods. The games are classified in terms of the size and shape of their pay-off matrices.

4.8.1 $2 \times n$ and $m \times 2$

As explained in the previous section, a $2 \times n$ or $m \times 2$ game must have a solution in common with some 2×2 sub-game. Hence, a $2 \times n$ or $m \times 2$ game is solved by one of the following methods:

(i) finding a saddle-point,

(ii) reducing the game to a 2×2 sub-game whose solution also satisfies the original game,

(iii) finding, by trial and error, a 2×2 sub-game whose solution also satisfies the original game.

Example 4.10

Solve the matrix game

$$A \overset{B}{\begin{pmatrix} -5 & 2 & 7 & -1 & 3 & -4 \\ 6 & 1 & 4 & -6 & -3 & -1 \end{pmatrix}}.$$

Solution

There is no saddle-point. The game may be reduced by *dominance* considerations: B will never use strategy B_2, because term for term it gives him greater losses than B_4, regardless of A's strategy. We say that B_2 *dominates* B_4 (the row or column containing the larger numbers is always the dominant one); similarly B_3 and B_5 dominate B_4. The game reduces to

$$\begin{pmatrix} -5 & -1 & -4 \\ 6 & -6 & -1 \end{pmatrix}. \tag{4.39}$$

Consider the 2×2 sub-game

$$\begin{pmatrix} -5 & -1 \\ 6 & -6 \end{pmatrix}. \tag{4.40}$$

A's optimal mixed strategy is given by

$$-5u_1 + 6u_2 = -u_1 - 6u_2; \ u_1 + u_2 = 1,$$

i.e.

$$u_1 = 3/4, \ u_2 = 1/4,$$

and the value of the sub-game is $-9/4$. Against B_3 in (4.39), this mixed strategy yields

$$\frac{3}{4}(-4) + \frac{1}{4}(-1) = -\frac{13}{4} < -\frac{9}{4},$$

and therefore cannot be optimal for the 2×3 game (4.39), for if A uses the mixed strategy (3/4, 1/4), then B will use B_3 in preference to his optimal mixed strategy for the 2×2 sub-game (4.40).

Continuing the trial-and-error process, consider the 2×2 sub-game

$$\begin{pmatrix} -1 & -4 \\ -6 & -1 \end{pmatrix}. \tag{4.41}$$

A's optimal mixed strategy is

$$u_1 = 5/8, \quad u_2 = 3/8,$$

and the value of the sub-game is $-23/8$. Against B_1 in (4.39), this mixed strategy yields

$$\frac{5}{8}(-5) + \frac{3}{8}(6) = -\frac{7}{8} > -\frac{23}{8}.$$

Hence B would not be so foolish as to use strategy B_1, and the solution of the sub-game (4.41) also satisfies the original game. B's optimal mixed strategy for the sub-game (4.41) is

$$v_1 = 3/8, \quad v_2 = 5/8.$$

The solution of the original 2×6 game is therefore

$$\mathbf{u}^* = [5/8, 3/8], \ \mathbf{v}^* = [0, 0, 0, 3/8, 0, 5/8]; \ V = -23/8.$$

The search for the correct 2×2 sub-game in Example 4.10 may be considerably speeded up by the graphical procedure shown in Figure 4.1. Strategy B_1 is represented by the line joining the point -5 on the A_1-axis to the point 6 on the A_2-axis. Similarly for B's other strategies. Remembering that the elements in the pay-off matrix represent A's possible gains, B need only consider the strategies that form the lower boundary of the diagram. (Notice that the dominance of strategies B_2, B_3 and B_5 shows clearly in the diagram.)

Let P be the highest point on the lower boundary of the diagram. Then P determines the two pure strategies that must form B's optimal mixed strategy. The point Q is worse for B, since it allows A to gain either -1 or $+6$ by using

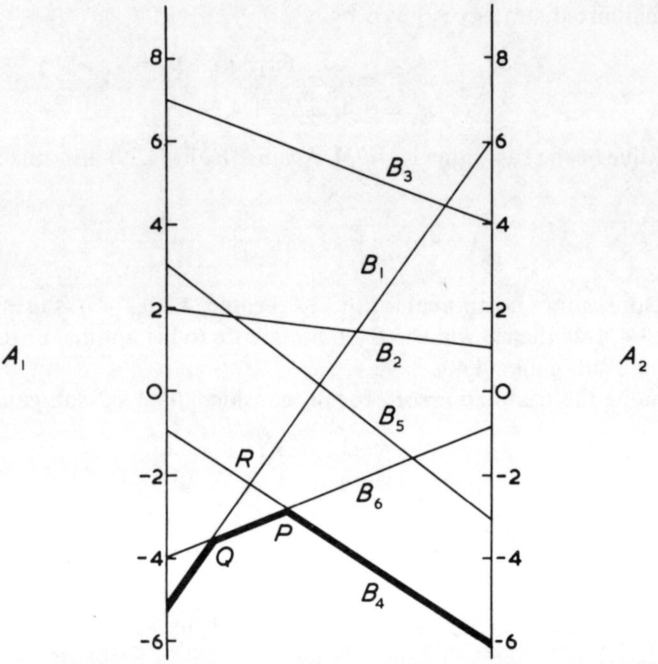

Figure 4.1 Solution of 2 × 6 game (Example 4.10)

strategy A_2 all the time (both these pay-offs being greater than the value of the game). The point R is also clearly worse for B; in this case A, as well as B, would use a mixed strategy.

The complete solution of the original problem can, in fact, be obtained graphically by drawing a horizontal line through P to intersect the A_1- and A_2-axes in C and D, respectively (not shown in Figure 4.1). A little elementary geometry shows that A's optimal mixed strategy is given by

$$\frac{u_1}{u_2} = \frac{PD}{CP}.$$

Also, if the lines B_4 and B_6 meet the A_1-axis in E and F, respectively, then B's optimal mixed strategy is given by

$$\frac{v_1}{v_2} = \frac{CF}{EC}.$$

A similar graphical method may be used for an $m \times 2$ game. The point that determines the required pure strategies for A is then the lowest point on the upper boundary of the diagram, since A is the maximizing player.

Example 4.11

Solve the matrix game

$$
\begin{array}{cc} & B \\ A & \begin{pmatrix} 2 & 8 \\ 1 & 10 \\ 3 & 6 \\ 0 & 12 \\ 6 & 0 \\ 5 & 2 \\ 4 & 1 \end{pmatrix}. \end{array}
$$

Solution

In Figure 4.2 the lines representing the pure strategies $A_1, \ldots, A_6$ are concurrent at the lowest point on the upper boundary of the diagram. This means that there are alternative solutions; from the diagram we see that the following pairs of pure strategies can form optimal mixed strategies for A:

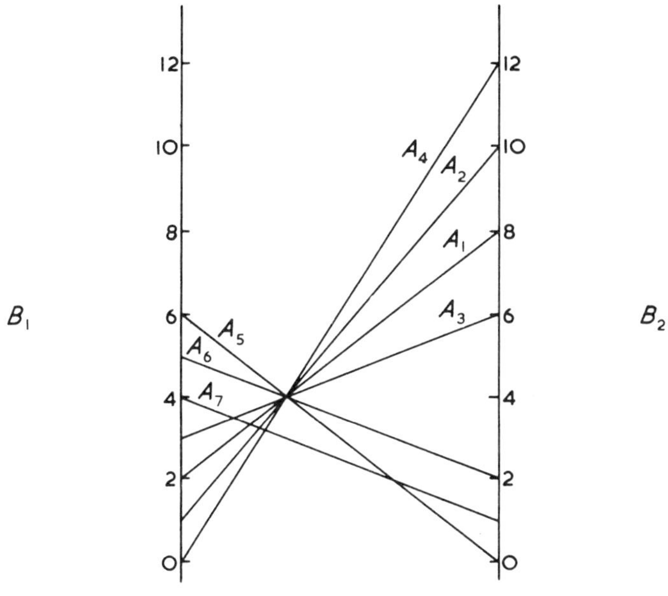

Figure 4.2 Solution of 7 × 2 game (Example 4.11)

(A_1, A_5), (A_1, A_6), (A_2, A_5), (A_2, A_6), (A_3, A_5), (A_3, A_6), (A_4, A_5), (A_4, A_6). The optimal mixed strategies are calculated for the various 2×2 sub-games, and are found to be, respectively,

$$
\begin{aligned}
(u_1, u_2) &= (1/2,\ 1/2),\ (1/3,\ 2/3),\ (2/5,\ 3/5),\ (1/4,\ 3/4),\ (2/3,\ 1/3), \\
&\quad\ (1/2,\ 1/2),\ (1/3,\ 2/3),\ (1/5,\ 4/5), \\
(v_1, v_2) &= (2/3,\ 1/3).
\end{aligned}
$$

The most general optimal mixed strategy for A is given by a convex combination of the optimal mixed strategies for the above 2×2 sub-games. Hence the most general solution of the original 7×2 game is

$$\mathbf{u}^* = [\tfrac{1}{2}\alpha+\tfrac{1}{3}\beta, \tfrac{2}{5}\gamma+\tfrac{1}{4}\delta, \tfrac{2}{3}\varepsilon+\tfrac{1}{2}\zeta, \tfrac{1}{3}\eta+\tfrac{1}{5}\theta, \tfrac{1}{2}\alpha+\tfrac{3}{5}\gamma+\tfrac{1}{3}\varepsilon+\tfrac{2}{3}\eta, \tfrac{2}{3}\beta+\tfrac{3}{4}\delta+\tfrac{1}{2}\zeta+\tfrac{4}{5}\theta, 0],$$

where

$$\alpha+\beta+\ \ldots\ +\theta = 1, \quad \alpha, \beta, \ldots, \theta \geqslant 0,$$

$\mathbf{v}^* = [2/3, 1/3]$.

The value of the game is easily obtained; for example, $\mathbf{v}^*$ and A_1 give

$$V = \tfrac{2}{3}(2)+\tfrac{1}{3}(8) = 4.$$

4.8.2 3×3

A 3×3 game is solved by one of the following processes:

(i) finding a saddle-point,

(ii) reducing the game to a 2×3 or 3×2 sub-game, and thence to a 2×2 sub-game whose solution also satisfies the original game,

(iii) finding, by trial and error, a 2×2 sub-game whose solution also satisfies the original game,

(iv) using a mixed strategy involving all three pure strategies.

Example 4.7, page 172, is a 3×3 game whose solution was found by method (iv).

Example 4.12

Solve the matrix game

$$A \overset{B}{\begin{pmatrix} 3 & 8 & 4 \\ 2 & 4 & 6 \\ 4 & 1 & 5 \end{pmatrix}}.$$

Solution

There is no saddle-point. Strategy B_3 dominates B_1; hence the game reduces to

$$\begin{pmatrix} 3 & 8 \\ 2 & 4 \\ 4 & 1 \end{pmatrix}.$$

Now A_1 dominates A_2, and the game reduces further to

$$\begin{pmatrix} 3 & 8 \\ 4 & 1 \end{pmatrix},$$

whose solution is

$$(u_1, u_2) = (3/8, 5/8), \quad (v_1, v_2) = (7/8, 1/8).$$

The solution of the original game is therefore

$$\mathbf{u}^* = [3/8, 0, 5/8], \quad \mathbf{v}^* = [7/8, 1/8, 0]; \quad V = 29/8.$$

4.8.3 $3 \times n$ and $m \times 3$

A $3 \times n$ or $m \times 3$ game must have a solution in common with some 3×3 sub-game. It is solved by one of the following processes:

(i) finding a saddle-point,

(ii) reducing the game to a $2 \times n$ or $m \times 2$ sub-game, and thence to a 2×2 sub-game whose solution also satisfies the original game,

(iii) finding, by trial and error, a 2×2 or 3×3 sub-game whose solution also satisfies the original game.

4.8.4 4×4 and larger

In general, a large game is solved by one of the following processes:

(i) finding a saddle-point,

(ii) reducing it to a square matrix game, and then finding, by further reduction, or by trial and error, a square matrix game of lower order whose solution also satisfies the original game. This process can be carried out systematically; for example, given an $n \times n$ game, consider all $(n-1) \times (n-1)$ games, etc.

The search for solutions of games of types 4.8.3 and 4.8.4 may be extremely laborious. However, the reduction process can sometimes be speeded up by using the idea of *matrix dominance*. Suppose that the pay-off matrix is partitioned into four sub-matrices **P**, **Q**, **R**, **S**:

$$\begin{array}{cc} & B \\ A & \left(\begin{array}{c|c} \mathbf{P} & \mathbf{Q} \\ \hline \mathbf{R} & \mathbf{S} \end{array}\right). \end{array}$$

For brevity, we shall use the word 'strategy' to mean 'a pure or mixed strategy'. If (i) *each* column of **Q** dominates *some* column of **P**, then, whenever A uses a strategy from $\mathbf{P}|\mathbf{Q}$, B will use a strategy from $\dfrac{\mathbf{P}}{\mathbf{R}}$.

Also, if

(ii) *each* row of **R** is dominated by *some* row of **P**, then, whenever B uses a strategy from $\dfrac{\mathbf{P}}{\mathbf{R}}$, A will use a strategy from $\mathbf{P}|\mathbf{Q}$.

Now suppose that both (i) and (ii) hold. Then, if A uses a strategy from $\mathbf{R}|\mathbf{S}$, B will again use a strategy from $\dfrac{\mathbf{P}}{\mathbf{R}}$, so that A's pay-off will be determined by **R**, and he will regret not having chosen a strategy from **P**. Also, if B uses a strategy from

$\frac{\mathbf{Q}}{\mathbf{S}}$, then A will again use a strategy from $\mathbf{P} \vdots \mathbf{Q}$, so that B's losses will be determined by $\mathbf{Q}$, and he will regret not having chosen a strategy from $\mathbf{P}$.

Thus, strategies involving $\mathbf{Q}$ and $\mathbf{R}$ cannot be optimal, and the game reduces to $\mathbf{P}$. It is interesting that this result is quite independent of $\mathbf{S}$. The ordering of the rows and columns in the pay-off matrix may be changed, if desired, to make matrix dominance appear more obvious, as shown in the following example.

Example 4.13

Solve the matrix game

$$\begin{array}{cc} & B \\ A & \begin{pmatrix} 6 & 4 & 9 & 3 & 7 \\ 0 & 2 & 9 & 8 & 5 \\ 5 & 3 & 4 & 2 & 4 \\ 1 & 6 & 2 & 1 & 8 \\ 1 & 6 & 1 & 3 & 6 \end{pmatrix}. \end{array}$$

Solution

Interchange rows 3 and 5, and columns 3 and 4. This gives

$$\left(\begin{array}{c|c} \mathbf{P} & \mathbf{Q} \\ \hline \mathbf{R} & \mathbf{S} \end{array}\right) = \left(\begin{array}{ccc|cc} 6 & 4 & 3 & 9 & 7 \\ 0 & 2 & 8 & 9 & 5 \\ 1 & 6 & 3 & 1 & 6 \\ \hline 1 & 6 & 1 & 2 & 8 \\ 5 & 3 & 2 & 4 & 4 \end{array}\right).$$

Conditions (i) and (ii) for matrix dominance apply; hence the game reduces to

$$\begin{pmatrix} 6 & 4 & 3 \\ 0 & 2 & 8 \\ 1 & 6 & 3 \end{pmatrix}.$$

Solving this 3×3 sub-game by using mixed strategies involving all three pure strategies for each player, we find that the solution of the 5×5 game in its original form is

$$\mathbf{u}^* = [36/57, 11/57, 0, 0, 10/57], \quad \mathbf{v}^* = [10/57, 25/57, 0, 22/57, 0];$$
$$V = 226/57.$$

Exercises

1. Three factories, F_1, F_2 and F_3, are capable of producing for export 1 000, 800 and 500 cars, respectively, each week. The cars are to be delivered to four ports,

P_1, P_2, P_3 and P_4, the numbers required at the ports being 300, 700, 500 and 400, respectively. The costs (in thousands of pounds) of manufacturing and delivering 100 cars are shown in the following table.

	P_1	P_2	P_3	P_4
F_1	75	90	65	70
F_2	63	72	74	78
F_3	84	88	85	80

Assuming that there is no penalty for underproduction at any factory, determine the production schedule and transportation pattern that satisfies the requirements of the ports while minimizing the total cost.

Exercises 2–16 are transportation problems for which the tables give unit costs, origin availabilities and destination requirements. Unless otherwise stated, find, in each case, the optimal transportation schedules (including alternative optima) and the minimum total cost.

2.

	D_1	D_2	D_3	Available
O_1	3	7	8	12
O_2	3	6	5	17
O_3	7	2	9	21
O_4	10	8	4	14
Required	16	20	28	

3. Assume that the penalties for non-delivery of goods to D_1, D_2 and D_3 are 5, 10 and 15 per unit, respectively.

	D_1	D_2	D_3	Available
O_1	23	24	23	5
O_2	23	25	24	8
O_3	24	25	23	7
O_4	25	23	25	6
Required	8	9	10	

4. Assume that surplus goods are stored, and that the unit costs for storage at O_1, O_2 and O_3 are 2, 4 and 5, respectively.

	D_1	D_2	D_3	D_4	Available
O_1	3	6	2	1	20
O_2	6	3	4	7	40
O_3	6	5	8	9	50
Required	10	25	35	15	

5.

	D_1	D_2	D_3	D_4	D_5	D_6	Available
O_1	5	10	15	8	9	7	30
O_2	14	13	10	9	20	21	40
O_3	15	11	13	25	8	12	10
O_4	9	19	12	8	6	13	100
Required	50	20	10	35	15	50	

6. Obtain one degenerate and four non-degenerate optimal solutions of the following transportation problem.

	D_1	D_2	D_3	D_4	D_5	Available
O_1	10	11	10	9	8	20
O_2	7	9	8	7	9	10
O_3	8	11	10	9	10	30
Required	10	5	15	20	10	

7. Obtain three distinct optimal solutions of the following transportation problem. Prove that there are nineteen non-degenerate solutions, but that none of them is optimal.

	D_1	D_2	D_3	D_4	Available
O_1	5	4	3	4	4
O_2	4	3	2	4	3
O_3	3	2	4	2	2
O_4	2	5	5	5	1
Required	1	7	1	1	

8. Assume that surplus goods are stored free of charge.

	D_1	D_2	D_3	D_4	Available
O_1	3	5	2	2	7
O_2	4	5	2	1	2
O_3	2	2	1	2	3
O_4	2	1	2	3	3
O_5	1	2	3	2	6
Required	8	2	7	2	

9.

	D_1	D_2	D_3	D_4	Available
O_1	2	2	1	3	10
O_2	3	1	3	4	9
O_3	4	3	2	3	11
Required	6	4	12	8	

10.

	D_1	D_2	D_3	D_4	D_5	Available
O_1	4	3	2	5	6	70
O_2	8	4	4	5	7	80
O_3	6	8	6	7	5	60
O_4	4	3	5	2	4	120
Required	60	50	50	70	100	

11. Obtain an optimal solution of the following transportation problem. Is there an optimal degenerate solution?

	D_1	D_2	D_3	D_4	D_5	Available
O_1	4	5	5	2	1	10
O_2	3	4	2	4	2	1
O_3	1	3	5	4	2	4
O_4	4	1	2	3	5	23
Required	13	1	19	4	1	

12.

	D_1	D_2	D_3	D_4	D_5	Available
O_1	5	2	3	6	1	4
O_2	7	8	3	3	8	20
O_3	4	0	1	7	9	6
O_4	2	4	5	6	9	7
Required	10	11	3	5	8	

13. Obtain an optimal solution of the following transportation problem. Is the solution unique?

	D_1	D_2	D_3	D_4	Available
O_1	18	16	15	9	20
O_2	11	12	14	3	20
O_3	4	5	4	3	20
Required	13	15	7	15	

14. Obtain an optimal solution of the following transportation problem. There is a penalty of 5 per unit for any non-delivery of goods.

	D_1	D_2	D_3	D_4	D_5	Available
O_1	10	15	10	12	20	8
O_2	5	10	8	15	10	7
O_3	15	10	12	12	10	6
Required	5	9	2	4	5	

15.

	D_1	D_2	D_3	D_4	D_5	D_6	Available
O_1	1	4	0	1	2	3	13
O_2	4	8	2	5	9	8	16
O_3	6	9	1	2	7	9	7
Required	4	5	6	6	7	8	

16.

	D_1	D_2	D_3	D_4	D_5	D_6	Available
O_1	3	6	2	1	3	3	20
O_2	6	3	4	2	2	2	41
O_3	6	4	8	5	3	1	49
Required	9	26	45	15	10	5	

17. A shipping company has to send ships from five ports of departure to four ports of destination. The numbers of ships available and required, and the costs of the voyages for one ship (in hundreds of £), are shown in the following table. No other costs are involved. The company wishes to minimize the total cost.

	O_1	O_2	O_3	O_4	O_5	No. of ships required at ports of destination
D_1	15	25	30	5	15	8
D_2	10	20	25	20	25	8
D_3	5	25	20	15	10	7
D_4	20	30	10	30	5	6
No. of ships available at ports of departure	5	7	9	8	4	

(a) Find an optimal transportation schedule and the minimum total cost.
(b) Prove that there are only two distinct optimal solutions.

18. Find four distinct optimal solutions of the following transportation problem, and prove that every optimal solution of the problem is degenerate.

	D_1	D_2	D_3	D_4	D_5	Available
O_1	2	1	1	2	3	19
O_2	1	2	3	2	1	10
O_3	3	1	2	2	1	13
O_4	2	3	3	2	2	4
Required	10	1	4	13	1	

19. Five squirrels agree to compile five hoards of nuts collected from three trees. The distances in metres from the trees T_i to the hoards H_j are given in the following table, together with the number of nuts available and required. Find the

transportation pattern that minimizes the total distance covered, assuming that a squirrel can carry only one nut at a time. (Ignore return journeys.)

	H_1	H_2	H_3	H_4	H_5	Available
T_1	70	30	20	40	20	50
T_2	60	50	50	60	10	70
T_3	30	20	50	90	60	90
Required	20	60	80	40	10	

By how much would the distance from T_1 to H_4 have to change before the present optimal solution became non-optimal?

20. In the following transportation problem, if a unit from any source is not transported, then a storage cost is incurred. The storage costs per unit at sources *A*, *B*, and *C* are 5, 4, and 3, respectively. However, all the supply at source *B* must be transported, to make room for a new product. Find the optimal solution.

		Destinations			
		X	Y	Z	Available
	A	1	2	1	20
Sources	B	0	4	5	40
	C	2	3	3	30
Required		30	20	20	

Does the constraint on source *B* make any difference to the optimal solution?

Find optimal assignment patterns (including alternative optima) for the job-rating matrices of Exercises 21–24.

21.

$$\mathbf{R} = \begin{pmatrix} 9 & 8 & 7 & 6 \\ 5 & 4 & 3 & 2 \\ 3 & 4 & 5 & 6 \\ 7 & 8 & 9 & 10 \end{pmatrix}.$$

22.

$$\mathbf{R} = \begin{pmatrix} 81 & 80 & 75 & 72 & 93 \\ 47 & 51 & 50 & 54 & 49 \\ 61 & 63 & 59 & 62 & 62 \\ 47 & 45 & 48 & 46 & 47 \\ 50 & 53 & 48 & 52 & 51 \end{pmatrix}.$$

23.

$$\mathbf{R} = \begin{pmatrix} 16 & 11 & 11 & 12 & 9 \\ 3 & 15 & 16 & 14 & 8 \\ 8 & 2 & 13 & 12 & 17 \\ 12 & 1 & 20 & 20 & 10 \\ 18 & 3 & 17 & 12 & 17 \end{pmatrix}.$$

24.

$$\mathbf{R} = \begin{pmatrix} 10 & 9 & 4 & 12 & 7 & 2 & 7 \\ 12 & 9 & 5 & 8 & 7 & 2 & 7 \\ 10 & 9 & 4 & 13 & 7 & 13 & 7 \\ 10 & 1 & 4 & 13 & 7 & 10 & 7 \\ 12 & 6 & 5 & 8 & 8 & 2 & 7 \\ 2 & 19 & 10 & 2 & 5 & 13 & 19 \\ 10 & 4 & 2 & 12 & 4 & 8 & 1 \end{pmatrix}.$$

25. For the job-rating matrix of Exercise 23, find the assignment patterns that *minimize* the sum of the ratings.

Solve the matrix games of Exercises 26–33, in which *A* is the maximizing player.

26.

$$\begin{array}{c} \\ A \end{array} \begin{array}{c} B \\ \begin{pmatrix} 2 & 5 & 3 & 8 & 1 & 4 \\ 4 & 7 & 1 & 2 & 6 & 5 \end{pmatrix}. \end{array}$$

27.

$$A \quad \overset{B}{\begin{pmatrix} 8 & 1 \\ 2 & 4 \\ 1 & 3 \\ 7 & 5 \\ 2 & 8 \end{pmatrix}}.$$

28.

$$A \quad \overset{B}{\begin{pmatrix} 16 & 17 & 18 & 19 & 20 \\ 12 & 9 & 6 & 3 & 0 \end{pmatrix}}.$$

29.

$$A \quad \overset{B}{\begin{pmatrix} 1 & 5 & 6 & 8 & 1 & 3 \\ 8 & 2 & 3 & 5 & 9 & 2 \\ 3 & 9 & 1 & 5 & 2 & 6 \\ 1 & 8 & 5 & 7 & 3 & 3 \\ 4 & 8 & 1 & 2 & 6 & 7 \\ 2 & 6 & 2 & 4 & 7 & 1 \end{pmatrix}}.$$

30.

$$A \overset{B}{\begin{pmatrix} 3 & 2 & 1 & 0 \\ 1 & 1 & 2 & 6 \\ 1 & 9 & 7 & 3 \end{pmatrix}}.$$

31.

$$A \overset{B}{\begin{pmatrix} 5 & 3 & 5 & 5 & 5 \\ 6 & 6 & 2 & 6 & 6 \\ 7 & 7 & 7 & 1 & 7 \\ 8 & 8 & 8 & 8 & 0 \end{pmatrix}}.$$

32.

$$A \overset{B}{\begin{pmatrix} -6 & -1 & 1 & 4 & 7 & 4 & 3 \\ 7 & -2 & 6 & 3 & -2 & -5 & 7 \end{pmatrix}}.$$

33.

$$A \overset{B}{\begin{pmatrix} 1 & 4 & 7 & 10 \\ 7 & 19 & 13 & 16 \\ 22 & 16 & 19 & 13 \\ 16 & 13 & 22 & 10 \end{pmatrix}}.$$

34. The game of Fifouree is played as follows. A chooses one of the integers $1, 2, 3, 4, 5$, and B, independently, chooses one of the integers $1, 2, 3, 4$. The pay-off to A (in pence) is the remainder when the sum of the two chosen integers is divided by three.

Find the most general optimal strategies for A and B, and determine the value of the game.

35. A and B each choose one of the integers $1, 2, 3, 4$, independently of one another. If both choose the same integer, then A pays B that number of pence. If they choose different integers, then B pays A the number of pence equal to the integer A has chosen.

Find optimal strategies for A and B, and determine the value of the game.

36. Repeat Exercise 35 when the integers from which A and B may choose are $1, 2, 3, 4, 5$.

37. Reduce the following game to a pair of dual linear programming problems, and solve one of these problems; thence obtain optimal strategies for A and B, and

determine the value of the game:

$$
\begin{array}{cc} & B \\ A & \begin{pmatrix} 9 & 1 \\ 5 & 7 \\ 8 & 3 \end{pmatrix} \end{array}
$$

38. Prove or disprove that it is possible for a 3×3 matrix game with a singular pay-off matrix and no saddle-point to have a solution with mixed strategies involving all three pure strategies for each player.

39. The celebrated gamesters Lin Prog and Theo Gam play as follows: L.P. chooses a letter from LINEAR PROGRAMMING, and T. G., independently, chooses a letter from THEORY OF GAMES. The pay-off to L.P. is:

(i) zero if both players choose the same letter—this rule takes precedence over rule (ii),

(ii) $+1$ if both players choose vowels or if both choose consonants,

(iii) -1 otherwise.

Find a set of optimal strategies for the two players, and determine the value of the game.

5

The Ellipsoid Algorithm

5.1 Introduction

The simplex method is an exponential-time algorithm, i.e. in the worst case the number of possible arithmetic steps ($+$, $-$, $\times$, $/$, or $\surd$) which are required in order to reach an optimal solution increases exponentially with the number of variables, n. On the other hand, the Shor-Khachiyan ellipsoid method [1], [4], [6], [14], [25] is a polynomial-time algorithm, i.e. the number of possible steps is at most Kn^{α}, where K and α are constants independent of n, and this is true whether exact arithmetic or finite precision arithmetic is used. Prior to its application to linear progamming problems, the ellipsoid method was used by Shor [33] on convex programming problems. It was not known whether the general linear programming problem was solvable in polynomial time until Khachiyan [25] settled the matter in 1979 by showing that it could be solved by the ellipsoid method.

However, this does not mean that the simplex method is obsolete, for an upper bound to the number of steps required in each method depends also on the constant which multiplies the dominant term. In the Shor-Khachiyan method this constant, K, can be extremely large, owing to the very great accuracy that the method usually demands. Also, it has been found in practice that the simplex method works well for most linear programming problems, and there is some recent theoretical evidence to support the general experience that the exponential upper bound on the number of steps is often unduly pessimistic.

In the present section we give a general outline of the Shor-Khachiyan algorithm. A more detailed mathematical account follows in later sections.

With the usual notation ($\mathbf{A}$ is an $m \times n$ matrix, $\mathbf{x}$ an n-vector, $\mathbf{b}$ an m-vector), the Shor-Khachiyan algorithm finds a solution, if one exists, of the inequality

$$\mathbf{Ax} \leqslant \mathbf{b}, \tag{5.1}$$

where all the constants a_{ij}, b_i are integers, and $m \geqslant 2$, $n \geqslant 2$. In practice, the use of integers is not a restriction, since the constants may be expressed as rational numbers to any desired accuracy and a scaling factor then applied. For the sake of simplicity, we assume throughout that exact arithmetic is used in the calculations. Khachiyan's results [25] are based on finite precision arithmetic, but it turns out that the differences between the two approaches are relatively minor.

In order to apply the algorithm to a standard linear programming problem the objective function must first be eliminated, and this can be done using the theory of duality (Section 3.2). Hence the problem

$$\left.\begin{aligned} &\text{Maximise } z = \mathbf{c}'\mathbf{x}, \\ \text{subject to} \quad & \\ &\mathbf{Ax} \leqslant \mathbf{b}, \quad \mathbf{x} \geqslant \mathbf{0}, \end{aligned}\right\} \tag{5.2}$$

may be expressed in the form (5.1), provided that **A** and **b** are suitably reinterpreted. In the usual case, when problem (5.2) has a unique optimal solution, the inequality (5.1) is satisfied at a single point.

An essential feature of the theory of the ellipsoid method is that the set of solution points of the inequality under consideration should have a non-zero volume. Since it is usually not known *a priori* whether this is the case or not for (5.1), Khachiyan considers instead the perturbed system

$$\mathbf{Ax} \leqslant \mathbf{b} + 2^{-L}\mathbf{e}, \tag{5.3}$$

where L is a sufficiently large integer (to be defined later) and $\mathbf{e} = [1, 1, \ldots, 1]$. It will be shown in Theorem 5.9 that the inequality (5.1) has a solution if and only if the perturbed inequality (5.3) has a solution. Furthermore, the algorithm can be modified so that the perturbation term $2^{-L}\mathbf{e}$ is ignorable in practice (cf. Section 5.5), and hence the perturbation may be regarded as a purely theoretical device. It is therefore convenient to assume for the time being that the solution set, if non-empty, of the inequality (5.1) has a non-zero volume; this assumption will be relaxed later.

To find a solution of the inequality (5.1), the algorithm begins with a sphere E_0, centre the origin and volume $V(E_0)$, which contains some solution points of the inequality. We may assume that the centre of the sphere, $\mathbf{x}_0 = \mathbf{0}$, is not a solution point, for otherwise there is no need to proceed further. At the end of the kth iteration, $k = 1, 2, 3, \ldots$, we have an ellipsoid E_k, centre $\mathbf{x}_k$ and volume $V(E_k)$, which contains some solution points ($k = 0$ corresponds to the initial sphere). The algorithm terminates if either $\mathbf{x}_k$ is a solution point, or $V(E_k)$ is so small that E_k cannot contain a solution point (and therefore a set of solution points of a certain small but finite volume). The latter condition gives an upper bound for the number of iterations required (cf. Theorem 5.8 *et seq.*), and in this case the inequality (5.1) has no solution.

In the $(k+1)$th iteration, a hyperplane is found which contains $\mathbf{x}_k$ and which divides E_k into two halves, E_{k-} and E_{k+}, such that $\mathbf{Ax} \leqslant \mathbf{b}$ in E_{k-} and $\mathbf{Ax} > \mathbf{b}$ in E_{k+}. Thus, the semi-ellipsoid E_{k-} contains the same solution points of the inequality (5.1) as E_k. An ellipsoid E_{k+1}, centre $\mathbf{x}_{k+1}$, is then found which contains the whole of E_{k-} and whose volume satisfies

$$V(E_{k+1}) < \gamma V(E_k),$$

where γ is a constant depending only on n and having the property that $0 < \gamma < 1$. Hence the volumes of successive ellipsoids E_k decrease faster than the terms of a geometric progression with common ratio γ. The steps in the Shor-Khachiyan algorithm are collected together for reference at the end of the chapter.

5.2 Starting the Algorithm

Since we are primarily concerned with the solution of linear programming problems, we assume at the outset that problem (5.2) is given. First of all, it is necessary to reduce this problem to the form (5.1); the transformation includes convenient redefinitions of **A** and **b**. The dual of problem (5.2) is

$$\left.\begin{aligned} &\text{Minimize } w = \mathbf{b}'\mathbf{y}, \\ &\text{subject to} \\ &\mathbf{A}'\mathbf{y} \geqslant \mathbf{c}, \quad \mathbf{y} \geqslant \mathbf{0}. \end{aligned}\right\} \tag{5.4}$$

From Theorem 3.2, we know that feasible solutions of (5.2) and (5.4) always satisfy $\mathbf{c}'\mathbf{x} \leqslant \mathbf{b}'\mathbf{y}$ and, from Theorem 3.3, these solutions are optimal if the equality holds. Hence the inequality $\mathbf{c}'\mathbf{x} \geqslant \mathbf{b}'\mathbf{y}$ ensures that the feasible solutions are optimal. Problem (5.2) may therefore be replaced by the set of inequalities

$$\begin{aligned} \mathbf{A}\mathbf{x} &\leqslant \mathbf{b}, \\ \mathbf{A}'\mathbf{y} &\geqslant \mathbf{c}, \\ \mathbf{c}'\mathbf{x} &\geqslant \mathbf{b}'\mathbf{y}, \\ \mathbf{x} &\geqslant \mathbf{0}, \\ \mathbf{y} &\geqslant \mathbf{0}. \end{aligned}$$

This may be written in the form

$$\begin{pmatrix} \mathbf{A} & \vdots & \mathbf{O} \\ \mathbf{O} & \vdots & -\mathbf{A}' \\ -\mathbf{c}' & \vdots & \mathbf{b}' \\ -\mathbf{I}_n & \vdots & \mathbf{O} \\ \mathbf{O} & \vdots & -\mathbf{I}_m \end{pmatrix} \begin{pmatrix} \mathbf{x} \\ \hdashline \mathbf{y} \end{pmatrix} \leqslant \begin{pmatrix} \mathbf{b} \\ -\mathbf{c} \\ 0 \\ \mathbf{0}_n \\ \mathbf{0}_m \end{pmatrix},$$

where $\mathbf{I}_n$ is the unit matrix of order n, and $\mathbf{0}_n$ is the n-vector of zeros. Thus, problem (5.2) has been reduced to the form (5.1), where we may assume that **A** is an $m \times n$ matrix with $m > n$.

At this point it is necessary to consider how the constants in the inequality (5.1) are represented. It is convenient to assume that they are expressed in binary digits, or bits. A useful measure of the amount of data is given by the total number of bits that are required to represent the inequality completely. Now an integer $p > 0$ can be represented by

$$1 + [\log_2 p]$$

bits, where $[t]$ means the largest integer less than or equal to t, and the log is to base 2. Also, the integer $p = 0$ requires one bit, and a sign requires one bit. Since $\mathbf{A} = \{a_{ij}\}$ is an $m \times n$ matrix, the inequality (5.1) is defined by the integers a_{ij}, b_i, m, and n. Thus, the length L of the input, i.e. the number of bits that are required to represent the integers and their signs, is taken to be

$$L = \left\{2mn + \sum_{\substack{i=1 \\ a_{ij} \neq 0}}^{m} \sum_{j=1}^{n} [\log_2 |a_{ij}|]\right\} + \left\{2m + \sum_{\substack{i=1 \\ b_i \neq 0}}^{m} [\log_2 |b_i|]\right\}$$

$$+ \{2 + [\log_2 m]\} + \{2 + [\log_2 n]\}$$

$$= \sum_{\substack{i=1 \\ a_{ij} \neq 0}}^{m} \sum_{j=1}^{n} [\log_2 |a_{ij}|] + \sum_{\substack{i=1 \\ b_i \neq 0}}^{m} [\log_2 |b_i|] + [\log_2 m] + [\log_2 n]$$

$$+ 2mn + 2m + 4. \tag{5.5}$$

An upper bound for L is easily found in terms of σ, the modulus of the numerically largest number in the data. We find that

$$L \leqslant m(m+n)(2 + \log_2 \sigma) + 4.$$

We now prove that if the inequality (5.1) has a solution, then the set of solution points within a distance 2^L of the origin has a non-zero volume. The proof is contained in the following three theorems. As stated earlier, we assume here that the solution set, if non-empty, of the inequality (5.1) has a non-zero volume.

■ Theorem 5.1

Let $\mathbf{v} = [v_1, \ldots, v_n]$ be a vertex of the polyhedron defined by the $m+n$ inequalities

$$\mathbf{Ax} \leqslant \mathbf{b},$$
$$\mathbf{x} \geqslant \mathbf{0},$$

and let $v_M = \max_{1 \leqslant k \leqslant n} \{v_k\}$. Then

$$v_M < \frac{2^L}{mn},$$

and the v_k are rational numbers with denominators less than $2^L/mn$ in absolute value.

Proof

Each vertex of the polyhedron is determined by the solution of n of the $m+n$ equations

$$\mathbf{Ax} = \mathbf{b}, \quad \mathbf{x} = \mathbf{0}.$$

Using Cramer's rule we find that, for any vertex $\mathbf{v}$, each v_k, $k = 1, \ldots, n$, is either zero or equal to D_k/D, where D_k and D are determinants of order n with entries from $\{a_{ij}, b_i, 0, 1\}$. Hence D_k and D are integers.

Let $\mathbf{d}_j$, $j = 1, \ldots, n$, be the column vectors of the matrix associated with D. These column vectors are of two types corresponding to $\mathbf{Ax} = \mathbf{b}$ and $\mathbf{x} = \mathbf{0}$, respectively: either $\mathbf{d}_j$ consists of entries entirely from $\{a_{ij}\}$ or it is a unit vector. By Hadamard's inequality,

$$|D| \leqslant \prod_{j=1}^{n} |\mathbf{d}_j|,$$

and since

$$\begin{aligned}|\mathbf{d}_j|^2 &= d_{ij}^{\ 2} + \ldots + d_{nj}^{\ 2}\\ &\leqslant (|d_{ij}|+1)^2 \times \ldots \times (|d_{nj}|+1)^2,\end{aligned}$$

we have

$$|D| \leqslant \prod_{j=1}^{n} \prod_{i=1}^{n} (|d_{ij}|+1) < 2^{L-\log_2 mn}.$$

The last step follows from the definition of L, after some manipulation. For

$$\begin{aligned}L - [\log_2 m] - [\log_2 n] = &\sum_{\substack{i=1\\ a_{ij}\neq 0}}^{m} \sum_{j=1}^{n} [\log_2 |a_{ij}|] + \sum_{\substack{i=1\\ b_i \neq 0}}^{m} [\log_2 |b_i|]\\ &+ 2mn + 2m + 4,\end{aligned}$$

and

$$[\log_2 m] + [\log_2 n] \geqslant \log_2 mn - 2.$$

Furthermore, for $a = 1, 2, 3, \ldots$, the reader will easily convince himself that

$$\log_2 (a+1) \leqslant [\log_2 a] + 1.$$

Hence, since every d_{ij} is either an a_{ij} or is equal to unity,

$$\begin{aligned}\sum_{j=1}^{n} \sum_{i=1}^{n} \log_2 (|d_{ij}|+1) &\leqslant \sum_{\substack{j=1\\ |d_{ij}|\neq 0}}^{n} \sum_{i=1}^{n} [\log_2 |d_{ij}|] + n^2\\ &< \sum_{\substack{i=1\\ |d_{ij}|\neq 0}}^{m} \sum_{j=1}^{n} [\log_2 |d_{ij}|] + mn\\ &= L - [\log_2 m] - [\log_2 n] - mn - 2m - 4\\ &< L - \log_2 mn,\end{aligned}$$

which leads immediately to the desired result. Hence,

$$|D| < \frac{2^L}{mn}.$$

Similarly, a column vector $\mathbf{d}_j$ of D_k consists of entries entirely from $\{a_{ij}, b_i\}$, or else it is a unit vector. Hence,

$$|D_k| < \frac{2^L}{mn}.$$

This completes the proof, since D_k and D are integers.

■ **Theorem 5.2**

Let $\mathbf{v} = [v_1, \ldots, v_n]$ be a vertex of the polyhedron defined by the $m+2n$ inequalities

$$\mathbf{Ax} \leqslant \mathbf{b},$$
$$\mathbf{x} \geqslant \mathbf{0},$$
$$\mathbf{x} \leqslant \left[\frac{2^L}{n}\right]\mathbf{e},$$

where $\mathbf{e} = [1, 1, \ldots, 1]$. Then the v_k are rational numbers with denominators less than $2^L/mn$ in absolute value.

Proof

The proof is closely similar to that of Theorem 5.1. Again using Cramer's rule, we find that each v_k is either zero or equal to D_k/D, where D_k and D are integers. The column vectors $\mathbf{d}_j$ of D are now taken from the matrix

$$\begin{pmatrix} \mathbf{A} \\ \hline \mathbf{I}_n \end{pmatrix}$$

instead of $\mathbf{A}$, where the $\mathbf{I}_n$ comes from the last n inequalities. Let $\mathbf{d}'_i$, $i = 1, \ldots, m+n$, be the rows of this matrix. By Hadamard's inequality,

$$|D| \leqslant \prod_{i=1}^{m+n} |\mathbf{d}'_i|$$

$$= \prod_{i=1}^{m} |\mathbf{d}'_i|,$$

since the last n rows of the matrix are unit vectors,

$$< \frac{2^L}{mn},$$

as in Theorem 5.1, *mutatis mutandis.*

N.B. The particular form of the right-hand side of the last n inequalities in the statement of the theorem is not used in the above proof, but is needed in the proof of the next theorem.

Theorem 5.3

If the inequality (5.1) has a solution, then the volume of the solution points inside the sphere $|\mathbf{x}| \leqslant 2^L$ is at least $2^{-(n+1)L}$.

Proof

Without loss of generality we may assume that the inequality (5.1) has a solution with $\mathbf{x} > \mathbf{0}$, so that the polyhedron

$$\left.\begin{aligned} \mathbf{Ax} &\leqslant \mathbf{b}, \\ \mathbf{x} &\geqslant \mathbf{0}, \end{aligned}\right\} \tag{5.6}$$

has an interior point. Also, for any vertex $\mathbf{v}$ of (5.6), Theorem 5.1 gives

$$v_M < \frac{2^L}{mn} < \left[\frac{2^L}{n}\right],$$

since $2^L > mn$ and $m \geqslant 2$. Thus (5.6) has an interior point $\mathbf{x}^*$ with $x_M^* < [2^L/n]$, and hence so has the polyhedron

$$\left.\begin{aligned} \mathbf{Ax} &\leqslant \mathbf{b}, \\ \mathbf{x} &\geqslant \mathbf{0}, \\ \mathbf{x} &\leqslant \left[\frac{2^L}{n}\right]\mathbf{e}. \end{aligned}\right\} \tag{5.7}$$

The polyhedron (5.7) must therefore have $n+1$ vertices, $\mathbf{v}_0, \mathbf{v}_1, \ldots, \mathbf{v}_n$, that do not lie on the same hyperplane (e.g. the origin, together with a point on each coordinate axis).

The volume of the n-dimensional simplex with vertices $\mathbf{v}_0, \mathbf{v}_1, \ldots, \mathbf{v}_n$ is

$$\frac{1}{n!}\left|\det\begin{pmatrix} 1 & \ldots & 1 \\ \mathbf{v}_0 & \ldots & \mathbf{v}_n \end{pmatrix}\right|,$$

particular cases being the area of a triangle ($n = 2$) and the volume of a tetrahedron ($n = 3$). Since a simplex, by definition, is the smallest convex set containing all its vertices, the volume V of the polyhedron (5.7) is greater than or equal to that of the above simplex. From Theorem 5.2, we can write

$$\mathbf{v}_i = \frac{\mathbf{u}_i}{D_i}, \quad i = 0, 1, \ldots, n,$$

where the $\mathbf{u}_i$ are vectors with integer components and the determinants D_i are integers satisfying $D_i < 2^L/n$. Hence,

$$\left|\det\begin{pmatrix}1 & \dots & 1\\ \mathbf{v}_0 & \dots & \mathbf{v}_n\end{pmatrix}\right| = \left|\det\begin{pmatrix}1 & \dots & 1\\ \dfrac{\mathbf{u}_0}{D_0} & \dots & \dfrac{\mathbf{u}_n}{D_n}\end{pmatrix}\right|$$

$$= \left|\frac{1}{D_0 \dots D_n}\det\begin{pmatrix}D_0 & \dots & D_n\\ \mathbf{u}_0 & \dots & \mathbf{u}_n\end{pmatrix}\right|$$

$$\geqslant \frac{1}{|D_0| \dots |D_n|},$$

since

$$\det\begin{pmatrix}D_0 & \dots & D_n\\ \mathbf{u}_0 & \dots & \mathbf{u}_n\end{pmatrix}$$

is a non-zero integer. Finally,

$$V \geqslant \frac{1}{n!\,|D_0| \dots |D_n|}$$

$$> \frac{1}{n!}\left(\frac{2^L}{n}\right)^{-(n+1)}$$

$$> 2^{-(n+1)L},$$

for n^{n+1} is obviously greater than $n!$ if $n \geqslant 2$.

5.3 Transformation of the Ellipsoid E_k

We have proved in the preceding section that a sphere, centre the origin and of radius 2^L, contains a set X_s, say, of solution points of the inequality (5.1), and that the volume of X_s is at least $2^{-(n+1)L}$ (assuming always that X_s, if non-empty, has a non-zero volume). The next step in the algorithm is to find an ellipsoid of smaller volume than the sphere but which contains the whole of X_s. It is convenient, however, to consider the general step, i.e. the transformation of the ellipsoid E_k to the ellipsoid E_{k+1}, where E_0 is the initial sphere.

Let $\mathbf{x}_k$ be the centre of E_k. Suppose that $\mathbf{x}_k$ is not a solution point of the inequality (5.1) and that a component of (5.1) violated at $\mathbf{x}_k$ is

$$\mathbf{a}'\mathbf{x} < \delta.$$

Then the hyperplane

$$\mathbf{a}'(\mathbf{x} - \mathbf{x}_k) = 0,$$

which passes through $\mathbf{x}_k$ and has $\mathbf{a}$ as a normal, divides E_k into two half-ellipsoids, E_{k-}, E_{k+}, defined by

$$E_{k-}: \quad \mathbf{x} \in E_k, \quad \mathbf{a}'(\mathbf{x} - \mathbf{x}_k) \leqslant 0,$$

$$E_{k+}: \quad \mathbf{x} \in E_k, \quad \mathbf{a}'(\mathbf{x} - \mathbf{x}_k) > 0.$$

The semi-ellipsoid E_{k+} consists entirely of points that violate (5.1), since $\mathbf{a}'\mathbf{x}_k \geqslant \delta$, and is therefore discarded. The ellipsoid E_{k+1}, which we now construct, contains the whole of E_{k-} and hence the whole of X_s. Incidentally, an interesting property of E_{k+1} is that it is the ellipsoid of smallest volume that contains the whole of E_{k-}. This property is proved in Appendix B of reference [6].

The ellipsoid E_k, with centre $\mathbf{x}_k$ and matrix $\mathbf{B}_k$, is defined by

$$(\mathbf{x}-\mathbf{x}_k)'\,\mathbf{B}_k^{-1}\,(\mathbf{x}-\mathbf{x}_k) \leqslant 1,$$

where $\mathbf{B}_k$, and hence $\mathbf{B}_k^{-1}$, is a positive definite symmetric matrix. The ellipsoid E_{k+1} has centre $\mathbf{x}_{k+1}$ and matrix $\mathbf{B}_{k+1}$, where

$$\mathbf{x}_{k+1} = \mathbf{x}_k - \frac{1}{n+1}\,\frac{\mathbf{B}_k\mathbf{a}}{(\mathbf{a}'\mathbf{B}_k\mathbf{a})^{1/2}}, \tag{5.8}$$

$$\mathbf{B}_{k+1} = \frac{n^2}{n^2-1}\left(\mathbf{B}_k - \frac{2}{n+1}\,\frac{\mathbf{B}_k\mathbf{a}\mathbf{a}'\mathbf{B}_k}{\mathbf{a}'\mathbf{B}_k\mathbf{a}}\right). \tag{5.9}$$

These are the central updating formulae of the ellipsoid algorithm.

The geometry of the n-dimensional ellipsoids E_k and E_{k+1} is shown diagrammatically in Figure 5.1. Note that E_k and E_{k+1} intersect the hyperplane $\mathbf{a}'(\mathbf{x}-\mathbf{x}_k) = 0$ in the same $(n-1)$-dimensional ellipsoid, and that they have a common tangent hyperplane at P, the boundary point in E_{k-} on the line of centres.

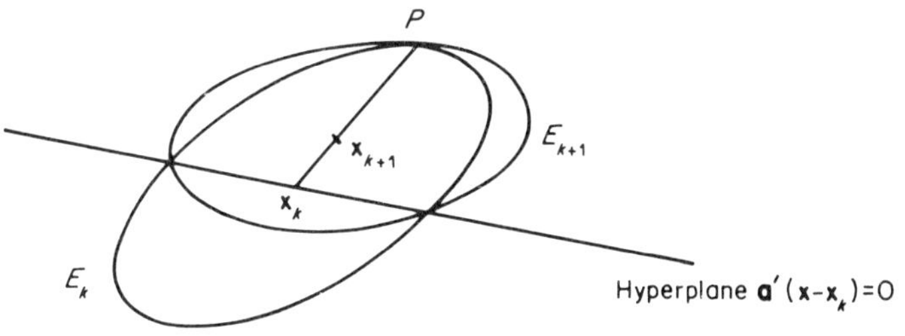

Figure 5.1 The ellipsoids E_k and E_{k+1}

We shall prove the following results in Theorems 5.5, 5.6, and 5.7, respectively:

(a) If $\mathbf{B}_k$ is symmetric and positive definite then so is $\mathbf{B}_{k+1}$.

(b) E_{k-} is contained in E_{k+1}.

(c) The volumes of E_{k+1} and E_k satisfy

$$V(E_{k+1}) < V(E_k)\exp\left(-\frac{1}{2(n+1)}\right).$$

The proofs are considerably simplified by noting that it is sufficient to consider the case where E_k is the unit sphere with centre the origin, and the vector $\mathbf{a}$ is simply the unit vector $\mathbf{v} = [-1, 0, \ldots, 0]$. This result follows from the fact that the properties (a), (b), and (c) above are invariant under a general linear transformation of Cartesian coordinates, usually called an *affine transformation*, viz.

$$T(\mathbf{x}) = \mathbf{x}_c + \mathbf{L}\mathbf{x}, \tag{5.10}$$

where $\mathbf{L}$ is a non-singular matrix. First, it is useful to consider briefly the geometrical interpretation of the transformation (5.10).

Consider the ellipsoid

$$\mathbf{x}'\mathbf{B}^{-1}\mathbf{x} \leqslant 1, \tag{5.11}$$

where the eigenvalues of the positive definite symmetric matrix $\mathbf{B}$ are $\lambda_j, j = 1, \ldots, n$. The λ_j are necessarily all strictly positive, and the corresponding eigenvectors $\mathbf{q}_j$ may be chosen to be the column vectors of an orthogonal matrix $\mathbf{Q}$ (i.e. $\mathbf{QQ}' = \mathbf{I}$). Thus,

$$\mathbf{B}\mathbf{q}_j = \lambda_j \mathbf{q}_j,$$

and hence

$$\mathbf{BQ} = \mathbf{Q}\mathbf{\Lambda},$$

where $\mathbf{\Lambda} = \operatorname{diag}(\lambda_1, \ldots, \lambda_n)$. Therefore

$$\mathbf{B} = \mathbf{Q}\mathbf{\Lambda}\mathbf{Q}^{-1} = \mathbf{Q}\mathbf{\Lambda}\mathbf{Q}' = \mathbf{Q}\mathbf{\Lambda}^{1/2}\mathbf{\Lambda}^{1/2}\mathbf{Q}' = \mathbf{LL}',$$

where

$$\mathbf{L} = \mathbf{Q}\mathbf{\Lambda}^{1/2}.$$

The ellipsoid (5.11) may be obtained by applying the transformation

$$T(\mathbf{x}) = \mathbf{L}\mathbf{x}$$

to the sphere

$$E\colon\ \mathbf{x}'\mathbf{x} \leqslant 1.$$

Note that the inverse transformation is

$$T^{-1}(\mathbf{x}) = \mathbf{L}^{-1}\mathbf{x}.$$

We find that if $\mathbf{x}$ is a point of $T(E)$, the set of points into which E is transformed by T, then, from the definition of E,

$$[T^{-1}(\mathbf{x})]'T^{-1}(\mathbf{x}) \leqslant 1,$$

i.e.

$$\mathbf{x}'(\mathbf{L}^{-1})'\mathbf{L}^{-1}\mathbf{x} = \mathbf{x}'(\mathbf{LL}')^{-1}\mathbf{x} = \mathbf{x}'\mathbf{B}^{-1}\mathbf{x} \leqslant 1,$$

so that $\mathbf{x}$ is a point of the ellipsoid (5.11), as required. In particular, the transformation T sends the unit vectors $\mathbf{e}_1, \ldots, \mathbf{e}_n$ into

$$\begin{aligned} T(\mathbf{e}_1, \ldots, \mathbf{e}_n) &= \mathbf{L}(\mathbf{e}_1, \ldots, \mathbf{e}_n) \\ &= \mathbf{Q}(\lambda_1^{1/2}\mathbf{e}_1, \ldots, \lambda_n^{1/2}\mathbf{e}_n) \\ &= (\lambda_1^{1/2}\mathbf{q}_1, \ldots, \lambda_n^{1/2}\mathbf{q}_n). \end{aligned}$$

This shows that n mutually orthogonal semi-axes of the sphere, along the coordinate directions, are transformed into mutually orthogonal semi-axes of the ellipsoid (5.11), in the directions of the eigenvectors $\mathbf{q}_j$, and that the lengths of the semi-axes of the ellipsoid are $\lambda_1^{1/2}, \ldots, \lambda_n^{1/2}$. It follows that

$$\frac{\text{vol. of ellipsoid}}{\text{vol. of sphere}} = (\lambda_1 \ldots \lambda_n)^{1/2} = |\det(\mathbf{L})|.$$

Remembering that $\mathbf{L} = \mathbf{Q}\Lambda^{1/2}$, the transformation (5.10) is now seen to consist of three elements:

(i) A rotation of the rectangular cartesian axes about the origin, due to the orthogonal matrix $\mathbf{Q}$.

(ii) Changes in length measured along these axes, by the factors $\lambda_1^{1/2}, \ldots, \lambda_n^{1/2}$, respectively.

(iii) A displacement $\mathbf{x}_c$ of the origin.

We now return to the proof that properties (a), (b), and (c) above are invariant under the transformation (5.10). The proof we shall give depends on the following theorem.

■ Theorem 5.4

Let $\mathbf{B}$ be an $n \times n$ symmetric, positive definite matrix, let $\mathbf{a} \neq \mathbf{0}$, $\mathbf{x}_1$, and $\mathbf{v} = [-1, 0, \ldots, 0]$ be n-vectors, and let α, β, and γ be positive constants. Then the transformation $T(\mathbf{x})$, of equation (5.10), which maps the sphere

$$E: \mathbf{x}'\mathbf{x} \leqslant 1$$

onto the ellipsoid

$$E_c: (\mathbf{x} - \mathbf{x}_c)'\mathbf{B}^{-1}(\mathbf{x} - \mathbf{x}_c) \leqslant 1, \tag{5.12}$$

also maps

$$\bar{E}: (\mathbf{x} + \alpha\mathbf{v})'\beta(\mathbf{I} - \gamma\mathbf{v}\mathbf{v}')^{-1}(\mathbf{x} + \alpha\mathbf{v}) \leqslant 1 \tag{5.13}$$

onto

$$\bar{E}_c: \left(\mathbf{x} - \mathbf{x}_c + \frac{\alpha\mathbf{B}\mathbf{a}}{(\mathbf{a}'\mathbf{B}\mathbf{a})^{1/2}}\right)'\beta\left(\mathbf{B} - \frac{\gamma\mathbf{B}\mathbf{a}\mathbf{a}'\mathbf{B}}{\mathbf{a}'\mathbf{B}\mathbf{a}}\right)^{-1}$$

$$\times\left(\mathbf{x} - \mathbf{x}^c + \frac{\alpha\mathbf{B}\mathbf{a}}{(\mathbf{a}'\mathbf{B}\mathbf{a})^{1/2}}\right) \leqslant 1. \tag{5.14}$$

Proof

We have already proved that $T(E) = E_c$ [cf. (i), (ii), and (iii) above]. It remains to prove that $T(\bar{E}) = \bar{E}_c$. We have

$$T(\mathbf{x}) \coloneqq \mathbf{x}_c + \mathbf{Q}\Lambda^{1/2}\mathbf{x},$$

where $\mathbf{Q}$ is orthogonal and $\boldsymbol{\Lambda}$ diagonal, and we now choose $\mathbf{Q}$ such that

$$\mathbf{v} = \frac{\mathbf{L}'\mathbf{a}}{|\mathbf{L}'\mathbf{a}|},$$

remembering that $\mathbf{v}$ is a unit vector. Geometrically, this is equivalent to choosing the orientation of the coordinate axes so that the negative x_1-axis is parallel to $\mathbf{a}$. Now

$$|\mathbf{L}'\mathbf{a}|^2 = \mathbf{a}'\mathbf{L}\mathbf{L}'\mathbf{a} = \mathbf{a}'\mathbf{B}\mathbf{a},$$

and hence

$$\mathbf{v}\mathbf{v}' = \frac{\mathbf{L}'\mathbf{a}\mathbf{a}'\mathbf{L}}{\mathbf{a}'\mathbf{B}\mathbf{a}}.$$

Thus, T maps $\bar{E}$ onto

$$(T^{-1}(\mathbf{x}) + \alpha\mathbf{v})'\beta(\mathbf{I} - \gamma\mathbf{v}\mathbf{v}')^{-1}(T^{-1}(\mathbf{x}) + \alpha\mathbf{v}) \leqslant 1,$$

and since

$$T^{-1}(\mathbf{x}) = \mathbf{L}^{-1}(\mathbf{x} - \mathbf{x}_c),$$

the left-hand side becomes

$$\begin{aligned}
&(L^{-1}(\mathbf{x} - \mathbf{x}_c) + \alpha\mathbf{v})'\beta(\mathbf{I} - \gamma\mathbf{v}\mathbf{v}')^{-1}(L^{-1}(\mathbf{x} - \mathbf{x}_c) + \alpha\mathbf{v}) \\
&= \left((\mathbf{x} - \mathbf{x}_c)'(\mathbf{L}^{-1})' + \frac{\alpha\mathbf{a}'\mathbf{L}}{(\mathbf{a}'\mathbf{B}\mathbf{a})^{1/2}}\right)\beta\left(\mathbf{I} - \frac{\gamma\mathbf{L}'\mathbf{a}\mathbf{a}'\mathbf{L}}{\mathbf{a}'\mathbf{B}\mathbf{a}}\right)^{-1} \\
&\quad\times\left(L^{-1}(\mathbf{x} - \mathbf{x}_c) + \frac{\alpha\mathbf{L}'\mathbf{a}}{(\mathbf{a}'\mathbf{B}\mathbf{a})^{1/2}}\right) \\
&= \left((\mathbf{x} - \mathbf{x}_c)' + \frac{\alpha\mathbf{a}'\mathbf{L}\mathbf{L}'}{(\mathbf{a}'\mathbf{B}\mathbf{a})^{1/2}}\right)(\mathbf{L}^{-1})'\beta\left(\mathbf{I} - \frac{\gamma\mathbf{L}'\mathbf{a}\mathbf{a}'\mathbf{L}}{\mathbf{a}'\mathbf{B}\mathbf{a}}\right)^{-1} \\
&\quad\times\mathbf{L}^{-1}\left(\mathbf{x} - \mathbf{x}_c + \frac{\alpha\mathbf{L}\mathbf{L}'\mathbf{a}}{(\mathbf{a}'\mathbf{B}\mathbf{a})^{1/2}}\right) \\
&= \left((\mathbf{x} - \mathbf{x}_c)' + \frac{\alpha\mathbf{a}'\mathbf{B}}{(\mathbf{a}'\mathbf{B}\mathbf{a})^{1/2}}\right)\beta\left(\mathbf{L}\mathbf{L}' - \frac{\gamma\mathbf{L}\mathbf{L}'\mathbf{a}\mathbf{a}'\mathbf{L}\mathbf{L}'}{\mathbf{a}'\mathbf{B}\mathbf{a}}\right)^{-1} \\
&\quad\times\left(\mathbf{x} - \mathbf{x}_c + \frac{\alpha\mathbf{B}\mathbf{a}}{(\mathbf{a}'\mathbf{B}\mathbf{a})^{1/2}}\right) \\
&= \left(\mathbf{x} - \mathbf{x}_c + \frac{\alpha\mathbf{B}\mathbf{a}}{(\mathbf{a}'\mathbf{B}\mathbf{a})^{1/2}}\right)'\beta\left(\mathbf{B} - \frac{\gamma\mathbf{B}\mathbf{a}\mathbf{a}'\mathbf{B}}{\mathbf{a}'\mathbf{B}\mathbf{a}}\right)^{-1} \\
&\quad\times\left(\mathbf{x} - \mathbf{x}_c + \frac{\alpha\mathbf{B}\mathbf{a}}{(\mathbf{a}'\mathbf{B}\mathbf{a})^{1/2}}\right).
\end{aligned}$$

We have therefore proved that $T(\bar{E}) = \bar{E}_c$.

If, in Theorem 5.4, we identify $\mathbf{x}_c$ with $\mathbf{x}_k$, and $\mathbf{B}$ with $\mathbf{B}_k$, and set

$$\alpha = \frac{1}{n+1}, \quad \beta = \frac{n^2-1}{n^2}, \quad \gamma = \frac{2}{n+1},$$

then E_c of (5.12) becomes E_k, and $\bar{E}_c$ of (5.14) becomes E_{k+1}. The significance of Theorem 5.4 is now clear. The general step in the algorithm transforms E_k into E_{k+1} [cf. equations (5.8) and (5.9)]; but the general linear transformation (5.10) transforms the sphere E into the ellipsoid E_c, and also transforms $\bar{E}$ into $\bar{E}_c$. Thus, if we wish to deduce any properties of E_k and E_{k+1} that remain invariant under the invertible transformation (5.10), we may replace E_k by E, and E_{k+1} by $\bar{E}$. It so happens that *all* the properties in which we are interested, viz. (a), (b), and (c) above, satisfy this condition. This may be proved as follows.

In each of the three proofs below we use the fact that any ellipsoid may be mapped onto the unit sphere, centre the origin, by a transformation of the form (5.10). Hence, any ellipsoid may be mapped onto any other ellipsoid; note that $T^{-1}(\mathbf{x})$ is also of the form (5.10).

(a) The matrix of an ellipsoid is transformed into another symmetric, positive definite matrix.

Proof

The transformation (5.10) applied to the sphere E leads to E_c of (5.12), where $\mathbf{B} = \mathbf{LL}'$. Hence, $\mathbf{B}$ is symmetric. Also,

$$\mathbf{x}'\mathbf{Bx} = \mathbf{x}'\mathbf{LL}'\mathbf{x} = (\mathbf{L}'\mathbf{x})'(\mathbf{L}'\mathbf{x}) > 0$$

for all $\mathbf{x} \neq \mathbf{0}$. Hence, $\mathbf{B}$ is positive definite. These two properties are preserved, since the matrix of E is $\mathbf{I}$, which is certainly symmetric and positive definite.

(b) The dividing hyperplane property is preserved.

Proof

Consider the hyperplane

$$H\colon \mathbf{a}'\mathbf{Lx} = 0,$$

which divides the sphere E into two halves. The transformation (5.10), with $\mathbf{x}_c = \mathbf{x}_k$, maps H onto

$$\bar{H}:\ \mathbf{a}'\mathbf{L}T^{-1}(\mathbf{x}) = 0,$$

i.e.

$$\mathbf{a}'(\mathbf{x} - \mathbf{x}_k) = 0.$$

Hence, the two halves of the sphere E, viz.

$$E_-: \mathbf{x} \in E, \quad \mathbf{a}'\mathbf{Lx} \leqslant 0; \qquad E_+: \mathbf{x} \in E, \quad \mathbf{a}'\mathbf{Lx} > 0,$$

are mapped onto E_{k-} and E_{k+}, respectively, and the required property is therefore preserved.

(c) $[V(E_{k+1})]/[V(E_k)]$ is invariant.

Proof

We have already proved that

$$\frac{V(\bar{E}_c)}{V(\bar{E})} = |\det(\mathbf{L})| = \frac{V(E_c)}{V(E)}.$$

Inserting appropriate values of the constants, we can identify E_k and E_{k+1} with E_c and $\bar{E}_c$, respectively, as indicated earlier. Hence,

$$\frac{V(E_{k+1})}{V(E_k)} = \frac{V(\bar{E})}{V(E)},$$

which depends only on n.

The next three theorems complete the proofs of the results (a), (b), and (c), page 203. In the proofs of these theorems we replace

$$E_k,\ \mathbf{x}_k,\ \mathbf{a},\ \mathbf{B}_k,\ \mathbf{L};\quad E_{k+1},\ \mathbf{x}_{k+1},\ \mathbf{B}_{k+1}$$

by

$$E,\ \mathbf{0},\ \mathbf{v},\ \mathbf{I},\ \mathbf{I};\quad \bar{E},\quad -\alpha\mathbf{v},\ \beta^{-1}(\mathbf{I}-\gamma\mathbf{v}\mathbf{v}'),$$

respectively, the validity of these substitutions having been proved in Theorem 5.4 *et seq.* We assume that $n \geqslant 2$.

■ **Theorem 5.5**

If $\mathbf{B}_k$ is symmetric and positive definite then so is $\mathbf{B}_{k+1}$, i.e. $\mathbf{B}_{k+1}$ defines an ellipsoid.

Proof

Replacing $\mathbf{B}_k$ by $\mathbf{I}$, and $\mathbf{B}_{k+1}$ by

$$\bar{\mathbf{B}} = \beta^{-1}(\mathbf{I}-\gamma\mathbf{v}\mathbf{v}'),$$

we have to prove that $\bar{\mathbf{B}}$ is symmetric and positive definite. The symmetry is obvious. Also, $\bar{\mathbf{B}}$ is a diagonal matrix whose elements are all positive. Hence it is positive definite.

■ Theorem 5.6

E_{k-} is contained in E_{k+1}.

Proof

Replacing E_k by E, etc. the hyperplane $\mathbf{v}'\mathbf{x} = 0$ divides E into two halves, viz.

$$E_{-}: \mathbf{x} \in E, \quad \mathbf{v}'\mathbf{x} \leqslant 0; \qquad E_{+}: \mathbf{x} \in E, \quad \mathbf{v}'\mathbf{x} > 0.$$

Let $\mathbf{y} \in E_{-}$. Then $|\mathbf{y}| \leqslant 1$ and $0 \leqslant y_1 \leqslant 1$. We have to show that $\mathbf{y} \in \bar{E}$, i.e.

$$(\mathbf{y} + \alpha\mathbf{v})'\overline{\mathbf{B}}^{-1}(\mathbf{y} + \alpha\mathbf{v}) \leqslant 1,$$

where $\overline{\mathbf{B}}$ is defined in the proof of Theorem 5.5. We find

$$\overline{\mathbf{B}}^{-1} = \frac{n^2 - 1}{n^2} \operatorname{diag}\left(\frac{n+1}{n-1}, 1, \ldots, 1\right),$$

and the left-hand side of the preceding inequality is

$$\mathbf{y}'\overline{\mathbf{B}}^{-1}\mathbf{y} - 2\alpha\mathbf{y}'\overline{\mathbf{B}}^{-1}\mathbf{v} + \alpha^2\mathbf{v}'\overline{\mathbf{B}}^{-1}\mathbf{v}$$

$$= \frac{n^2-1}{n^2}\left\{|\mathbf{y}|^2 + \left(\frac{n+1}{n-1} - 1\right)y_1^2 + \frac{2}{n+1}\left(\frac{n+1}{n-1}\right)y_1 + \frac{1}{(n+1)^2}\left(\frac{n+1}{n-1}\right)\right\}$$

$$= \frac{n^2-1}{n^2}\left\{|\mathbf{y}|^2 + \frac{2y_1^2}{n-1} + \frac{2y_1}{n-1} + \frac{1}{n^2-1}\right\}$$

$$= \frac{n^2-1}{n^2} \cdot |\mathbf{y}|^2 + \frac{2(n+1)}{n^2}y_1^2 - \frac{2(n+1)}{n^2}y_1 + \frac{1}{n^2}$$

$$= \frac{n^2-1}{n^2}(|\mathbf{y}|^2 - 1) + \frac{2(n+1)}{n^2}y_1(y_1 - 1) + 1$$

$$\leqslant 1,$$

which completes the proof.

■ Theorem 5.7

The volumes of E_{k+1} and E_k satisfy

$$V(E_{k+1}) < V(E_k)\exp\left(-\frac{1}{2(n+1)}\right).$$

Proof

Again replacing E_k by E, etc. we have to find an upper bound for $V(\bar{E})/V(E)$, where the transformation $E \to \bar{E}$ is defined by

$$\bar{E} = T(E), \quad T(\mathbf{x}) = -\alpha\mathbf{v} + \mathbf{L}\mathbf{x}, \quad \bar{\mathbf{B}} = \mathbf{L}\mathbf{L}' = \beta^{-1}(\mathbf{I} - \gamma\mathbf{v}\mathbf{v}').$$

We know that

$$V(\bar{E}) = |\det(\mathbf{L})|\, V(E),$$

and we have

$$|\det(\mathbf{L})| = \{\det(\bar{\mathbf{B}})\}^{1/2} = \left(\frac{n}{n+1}\right)\left(\frac{n^2}{n^2-1}\right)^{(n-1)/2}$$

$$= \left(1 - \frac{1}{n+1}\right)\left(1 + \frac{1}{n^2-1}\right)^{(n-1)/2}$$

$$< \exp\left(-\frac{1}{n+1}\right)\cdot \exp\left(\frac{n-1}{2(n^2-1)}\right)$$

$$= \exp\left(-\frac{1}{2(n+1)}\right).$$

The result follows immediately.

5.4 The Perturbed Inequality

We have assumed so far that if the inequality (5.1) has a solution, then the volume of the set of solution points is non-zero. We now wish to relax this assumption, and to this end we first prove the following theorem, which deals with the special case where the solution set of (5.1) is bounded above and below.

■ **Theorem 5.8**

Let X be the solution set of the inequality (5.1), and let $S(\mathbf{x}, y)$ denote the sphere with centre $\mathbf{x}$ and radius y. Suppose that *a priori* bounds on X are given in the form

$$S(\mathbf{a}^*, r) \subseteq X \subseteq S(\mathbf{a}_0, R),$$

where $\mathbf{a}^*$ is unknown, $\mathbf{a}_0$ is known, and $r < R$. If

$$E_0 = S(\mathbf{a}_0, R),$$

then the ellipsoid algorithm for finding a solution of (5.1) must terminate with $\mathbf{x}_k \in X$ for some k satisfying

$$k \leqslant 2n(n+1)\log_e\left(\frac{R}{r}\right).$$

Proof

The proof is by contradiction. From Theorem 5.7,

$$\frac{V(E_{k+1})}{V(E_k)} < \exp\left(-\frac{1}{2(n+1)}\right), \quad k = 0, 1, 2, \ldots.$$

Suppose that

$$k > 2n(n+1)\log_e\left(\frac{R}{r}\right).$$

Then

$$\begin{aligned} V(E_k) &= \frac{V(E_k)}{V(E_{k-1})} \cdot \frac{V(E_{k-1})}{V(E_{k-2})} \cdots \frac{V(E_1)}{V(E_0)} . V(E_0) \\ &< \exp\left(-\frac{k}{2(n+1)}\right) V(E_0) \\ &< \exp\left(-n \log_e\left(\frac{R}{r}\right)\right) V(E_0) \\ &= \left(\frac{r}{R}\right)^n V(E_0). \end{aligned}$$

Now E_0 is of radius R. Hence, if E_k were a sphere its radius would be less than r, and in any case E_k cannot contain a sphere of radius r.

On the other hand, $X \subseteq E_0$, by hypothesis, and hence $X \subseteq E_k$, by the method of construction of the ellipsoids. It follows that

$$S(\mathbf{a}^*, r) \subseteq X \subseteq E_k, \quad k = 0, 1, 2, \ldots.$$

This contradiction shows that the algorithm must terminate with $\mathbf{x}_k \in X$ for some $k \leqslant 2n(n+1)\log_e(R/r)$.

The result of Theorem 5.8 shows that the algorithm is a polynomial-time algorithm if r and R are regarded as part of the input, or if $\log_e(R/r)$ is polynomial in n. However, in order to provide a polynomial-time algorithm which is applicable in the most general case, we must assume that nothing is known about the inequality (5.1) apart from the values of the elements of $\mathbf{A}$ and $\mathbf{b}$. Theorem 5.3 shows that we can always take $R = 2^L$; but it may happen that $r = 0$, in which case

Theorem 5.8 is not applicable. Khachiyan [25] considers the perturbed inequality (5.3) and uses the following important theorem.

■ Theorem 5.9

The inequality (5.1) has a solution if and only if the perturbed inequality (5.3) has a solution.

Proof

The 'only if' part of the proof is trivial. The 'if' part relies on one of the variants of Farkas' lemma. This elegant proof is due to Karamardian [24]. Farkas' lemma and its variants are statements of the form that of two sets of linear constraints, just one has a solution.

The variant required here is concerned with the following sets of constraints:
(i) $\mathbf{Ax} \leqslant \mathbf{b}$, $\mathbf{x}$ unrestricted in sign,
(ii) $\mathbf{A}'\mathbf{y} = \mathbf{0}$, $\mathbf{y} > \mathbf{0}$, $\mathbf{b}'\mathbf{y} < 0$.
To prove this variant, we regard (i) as the constraints of the linear programming problem

$$\text{Maximize } z = \mathbf{c}'\mathbf{x}.$$

The dual of this problem is

$$\text{Minimize } w = \mathbf{b}'\mathbf{y},$$

subject to

$$\mathbf{A}'\mathbf{y} = \mathbf{c}, \quad \mathbf{y} \geqslant \mathbf{0}.$$

For any feasible solutions $\mathbf{x}$, $\mathbf{y}$ of the primal and dual problems, respectively, we know from equation (3.20) that

$$z \leqslant w, \quad \text{i.e. } \mathbf{c}'\mathbf{x} \leqslant \mathbf{b}'\mathbf{y}.$$

Now let $\mathbf{c} \to \mathbf{0}$. Then the dual constraints become $\mathbf{A}'\mathbf{y} = \mathbf{0}$, and for any feasible solution $(\mathbf{y} \geqslant \mathbf{0})$ of the dual, we have

$$\mathbf{b}'\mathbf{y} \geqslant \mathbf{0},$$

which contradicts the last constraint in (ii). Hence, if (i) has a solution, then (ii) does not, and conversely. This proves the required variant of Farkas' lemma.

We shall now show that if

$$\mathbf{Ax} \leqslant \mathbf{b} + 2^{-L}\mathbf{e} \tag{5.3}$$

has a solution, then so has $\mathbf{Ax} \leqslant \mathbf{b}$. The proof is by contradiction. Suppose that the first of these inequalities has a solution and the second has not. Then, from (ii) above, there exists an m-vector $\bar{\mathbf{y}}$ such that

$$\mathbf{A}'\bar{\mathbf{y}} = \mathbf{0}, \quad \bar{\mathbf{y}} > \mathbf{0}, \quad \mathbf{b}'\bar{\mathbf{y}} = -1. \tag{5.15}$$

Also, from Theorem 5.1, $\bar{\mathbf{y}}$ satisfies

$$\mathbf{e}'\bar{\mathbf{y}} < \frac{2^L}{n} < 2^L. \tag{5.16}$$

From (5.3) and (5.15), we have

$$0 = \bar{\mathbf{y}}'\mathbf{A}\mathbf{x} \leqslant \bar{\mathbf{y}}'\mathbf{b} + 2^{-L}\bar{\mathbf{y}}'\mathbf{e} = -1 + 2^{-L}\bar{\mathbf{y}}'\mathbf{e},$$

giving

$$\bar{\mathbf{y}}'\mathbf{e} \geqslant 2^L,$$

which contradicts (5.16) and completes the proof.

Suppose now that Y is the solution set of the perturbed inequality (5.3), which we write in the form

$$\mathbf{a}_i'\mathbf{x} \leqslant b_i + 2^{-L}, \quad i = 1, \ldots, m,$$

where $\mathbf{a}_i'$ is the ith row of $\mathbf{A}$, and suppose that the inequality (5.1) has a solution $\hat{\mathbf{x}}$. The reason for considering the perturbed inequality (5.3) is that the sphere

$$S\left(\hat{\mathbf{x}}, \frac{1}{\max_i |2^L\mathbf{a}_i'|}\right)$$

is contained in Y. This is proved in the following theorem.

■ **Theorem 5.10**

Let Y be the solution set of

$$\mathbf{a}_i'\mathbf{x} \leqslant b_i + 2^{-L}, \quad i = 1, \ldots, m,$$

and suppose that

$$\mathbf{a}_i'\mathbf{x} \leqslant b_i$$

has a solution $\hat{\mathbf{x}}$. Then

$$S\left(\hat{\mathbf{x}}, \frac{1}{\max_i |2^L\mathbf{a}_i'|}\right) \subseteq Y.$$

Proof

Let

$$\mathbf{x} = \hat{\mathbf{x}} + \frac{\boldsymbol{\theta}}{\max_i |2^L\mathbf{a}_i'|}, \quad 0 \leqslant |\boldsymbol{\theta}| \leqslant 1,$$

i.e. $\mathbf{x}$ is any point inside or on the sphere of centre $\hat{\mathbf{x}}$ and radius $1/\max_i |2^L\mathbf{a}_i'|$. Then

$$2^L\mathbf{a}_i'\mathbf{x}-2^Lb_i=2^L\mathbf{a}_i'\hat{\mathbf{x}}+\frac{2^L\mathbf{a}_i'\boldsymbol{\theta}}{\max_i|2^L\mathbf{a}_i'|}-2^Lb_i$$
$$\leqslant\frac{2^L\mathbf{a}_i'\boldsymbol{\theta}}{\max_i|2^L\mathbf{a}_i'|}$$
$$\leqslant\frac{|2^L\mathbf{a}_i'|}{\max_i|2^L\mathbf{a}_i'|}$$
$$\leqslant 1,$$

i.e.

$$\mathbf{x}\in Y,$$

or

$$S\left(\hat{\mathbf{x}},\frac{1}{\max_i|2^L\mathbf{a}_i'|}\right)\subseteq Y.$$

Since L is the total length of the input for the inequality (5.1), we must have

$$|\mathbf{a}_i|\leqslant 2^L.$$

It follows immediately from Theorem 5.10 that

$$S(\hat{\mathbf{x}},2^{-2L})\subseteq Y.$$

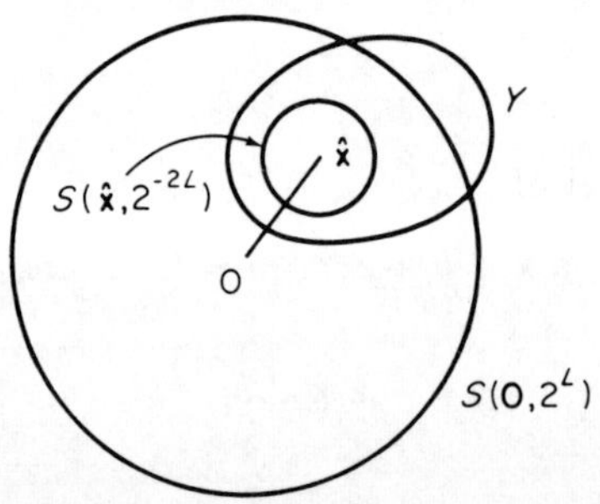

Figure 5.2 The position of $\hat{\mathbf{x}}$ relative to Y

This is illustrated in Figure 5.2. Now if $\hat{\mathbf{x}}\in X_S=X\cap S(\mathbf{0},2^L)$, then $\hat{\mathbf{x}}\in Y\cap S(\mathbf{0},2^L)$, and it is clear from Figure 5.2 that $\hat{\mathbf{x}}$ can be chosen to be within a distance 2^L-2^{-2L} of the origin O. Hence we can find a point $\hat{\mathbf{x}}$ such that

$$S(\hat{\mathbf{x}},2^{-2L})\subseteq Y\cap S(\mathbf{0},2^L)\subseteq S(\mathbf{0},2^L). \tag{5.17}$$

Finally, suppose that the conditions of Theorem 5.10 hold, and that the ellipsoid algorithm is applied to the perturbed inequality (5.3). Then the algorithm must terminate with a solution in not more than $6n(n+1)L$ iterations.

For we can apply Theorem 5.8 to the perturbed inequality (5.3), knowing that the restricted solution set $Y \cap S(\mathbf{0}, 2^L)$ is bounded by (5.17), where $\hat{\mathbf{x}}$ is, *a priori*, unknown. Thus, in Theorem 5.8, we can set $r = 2^{-2L}$, $R = 2^L$, to obtain:

$$k \leqslant 2n(n+1)\log_e(2^{3L}) = 6n(n+1)L.$$

As indicated earlier, it is not necessary in practice to use the perturbed inequality (5.3); the calculations can be performed using only the original inequality (5.1), as explained in the next section.

5.5 Concluding Remarks

We are not concerned here with the implementation of the algorithm. However, the following points are worth noting.

First, a BASIC program designed to illustrate the algorithm is given in Part 2 of reference [4]; also, references [17] and [18] contain detailed discussions of the implementation of the algorithm.

Secondly, it is not necessary to perturb the inequality (5.1) in the manner of (5.3). To see this, consider the ith component,

$$\mathbf{a}_i'\mathbf{x} \leqslant b_i, \tag{5.18}$$

of the inequality (5.1), and define the *residual* of (5.18) at $\mathbf{x}_k$ as

$$\theta_i(\mathbf{x}_k) = \mathbf{a}_i'\mathbf{x}_k - b_i.$$

In the $(k+1)$th iteration, suppose that the dividing hyperplane is chosen from those components of (5.3) which have residuals greater than 2^{-L}. Then the perturbation term $2^{-L}\mathbf{e}$ in (5.3) becomes ignorable, and the updating formulae for $\mathbf{x}_{k+1}$ and $\mathbf{B}_{k+1}$ remain unchanged. Let

$$\theta(\mathbf{x}_k) = \max_i \theta_i(\mathbf{x}_k).$$

If $\theta(\mathbf{x}_k) \leqslant 2^{-L}$, then $\mathbf{x}_k$ satisfies (5.3), and Theorem 5.9 shows that (5.1) also has a solution. Khachiyan [25] therefore chooses the dividing hyperplane from the component of (5.1) corresponding to $\theta(\mathbf{x}_k)$, and continues the iterations until the maximum residual is less than or equal to 2^{-L}, at which point it is known that the inequality (5.1) has a solution.

In this case, the current $\mathbf{x}_k$ is, in general, an approximate solution of the inequality (5.1) and hence of the original linear programming problem (5.2). This solution will usually be sufficiently accurate for practical purposes. However, since all the coefficients in the inequality (5.1) are integers, it is possible to obtain an exact solution from the approximate solution. The method is due to Grötschel, Lovász and Schrijver [19]. Let Δ be a positive integer. Then, using continued fractions, an approximate solution $\mathbf{x}$ may itself be approximated by

$$\mathbf{x}^* = [p_1/q_1, \ldots, p_n/q_n],$$

where p_j/q_j is the rational number, with the property $|q_j| \leqslant \Delta$, which is nearest to $x_j, j = 1, \ldots, n$. It can be shown that if $\Delta = 2^L$, then $|\mathbf{x}^* - \mathbf{x}| < 1/2\Delta^2$, and that in this case $\mathbf{x}^*$ is unique and is the exact optimal solution of the linear programming problem (5.2). Moreover, all these operations can be carried out in polynomial time. Further details of the method are given in reference [6].

Thirdly, the above proof that at most $6n(n+1)L$ iterations are required in order to show that the inequality (5.1) has no solution also applies to the inequality (5.3), and hence to Khachiyan's method of generating cuts from the components of (5.1) with maximum residuals. For the maximum number of iterations that are required does not depend on whether the cuts are generated from arbitrary violated constraints or from those with maximum residuals.

Finally, in order to avoid having to perform the full number of iterations in the case of a system of linear inequalities which have no solution, a second system can be chosen using Farkas' lemma or one of its variants. Just one of the systems then has a solution and, if the algorithm is applied simultaneously to both systems, the calculations terminate when this solution is found. For example, the systems

$$\mathbf{A}\mathbf{x} \leqslant \mathbf{b}, \quad \mathbf{x} \geqslant \mathbf{0},$$

$$\mathbf{A}'\mathbf{y} \geqslant \mathbf{0}, \quad \mathbf{y} > \mathbf{0}, \quad \mathbf{b}'\mathbf{y} < 0$$

form such a pair. With this method, the amount of computation in each iteration is, of course, doubled.

The Algorithm

The steps in the Shor-Khachiyan algorithm to find a solution of the inequality (5.1) are given below for reference.

Step 1. Set $\mathbf{x}_0 = \mathbf{0}$, $\mathbf{B}_0 = 2^{2L}\mathbf{I}$, $k = 0$, where L is given by equation (5.5).

Step 2. Terminate the algorithm if either

(a) the maximum residual $\theta(\mathbf{x}_k)$ of the m inequalities (5.1) at $\mathbf{x}_k$ is less than 2^{-L}, or

(b) $k = 6n(n+1)L$, in which case (5.1) has no solution. Otherwise, go to Step 3.

Step 3. Let

$$\mathbf{a}_i'\mathbf{x} \leqslant b_i$$

be the component of (5.1) with the largest residual at $\mathbf{x}_k$, and set

$$\mathbf{x}_{k+1} = \mathbf{x}_k - \frac{1}{n+1}\frac{\mathbf{B}_k\mathbf{a}_i}{(\mathbf{a}_i'\mathbf{B}_k\mathbf{a}_i)^{1/2}},$$

$$\mathbf{B}_{k+1} = \frac{n^2}{n^2-1}\left(\mathbf{B}_k - \frac{2}{n+1}\frac{\mathbf{B}_k\mathbf{a}_i\mathbf{a}_i'\mathbf{B}_k}{\mathbf{a}_i'\mathbf{B}_k\mathbf{a}_i}\right).$$

Set $k = k+1$ and go to Step 2.

N.B. In terms of the corresponding linear programming problem (5.2), termination at Step 2(a) gives an optimal (or near optimal) solution $\mathbf{x}_k$, while termination at Step 2(b) implies no feasible solution. Also, a slight extension of the algorithm enables an unbounded solution to be identified [6].

Exercises

1. Express the following linear programming problem in the form $\mathbf{Ax} \leqslant \mathbf{b}$:

$$\text{Maximize } z = 2x_1 + 3x_2,$$

subject to

$$\begin{aligned} x_1 + x_2 &\leqslant 1, \\ 2x_1 - 2x_2 &\geqslant 1, \\ x_1 + 4x_2 &\leqslant 2, \\ x_1, x_2 &\geqslant 0. \end{aligned}$$

Find the length L of the input for this problem.

2. If λ is an eigenvalue of a non-singular matrix, prove that λ^{-1} is an eigenvalue of its inverse. Hence, or otherwise, prove that if a matrix is positive definite and symmetric, then so is its inverse.

3. Prove the formula for the volume of a tetrahedron with vertices $\mathbf{v}_0, \mathbf{v}_1, \mathbf{v}_2, \mathbf{v}_3$ (see Theorem 5.3).

4. In Figure 5.1, verify that the position vector of the point P is

$$\mathbf{x}_k - \frac{\mathbf{B}_k \mathbf{a}}{(\mathbf{a}' \mathbf{B}_k \mathbf{a})^{1/2}}.$$

5. Prove that the number of arithmetic operations that are required in order to find a violated inequality in (5.1) is at most $O(mn)$, and to find $\mathbf{x}_{k+1}$ and $\mathbf{B}_{k+1}$ for the ellipsoid E_{k+1} is at most $O(n^2)$. Deduce that the total number of arithmetic operations in the ellipsoid algorithm for the inequality (5.1) is at most

$$O[(m+n)n^3 L].$$

6. Suppose that the length of the input of the inequality

$$\mathbf{Ax} \leqslant \mathbf{b}$$

is L. Prove that the length of the input of the inequality

$$2^L \mathbf{Ax} \leqslant 2^L \mathbf{b} + \mathbf{e}$$

is at most $(mn + m + 1)L$.

7. It is shown in books on many-variable calculus that the volume of an n-dimensional sphere of unit radius is

$$\frac{\pi^{3/2}}{\Gamma\left(\frac{n+2}{2}\right)}.$$

Verify this formula for the case $n = 3$. Prove that the ratio of the volumes of a four-dimensional sphere of radius r and a four-dimensional cube of side $2r$ is

$$\frac{\pi^{3/2}}{32} \quad (= 0.1740).$$

8. Prove that the volume of an n-dimensional sphere of radius 2^L is less than $2^{n(L+1)}$.

Suppose that the strict inequality $\mathbf{Ax} < \mathbf{b}$ has a solution, and that the ellipsoid method is applied directly, the cuts being generated from any violated component. Prove, by contradiction, that the solution must be found in not more than $4(n+1)^2 L$ iterations.

9. Suppose that Δ is a positive integer and that $\mathbf{x}^*$ has rational components with bounded denominators, i.e.

$$\mathbf{x}^* = [p_1/q_1, \ldots, p_n/q_n], \qquad \text{(a)}$$

where $|q_j| \leqslant \Delta, j = 1, \ldots, n$. Suppose also that

$$\mathbf{x}^* \in S(\mathbf{x}, 1/2\Delta^2) \quad \text{and} \quad \mathbf{y} \in S(\mathbf{x}, 1/2\Delta^2).$$

Prove that

$$|\mathbf{y} - \mathbf{x}^*| \leqslant \frac{1}{\Delta^2}.$$

Suppose further that $\mathbf{y}$ is also of the form (a), and that $y_j \neq x_j^*$ for some value of j. Deduce that

$$|y_j - x_j^*| \geqslant \frac{1}{\Delta^2}, \quad |\mathbf{y} - \mathbf{x}^*| \geqslant \frac{1}{\Delta^2},$$

and hence that $\mathbf{x}^*$, as defined above, is unique.

References

1. B. Aspvall and R. E. Stone, 'Khachiyan's linear programming algorithm', *J. of Algorithms*, **1**, No. 1, 1–13, 1980.
2. W. J. Baumol, *Economic Theory and Operations Analysis*, 4th edn, Prentice-Hall, New York, 1977.
3. E. M. L. Beale, 'Cycling in the dual simplex algorithm', *Naval Res. Logistics Quart.*, **1**, 36–47, 1954.
4. G. C. Berresford, A. M. Rockett, and J. C. Stevenson, 'Khachiyan's algorithm', Part 1: 'A new solution to linear programming problems'; Part 2: 'Problems with the algorithm', *BYTE*, **5**, No. 8, 198–208, and No. 9, 242–255, 1980.
5. G. Birkhoff and S. MacLane, *A Survey of Modern Algebra*, 4th edn, Collier-Macmillan, New York, 1977.
6. R. G. Bland, D. Goldfarb, and M. J. Todd, 'The ellipsoid method: a survey', *Oper. Res.*, **29**, No. 6, 1039–1091, 1981.
7. A. Charnes, W. W. Cooper, and A. Henderson, *An Introduction to Linear Programming*, Wiley, New York, 1953.
8. P. M. Cohn, *Linear Equations*, Routledge & Kegan Paul, London, 1971.
9. G. B. Dantzig, *Linear Programming and Extensions*, Princeton University Press, Princeton, New Jersey, 1963.
10. G. B. Dantzig, 'Maximization of a linear function of variables subject to linear inequalities', in: *Activity Analysis of Production and Allocation*, (T. C. Koopmans, Ed.), Wiley, New York, 1972.
11. G. B. Dantzig and W. Orchard-Hays, 'Notes on linear programming: Part V—alternate algorithm for the revised simplex method using product form for the inverse', *The RAND Corporation, Research Memorandum RM*-1268, 1953.
12. R. Dorfman, P. A. Samuelson, and R. M. Solow, *Linear Programming and Economic Analysis*, McGraw-Hill, New York, 1958.
13. L. R. Ford, Jr and D. R. Fulkerson, *Flows in Networks*, Princeton University Press, Princeton, New Jersey, 1962.
14. P. Gács and L. Lovász, 'Khachiyan's algorithm for linear programming', *Math. Program. Study*, **14**, 61–68, 1981.
15. D. Gale, *The Theory of Linear Economic Models*, McGraw-Hill, New York, 1960.
16. R. C. Geary and J. E. Spencer, *Elements of Linear Programming with Economic Applications*, 2nd rev. edn, Griffin, London, 1973.
17. J. L. Goffin, 'Convergence of a cyclic ellipsoid algorithm for systems of linear equalities', *Math. Programming*, **22**, No. 3, 239–260, 1982.
18. D. Goldfarb and M. J. Todd, 'Modifications and implementation of the ellipsoid algorithm for linear programming', *Math. Programming*, **23**, No. 1, 1–19, 1982.
19. M. Grötschel, L. Lovász, and A. Schrijver, 'The ellipsoid method and its consequences in combinatorial optimization', *Combinatorica*, **1**, No. 2, 169–197, 1981.
20. G. Hadley, *Linear Programming*, Addison-Wesley, Reading, Mass., 1962.
21. M. Hall, Jr, 'An algorithm for distinct representatives', *Am. Math. Monthly*, **63**, 716–717, 1956.

22. F. L. Hitchcock, 'The distribution of a product, from several sources to numerous localities, *J. Math. Phys.*, **20**, 224–230, 1941.
23. L. V. Kantorovich, 'Mathematical models in the organisation and planning of production', Leningrad University, 1939. Translated in *Management Sci.*, **6**, 366–422, 1960.
24. S. Karamardian, 'A note on Khachiyan's algorithm', *J. of Optimization Theory and Applications*, **32**, No. 4, 595–597, 1980.
25. L. G. Khachiyan, 'A polynomial algorithm in linear programming' (in Russian), *Doklady Akademiia Nauk SSSR*, **244**, No. 5, 1093–1096, 1979. Translated in *Soviet Mathematics Doklady*, **20**, No. 1, 191–194, 1979.
26. T. C. Koopmans, 'Optimum utilization of the transportation system', in: *Proceedings of the International Statistical Conferences*, Washington, D.C., 1947. Volume 5 reprinted as a supplement to *Econometrica*, **17**, 136–145, 1949.
27. H. W. Kuhn, 'The Hungarian method for the assignment problem', *Naval Res. Logistics Quart.*, **2**, 83–97, 1955.
28. H. W. Kuhn, 'Variants of the Hungarian method for assignment problems', *Naval Res. Logistics Quart.*, **3**, 253–258, 1956.
29. C. E. Lemke, 'The dual method of solving the linear programming problem', *Naval Res. Logistics Quart.*, **1**, 36–47, 1954.
30. J. Munkres, 'Algorithms for the assignment and transportation problems', *J. Soc. Ind. Appl. Math.* (SIAM), **5**, 32–38, 1957.
31. B. Noble and J. W. Daniel, *Applied Linear Algebra*, 2nd edn, Prentice-Hall, New York, 1977.
32. W. Orchard-Hays, 'Evolution of computer codes for linear programming', *The RAND Corporation Paper P*-810, 22–24, 1956.
33. N. Z. Shor, 'Cut-off method with space extension in convex programming problems' (in Russian), *Kibernetika*, **13**, No. 1, 94–95, 1977. Translated in *Cybernetics*, **13**, No. 1, 94–96, 1977.
34. J. von Neumann and O. Morgenstern, *Theory of Games and Economic Behavior*, Princeton University Press, Princeton, New Jersey, 1980.
35. G. R. Walsh, *Methods of Optimization*, Wiley, Chichester, 1979.
36. J. D. Williams, *The Compleat Strategyst* (rev. edn) McGraw-Hill, New York, 1966.

Suggestions for Further Reading

L. Cooper and D. Steinberg, *Methods and Applications of Linear Programming*, Saunders, Philadelphia, 1974.

R. Fletcher, *Practical Methods of Optimization: Vol. 1: Unconstrained Optimization; Vol. 2: Constrained Optimization*, Wiley, Chichester, 1980 and 1981, respectively.

S. I. Gass, *Linear Programming*, 4th edn, McGraw-Hill, New York, 1975.

P. L. Hammer and G. Zoutendijk (Eds.), *Mathematical Programming in Theory and Practice*, American Elsevier, New York, 1975.

W. Ledermann (Chief Ed.), *Handbook of Applicable Mathematics*, particularly Vol. I (Algebra), Vol. III (Numerical Methods), Vol. IV (Analysis), Wiley, Chichester, 1980, 1981, 1982, respectively.

W. McLewin, *Linear Programming and Applications*, Input–Output, Manchester Student Edition, 1980.

O. L. Mangasarian, *Nonlinear Programming*, McGraw-Hill, New York, 1969.

W. Orchard-Hays, *Advanced Linear-Programming Computing Techniques*, McGraw-Hill, New York, 1968.

H. A. Taha, *Operations Research*, 3rd edn, Macmillan, New York, 1982.

S. Vayda, *Linear Programming: Algorithms and Applications*, Chapman and Hall, London, 1981.

Answers to Exercises

Chapter 1

1. $(x_1^*, x_2^*) = (3/5, 8/5)$; $z^* = 36/5$.

2. $(x_1^*, x_2^*) = (9/5, 16/5)$; $z^* = 98/5$.

3. $(x_1^*, x_2^*) = (2, 2/3)$; $z^* = -10/3$.

4. No solution: constraints inconsistent.

5. Alternative optima: (x_1^*, x_2^*) is any point on the line segment joining the points (0, 12) and (1, 6). $z^* = 24$.

6. The feasible region consists of the single point (40/11, 7/11); hence there is no optimization problem.

7a. $(x_1^*, x_2^*) = (0, 3)$; $z^* = 27$.

7b. $(x_1^*, x_2^*) = (0, 9/7)$; $z^* = 27$.

8a. Unbounded solution with an unbounded value of z.

8b. No feasible solution.

9. $66\frac{2}{3}$ acres arable, $33\frac{1}{3}$ acres grass.

10. 2 large, 10 small tables.

11. Let x_1, x_2 be the numbers of cars manufactured for the home market and for export, respectively.

(a) $(x_1^*, x_2^*) = (45\frac{5}{7}, 68\frac{4}{7})$.

(b) $(x_1^*, x_2^*) = (0, 133\frac{1}{3})$ when $2 \geqslant k > 3/2$,
$= (20, 120)$ when $3/2 > k > 8/7$,
$= (57\frac{17}{19}, 86\frac{16}{19})$ when $8/7 > k \geqslant 0$.

When $k = 3/2$ or $8/7$ there are alternative optima, obtained by taking suitable linear combinations of adjacent optimal solutions.

12. The origin is always a feasible point, and may be the only feasible point. Either $z^* = 0$ (with or without alternative optima) or there is an unbounded solution with an unbounded value of z.

Chapter 2

1. *Notation*

x_1 wheat	acres	x_6 cows	
x_2 barley	acres	x_7 pigs	
x_3 oats	acres	x_8 hens	
x_4 sugar beet	acres	x_9 labour (non-overtime)	hours
x_5 grass	acres	x_{10} labour (overtime)	hours

Linear Programming Problem

$$\text{Maximize } z = 39x_1 + 36z_2 + 32x_3 + 92x_4 - 5x_5 + 195x_6 + 2x_7 + x_8 - 0{\cdot}50x_9 - 0{\cdot}75x_{10},$$

subject to

$$\begin{aligned}
x_1 + x_2 + x_3 + x_4 + x_5 &\leqslant 100,\\
x_1 + x_2 + x_3 + x_4 &\leqslant 60,\\
x_6 - 2x_5 &\leqslant 0,\\
12x_1 + 13x_2 + 14x_3 + 20x_4 + 5x_5 + 100x_6 + 25x_7 + 20x_8 - x_9 - x_{10} &\leqslant 2\,000,\\
30x_7 + 15x_8 &\leqslant 10\,000,\\
x_4 \leqslant 10, \quad x_9 \leqslant 2\,200, \quad x_j \geqslant 0, \quad j &= 1, \ldots, 10.
\end{aligned}$$

2. *Basic Solutions*

$$(x_1, x_2, x_3, x_4) = (0, \tfrac{1}{9}, \tfrac{22}{21}, \tfrac{29}{63}), (\tfrac{22}{9}, \tfrac{1}{9}, 0, \tfrac{1}{9}), (\tfrac{29}{9}, \tfrac{1}{9}, -\tfrac{1}{3}, 0).$$

Most General Solution

$$x_1 = \tfrac{22}{9}\mu + \tfrac{29}{9}\nu, \quad x_2 = \tfrac{1}{9}, \quad x_3 = \tfrac{22}{21}\lambda - \tfrac{1}{3}\nu, \quad x_4 = \tfrac{29}{63}\lambda + \tfrac{1}{9}\mu,$$

where $$\lambda + \mu + \nu = 1.$$

3. The row-sum check still works when artificial variables are present, provided they are all retained in the new tableau. If an artificial variable x_{Bi} is omitted from the new tableau on becoming non-basic, then σ_i in the old tableau is reduced by unity before the transformation of the σ column is carried out.

4. $(x_1{}^*, x_2{}^*, x_3{}^*) = (7/2, 0, 3/4)$; $z^* = 41/2$.

5. $(x_1{}^*, x_2{}^*, x_3{}^*, x_4{}^*) = (0, 4, 0, 0)$; $z^* = -20$.

6. $(x_1{}^*, x_2{}^*, x_3{}^*) = (0, 5/3, 35/3)$; $z^* = 55$.

7a. $(x_1{}^*, x_2{}^*, x_3{}^*) = (6, 0, 0)$; $z^* = 6$.

7b. Unbounded solution with an undounded value of z.
N.B. Note that the third constraint can be ignored *ab initio* because of the non-negativity restrictions.

8. Alternative optima:

$$(x_1{}^*, x_2{}^*, x_3{}^*) = (0, 1, 0) \textit{ or } (80/19, 9/19, 0) \textit{ or } (0, 1/11, 80/11);\ z^* = 8.$$

If these three optimal solutions are denoted by $\mathbf{x}_A{}^*, \mathbf{x}_B{}^*, \mathbf{x}_C{}^*$, respectively, then the most general optimal solution is

$$\mathbf{x}^* = \lambda \mathbf{x}_A{}^* + \mu \mathbf{x}_B{}^* + \nu \mathbf{x}_C{}^*, \quad \lambda + \mu + \nu = 1, \quad \lambda, \mu, \nu \geqslant 0.$$

9. $(x_1{}^*, x_2{}^*, x_3{}^*, x_4{}^*) = (3/5, 0, 0, 4/5)$; $z^* = 7/5$.

10. Unbounded solution with an unbounded value of z.

11. No feasible solution; original constraints inconsistent.

12. $(x_1{}^*, x_2{}^*, x_3{}^*) = (5/3, 10/3, 0)$; $z^* = 100/3$. One constraint redundant.

13. No feasible solution; non-feasible solutions exist—original constraints consistent.

14. As for 13.

15. $(x_1{}^*, x_2{}^*, x_3{}^*, x_4{}^*) = (9, 0, 0, 2)$ or $(1, 4, 0, 0)$; $z^* = -1$.

16. Unbounded solution with a finite value (-15) of z.

17. $(x_1{}^*, x_2{}^*, x_3{}^*) = (10/9, 16/9, 0)$; $z^* = 94/9$.

18. $(x_1{}^*, x_2{}^*, x_3{}^*) = (0, 1/2, 0)$; $z^* = -2$.

19. $(x_1{}^*, x_2{}^*, x_3{}^*) = (2, 0, 0)$; $z^* = 4$.

20. As for 13.

21. Unbounded solution with an unbounded value of z.

22. As for 21.

23. $(x_1^*, x_2^*, x_3^*) = (0, 2, 0)$; $z^* = 4$.

24. $(x_1^*, x_2^*, x_3^*) = (0, 0, -4)$; $z^* = 16$.

25. $(x_1^*, x_2^*, x_3^*) = (2, 1, 0)$ or $(4, 0, 0)$; $z^* = -4$.

26. There are four ways of subdividing the width of 120 cm. Let

$$X = \text{no. of strips 36 cm wide,}$$
$$Y = \text{no. of strips 30 cm wide.}$$

Then

$$(X, Y) = (3, 0), (2, 1), (1, 2) \text{ or } (0, 4),$$

and the widths used are, respectively, 108 cm, 102 cm, 96 cm, and 120 cm. Let x_1, x_2, x_3, x_4 (m) be the lengths associated with each of these methods of subdivision. Then the area wasted is

$$z = 0.01\,(12x_1 + 18x_2 + 24x_3)\ \text{m}^2.$$

The constraints are

$$\begin{aligned} 3x_1 + 2x_2 + x_3 \quad\quad\quad\quad & \geqslant 15, \\ x_2 + 2x_3 + 4x_4 \quad & \geqslant 20, \\ x_1, x_2, x_3, x_4 & \geqslant 0. \end{aligned}$$

We find

$$(x_1^*, x_2^*, x_3^*, x_4^*) = (5, 0, 0, 5)\ \text{m};\ z^* = 0.6\ \text{m}^2.$$

28(b). In each iteration, x_{Bh} is strictly increased in value, and positive x_{Bi} remain positive. Also, there is only a finite number of basic solutions. Hence, if a feasible solution exists, then a basic feasible solution must eventually appear.

28(c). The problem has no feasible solution.

29.

$$\alpha_i = \beta_{ik}/\beta_{rk}, \quad i \neq r,$$
$$\alpha_r = -1/\beta_{rk}.$$

[See equations (2.58a) and (2.58b).]

Chapter 3

1. Minimize $w = -5y_1 + 7y_2 - 5y_3$,

subject to

$$\begin{aligned} -7y_1 + 6y_2 + 8y_3 &\geqslant 7, \\ -2y_1 - y_2 - 2y_3 &\geqslant -8, \\ 3y_1 \quad\quad + 5y_3 &\geqslant 9, \\ y_1 + y_2 \quad\quad &\geqslant 10, \end{aligned}$$

$y_1 \geqslant 0$, y_2 unrestricted in sign, $y_3 \geqslant 0$.

2. $$\text{Minimize } w = \mathbf{b}'\mathbf{y} - \mathbf{x}_l{}'\mathbf{y}_1 + \mathbf{x}_u{}'\mathbf{y}_2,$$
subject to
$$\mathbf{A}'\mathbf{y} - \mathbf{y}_1 + \mathbf{y}_2 = \mathbf{c},$$
with y_i unrestricted in sign for all i, and $\mathbf{y}_1 \geqslant \mathbf{0}$, $\mathbf{y}_2 \geqslant \mathbf{0}$.
(The components of $\mathbf{y}_1$ and $\mathbf{y}_2$ are sets of dual variables corresponding to the lower and upper bounds, respectively, on the primal variables.)

8.

Optimal Dual Tableau (Exercise 8)

	$\mathbf{b}'$		3	−1	2	0	0	0	0
$\mathbf{b}_B$	Basic Variables		y_1	y_2	y_3	y_4	y_5	y_6	y_7
0	y_4	77/10	0	0	−9/20	1	−11/20	3/4	0
−1	y_2	1/5	0	1	−1/5	0	1/5	0	0
3	y_1	3/10	1	0	−1/20	0	1/20	−1/4	0
0	y_7	5/2	0	0	5/4	0	−1/4	1/4	1
	$w_i - b_i$	7/10	0	0	−39/20	0	−1/20	−3/4	0

Optimal Primal Tableau (Exercise 8)

	$\mathbf{c}'$		−9	−1	1	−3	0	0	0
$\mathbf{c}_B$	Basic Variables		x_1	x_2	x_3	x_4	x_5	x_6	x_7
−1	x_2	1/20	11/20	1	0	1/4	−1/20	−1/5	0
1	x_3	3/4	−3/4	0	1	−1/4	1/4	0	0
0	x_7	39/20	9/20	0	0	−5/4	1/20	1/5	1
	$z_j - c_j$	7/10	77/10	0	0	5/2	3/10	1/5	0

9.

Optimal Dual Tableau (Exercise 9)

	$\mathbf{b}'$		3	6	10	0	0	0
$\mathbf{b}_B$	Basic Variables		y_1	y_2	y_3	y_4	y_5	y_6
6	y_2	3	0	1	9	1	0	1
0	y_5	2	0	0	−31	−4	1	−3
3	y_1	5	1	0	21	3	0	2
	$w_i - b_i$	33	0	0	107	15	0	12

Optimal Primal Tableau (Exercise 9)

	c′		−1	10	4	0	0	0
$\mathbf{c}_B$	Basic Variables		x_1	x_2	x_3	x_4	x_5	x_6
−1	x_1	15	1	4	0	−3	−1	0
4	x_3	12	0	3	1	−2	−1	0
0	x_6	107	0	31	0	−21	−9	1
	$z_j - c_j$	33	0	−2	0	−5	−3	0

10.

Optimal Dual Tableau (Exercise 10)

	b′		4	11	−2	0	0	0
$\mathbf{b}_B$	Basic Variables		y_1	y_2	y_3	y_4	y_5	y_6
11	y_2	3/10	3/5	1	0	3/10	0	1/10
0	y_5	4	−7	0	0	−2	1	−1
−2	y_3	11/10	−4/5	0	1	1/10	0	−3/10
	$w_i - b_i$	11/10	21/5	0	0	31/10	0	17/10

Optimal Primal Tableau (Exercise 10)

	c′		2	5	−3	0	0	0
$\mathbf{c}_B$	Basic Variables		x_1	x_2	x_3	x_4	x_5	x_6
2	x_1	31/10	1	2	0	0	−3/10	−1/10
−3	x_3	17/10	0	1	1	0	−1/10	3/10
0	x_4	21/5	0	7	0	1	−3/5	4/5
	$z_j - c_j$	11/10	0	−4	0	0	−3/10	−11/10

11. y_4, y_5, y_6 are slack and surplus variables associated with the first three dual constraints. The fourth dual constraint is an equality.

Optimal Dual Tableau (Exercise 11)

	b′		3	−1	2	0	0	0
$\mathbf{b}_B$	Basic Variables		y_1	y_2	y_3	y_4	y_5	y_6
0	y_4	43/5	0	0	0	1	−16/25	21/25
−1	y_2	3/5	0	1	0	0	4/25	1/25
3	y_1	2/5	1	0	0	0	1/25	−6/25
2	y_3	2	0	0	1	0	−1/5	1/5
	$w_i - b_i$	23/5	0	0	0	0	−11/25	−9/25

Optimal Primal Tableau (Exercise 11)

	c′		−9	−1	1	−3	0	0	0
c_B	Basic Variables		x_1	x_2	x_3	x_4	x_5	x_6	x_7
−1	x_2	11/25	16/25	1	0	0	−1/25	−4/25	1/5
1	x_3	9/25	−21/25	0	1	0	6/25	−1/25	−1/5
−3	x_4	−39/25	−9/25	0	0	1	−1/25	−4/25	−4/5
	$z_j - c_j$	23/5	43/5	0	0	0	2/5	3/5	2

12. No feasible solution; non-feasible solutions exist—original constraints consistent.

13. In the usual notation, $(x_1^*, x_2^*) = (4, 3)$; $z^* = 18$.

14. $z^* = 64$.

15. $(x_1^*, x_2^*, x_3^*) = (4, 7, 3)$; $z^* = 43$.

16. $(x_1^*, x_2^*, x_3^*) = (89/65, 216/65, 17/13)$; $z^* = 784/65$.

17. $(x_1^*, x_2^*, x_3^*, x_4^*) = (14/5, 0, 26/5, 38/5)$; $z^* = -214/5$.

18. $(x_1^*, x_2^*, x_3^*, x_4^*) = (14, 0, 22, 2)$; $z^* = -166$.

19. $(x_1^*, x_2^*, x_3^*) = (0, 28, 24)$; $z^* = 52$.

20. Unbounded solution with an unbounded value of z.

21. *Primal*: Minimize $w = \mathbf{b}'\mathbf{y}$,
subject to $\mathbf{P}'\mathbf{y} \geqslant \mathbf{c}$, $\mathbf{y} \geqslant \mathbf{0}$, where $\mathbf{P} = \{p_{ij}\}$.

Dual: Maximize $z = \mathbf{c}'\mathbf{x}$,
subject to $\mathbf{Px} \leqslant \mathbf{b}$, $\mathbf{x} \geqslant \mathbf{0}$.

Dual Variables: x_j = shadow price of one unit of nutrient j.

Dual Constraints: Shadow price of one unit of food $i \leqslant$ Cost of one unit of food i.

Dual Objective Function: Maximize the shadow price of the balanced diet.

In an optimal solution, the only foods used are those for which the shadow price is equal to the cost, and therefore, for the balanced diet, maximum shadow price is equal to minimum cost.

22. Entries in the last column of the revised simplex tableau are ignored when taking the row sums. The last column remains unchecked.

23. $(x_1^*, x_2^*) = (5/17, 60/17)$; $z^* = 65/17$.
    $(y_1^*, y_2^*) = (1/17, 3/17)$; $w^* = 65/17$.

24. $(x_1^*, x_2^*, x_3^*) = (0, 15, 12)$; $z^* = 33$.
    $(y_1^*, y_2^*, y_3^*) = (5, 3, 0)$; $w^* = 33$.

25. The new optimal (or unbounded) solutions are:
    (a) $(x_1^*, x_2^*, x_3^*, x_4^*) = (0, 1/2, 3/4, 0)$; $z^* = 1/4$.
    (b) $(x_1^*, x_2^*, x_3^*, x_4^*) = (0, 9/20, 3/4, 0)$; $z^* = 3/10$.
    (c) Unbounded solution with an unbounded value of z.
    (d) $(x_1^*, x_2^*, x_3^*, x_4^*, x_8^*) = (0, 0, 1/12, 0, 1/3)$; $z^* = 41/12$.

26. $(x_1^*, x_2^*, x_3^*, x_4^*) = (1, 1, 0, 0)$; $z^* = 18$.
    $(x_1^*, x_2^*, x_3^*, x_4^*) = (0, 0, 2, 0)$; $z^* = 8$.

27. $(x_1^*, x_2^*, x_3^*) = (3, 0, 12)$; $z^* = 18$.
    $(x_1^*, x_2^*, x_3^*) = (0, 1/5, 0)$; $z^* = 7/5$.

28. (a) $(x_1^*, x_2^*, x_3^*) = (0, 38/7, 11/7)$; $z^* = -103/7$.
    (b) $(x_1^*, x_2^*, x_3^*) = (0, 5, 0)$; $z^* = -15$.

29. (a) Optimal solution unchanged.
    (b) Unbounded solution with an unbounded value of z.
    (c) $(x_1^*, x_2^*, x_3^*, x_4^*, x_5^*) = (0, 1/2, 4, 0, 11/2)$; $z^* = 35$.
    (d) $(x_1^*, x_2^*, x_3^*, x_4^*, x_5^*) = (1, 0, 5, 0, 7)$; $z^* = 26$.
    (e) Unbounded solution with a finite value (46) of z.
    (f) Optimal solution unchanged.
    (g) Unbounded solution with an unbounded value of z.
    (h) $(x_1^*, x_2^*, x_3^*, x_4^*, x_5^*, x_9^*) = (0, 0, 7, 0, 5, 3)$; $z^* = 52$.

30. $(x_1^*, x_2^*) = \left(\dfrac{32+14\theta}{22+7\theta}, \dfrac{42}{22+7\theta}\right)$; $z^* = \dfrac{254+56\theta}{22+7\theta}$.

31. $\underline{\phi \geqslant -1}$ $\mathbf{x}^* = [0, \frac{1}{2}(3+\phi), 2(2+\phi), 0, \frac{13}{2}(1+\phi)]$; $z^* = 43 + 30\phi$.

$\underline{\phi \geqslant -\frac{21}{20}}$ $\mathbf{x}^* = [0, 0, 5 + \frac{7}{3}\phi, 1 + \frac{1}{3}\phi, 7 + \frac{20}{3}\phi]$; $z^* = 43 + 30\phi$.

$\underline{\phi \leqslant -1}$ $\mathbf{x}^* = [-\frac{13}{5}(1+\phi), \frac{1}{5}(1-4\phi), \frac{1}{5}(7-3\phi), 0, 0]$; $z^* = \frac{1}{5}(228 + 163\phi)$.

$\underline{\phi \leqslant -\frac{21}{20}}$ $\mathbf{x}^* = [-\frac{1}{8}(21+20\phi), 0, \frac{3}{2} - \phi, \frac{1}{8}(1-4\phi), 0]$; $z^* = \frac{5}{8}(73 + 52\phi)$.

$\underline{-\frac{21}{20} \leqslant \phi \leqslant -1}$ $\mathbf{x}^* = [0, 21 + 20\phi, -(9 + 11\phi), -13(1+\phi), 0]$;

$z^* = 43 + 30\phi$.

Chapter 4

1.

	P_1	P_2	P_3	P_4
F_1	100		500	400
F_2	200	600		
F_3		100		

Minimum cost = £1 326 000.

2.

	D_1	D_2	D_3
O_1	12		
O_2	4		13
O_3		20	1
O_4			14

or

	D_1	D_2	D_3
O_1	12		
O_2	3		14
O_3	1	20	
O_4			14

Minimum cost = 218.

3.

	D_1	D_2	D_3
O_1		2	3
O_2	7	1	
O_3			7
O_4		6	
†O_5	1		

or

	D_1	D_2	D_3
O_1		3	2
O_2	7		1
O_3			7
O_4		6	
†O_5	1		

Minimum cost = 607.

†O_5 is a fictitious origin.

4.

	D_1	D_2	D_3	D_4	†D_5
O_1			5	15	
O_2		10	30		
O_3	10	15			25

Minimum cost = 435

†D_5 is a fictitious destination.

5.

	D_1	D_2	D_3	D_4	D_5	D_6
O_1						30
O_2		20	10	10		
O_3						10
O_4	50			25	15	10

or

	D_1	D_2	D_3	D_4	D_5	D_6
O_1						30
O_2		10	10	20		
O_3		10				
O_4	50			15	15	20

Minimum cost = 1650.

6. *Degenerate:*

	D_1	D_2	D_3	D_4	D_5
O_1				10	10
O_2				10	
O_3	10	5	15		

Non-degenerate:

	D_1	D_2	D_3	D_4	D_5
O_1			10		10
O_2		5		5	
O_3	10		5	15	

	D_1	D_2	D_3	D_4	D_5
O_1				10	10
O_2		5		5	
O_3	10		15	5	

	D_1	D_2	D_3	D_4	D_5
O_1		5		5	10
O_2				10	
O_3	10		15	5	

	D_1	D_2	D_3	D_4	D_5
O_1				10	10
O_2			10		
O_3	10	5	5	10	

Minimum cost = 525.

N.B. There are several other optimal solutions.

7.

	D_1	D_2	D_3	D_4
O_1		3		1
O_2		2	1	
O_3		2		
O_4	1			

	D_1	D_2	D_3	D_4
O_1		2	1	1
O_2		3		
O_3		2		
O_4	1			

	D_1	D_2	D_3	D_4
O_1		3	1	
O_2		3		
O_3		1		1
O_4	1			

Minimum cost = 30.

In a non-degenerate solution there must be $(m+n-1) = 7$ non-zero entries; hence the D_2 column must contain 4 non-zero entries, and a 1 must be entered in each of the columns D_1, D_3 and D_4 in one or more of the first three rows. This can be done in 27 ways. But not more than one 1 is allowed in row 3 (which excludes 7 cases), and not more than two 1's are allowed in row 2 (which excludes one more case). These restrictions limit the number of non-degenerate solutions to 19. The lowest cost for a non-degenerate solution is 34, which is greater than the optimal cost of 30.

8.

	D_1	D_3	D_3	D_4	†D_5
O_1			5		2
O_2				2	
O_3	1		2		
O_4	1	2			
O_5	6				

or

	D_1	D_2	D_3	D_4	†D_5
O_1	1		4		2
O_2				2	
O_3			3		
O_4	1	2			
O_5	6				

Minimum cost = 26. †D_5 is a fictitious destination.

9.

	D_1	D_2	D_3	D_4
O_1	1		9	
O_2	5	4		
O_3			3	8

Minimum cost = 60.

10.

	D_1	D_2	D_3	D_4	D_5
O_1	50		20		
O_2		50	30		
O_3					60
O_4	10			70	40

Minimum cost = 1200.

11.

	D_1	D_2	D_3	D_4	D_5
O_1	5			4	1
O_2	1				
O_3	4				
O_4	3	1	19		

Minimum cost = 87.

There is no alternative optimum, and hence no optimal degenerate solution.

12.

	D_1	D_2	D_3	D_4	D_5
O_1					4
O_2	3	5	3	5	4
O_3		6			
O_4	7				

Minimum cost = 135.

13.

	D_1	D_2	D_3	D_4	$†D_5$
O_1		10			10
O_2	5			15	
O_3	8	5	7		

Minimum cost = 345. $†D_5$ is a fictitious destination. The solution is not unique.

14.

	D_1	D_2	D_3	D_4	D_5
O_1	2		2	4	
O_2	3				4
O_3		6			
$†O_4$		3			1

Minimum cost = 223. $†O_4$ is a fictitious origin.
N.B. There are several other optimal solutions.

15.

	D_1	D_2	D_3	D_4	D_5	D_6
O_1					7	6
O_2	4	5	5			2
O_3			1	6		

Minimum cost = 127.

16.

	D_1	D_2	D_3	D_4	D_5	D_6
O_1			20			
O_2			25	15	1	
O_3	9	26			9	5

or

	D_1	D_2	D_3	D_4	D_5	D_6
O_1	1		19			
O_2			26	15		
O_3	8	26			10	5

Minimum cost = 362.

17.

	O_1	O_2	O_3	O_4	O_5
D_1				8	
D_2	1	7			
D_3	4				3
D_4			5		1
$†D_5$			4		

or

	O_1	O_2	O_3	O_4	O_5
D_1				8	
D_2	2	6			
D_3	3				4
D_4			6		
$†D_5$		1	3		

Minimum cost = £29,500. $†D_5$ is a fictitious destination.

18.

	D_1	D_2	D_3	D_4	D_5	$†D_6$
O_1		1	4	1		13
O_2	10					
O_3				12	1	
O_4						4

or

	D_1	D_2	D_3	D_4	D_5	$†D_6$
O_1			4	2		13
O_2	10					
O_3		1		11	1	
O_4						4

or

	D_1	D_2	D_3	D_4	D_5	$\dagger D_6$
O_1		1	4	13		1
O_2	10					
O_3					1	12
O_4						4

or

	D_1	D_2	D_3	D_4	D_5	$\dagger D_6$
O_1		1	4			14
O_2	10					
O_3				12	1	
O_4				1		3

Minimum cost = 42. $\dagger D_6$ is a fictitious destination.

19.

	H_1	H_2	H_3	H_4	H_5
T_1			50		
T_2			20	40	10
T_3	20	60	10		

Minimum distance = 6.8 km.
The distance from T_1 to H_4 would have to decrease by more than 10 m.

20.

	X	Y	Z	†F
A			20	
B	30	10		
C		10		20

Minimum cost = 150. †F is a fictitious destination.

If the constraint on source B is removed then the optimal solution is:

	X	Y	Z	†F
A			20	
B	30			10
C		20		10

The minimum cost is unchanged.

21. Four optimal solutions:

$r_{11}, r_{22}, r_{33}, r_{44}$;
$r_{11}, r_{22}, r_{34}, r_{43}$;
$r_{12}, r_{21}, r_{33}, r_{44}$;
$r_{12}, r_{21}, r_{34}, r_{43}$.

22. $r_{15}, r_{24}, r_{31}, r_{43}, r_{52}$.

23. $r_{11}, r_{22}, r_{35}, r_{44}, r_{53}$.

24. Four optimal solutions:

$r_{12}, r_{21}, r_{36}, r_{43}, r_{55}, r_{67}, r_{74}$;
$r_{12}, r_{21}, r_{36}, r_{45}, r_{53}, r_{67}, r_{74}$;
$r_{12}, r_{23}, r_{36}, r_{44}, r_{55}, r_{67}, r_{71}$;
$r_{12}, r_{23}, r_{36}, r_{45}, r_{51}, r_{67}, r_{74}$.

25. Two optimal solutions:

$r_{13}, r_{21}, r_{32}, r_{45}, r_{54}$;
$r_{15}, r_{21}, r_{33}, r_{42}, r_{54}$.

26. $\mathbf{u}^* = [5/7, 2/7]$, $\mathbf{v}^* = [0, 0, 5/7, 0, 2/7, 0]$; $V = 17/7$.

27. $\mathbf{u}^* = [0, 0, 0, 3/4, 1/4]$, $\mathbf{v}^* = [3/8, 5/8]$; $V = 23/4$.

28. A and B use the pure strategies A_1 and B_1, respectively.
$V = 16$ (saddle-point).

29. $\mathbf{u}^* = [33/74, 21/74, 0, 0, 10/37, 0]$,
$\mathbf{v}^* = [17/74, 0, 31/74, 0, 0, 13/37]$; $V = 281/74$.

30. $\mathbf{u}^* = [4/7, 2/7, 1/7]$,
$\mathbf{v}^* = [33/49, 0, 6/49, 10/49]$; $V = 15/7$.

31. $\mathbf{u}^* = [12/25, 6/25, 4/25, 3/25]$, $\mathbf{v}^* = [0, 1/50, 13/50, 17/50, 19/50]$
$V = 124/25$.

32. $\mathbf{u}^* = [9/14, 5/14]$, $\mathbf{v}^* = [1/14, 13/14, 0, 0, 0, 0, 0]$; $V = -19/14$.

33. $\mathbf{u}^* = [0, 1/2, 1/2, 0]$, $\mathbf{v}^* = [1/6, 0, 0, 5/6]$; $V = 29/2$.

34. $\mathbf{u}^* = [\frac{1}{3}\alpha, \frac{1}{3}\beta, \frac{1}{3}, \frac{1}{3}(1-\alpha), \frac{1}{3}(1-\beta)]$, $\mathbf{v}^* = [\frac{1}{3}\gamma, \frac{1}{3}, \frac{1}{3}, \frac{1}{3}(1-\gamma)]$
for any $\alpha, \beta, \gamma \in [0, 1]$; $V = 1\text{p}$.

35. $\mathbf{u}^* = [12/25, 6/25, 4/25, 3/25]$, $\mathbf{v}^* = [1/50, 13/50, 17/50, 19/50]$
$V = (24/25)\ \text{p}$.

36. $\mathbf{u}^* = [0, 30/77, 20/77, 15/77, 12/77]$,
$\mathbf{v}^* = [0, 17/154, 37/154, 47/154, 53/154]$; $V = (120/77)\ \text{p}$.

37. $\mathbf{u}^* = [0, 5/7, 2/7]$, $\mathbf{v}^* = [4/7, 3/7]$; $V = 41/7$.

38. The matrix game

$$A \begin{pmatrix} & B & \\ 0 & -1 & 1 \\ 1 & 0 & -1 \\ -1 & 1 & 0 \end{pmatrix}$$

satisfies the given conditions.

39. L.P. chooses I and $\{L$ or N or $P]$ each with probability $\frac{1}{2}$,
T.G. chooses $\{A$ or E or $O\}$ and G each with probability $\frac{1}{2}$;
$V = 0$.

Chapter 5

1.
$$\begin{aligned}
x_1 + x_2 &\leqslant 1\\
-2x_1 + 2x_2 &\leqslant -1,\\
x_1 + 4x_2 &\leqslant 2,\\
-y_1 + 2y_2 - y_3 &\leqslant -2,\\
-y_1 - 2y_2 - 4y_3 &\leqslant -3,\\
-2x_1 - 3x_2 + y_1 - y_2 + 2y_3 &\leqslant 0,\\
-\mathbf{x} \leqslant \mathbf{0},\ -\mathbf{y} &\leqslant \mathbf{0}.\\
m = 11,\ n = 5,\ L &= 155.
\end{aligned}$$

Index